SHORT STORIES
FOR ENGLISH COURSES

SHORT STORIES

FOR

ENGLISH COURSES

EDITED

WITH INTRODUCTION AND NOTES

BY

ROSA M. R. MIKELS

SHORTRIDGE HIGH SCHOOL, INDIANAPOLIS, IND.

CHARLES SCRIBNER'S SONS

NEW YORK   CHICAGO   BOSTON

9074

808.3

M

c 892

PRINTED AT
THE SCRIBNER PRESS
NEW YORK, U. S. A.

CONTENTS

PREFACE

Why must we confine the reading of our children to the older literary classics? This is the question asked by an ever-increasing number of thoughtful teachers. They have no wish to displace or to discredit the classics. On the contrary, they love and revere them. But they do wish to give their pupils something additional, something that pulses with present life, that is characteristic of to-day. The children, too, wonder that, with the great literary outpouring going on about them, they must always fill their cups from the cisterns of the past.

The short story is especially adapted to supplement our high-school reading. It is of a piece with our varied, hurried, efficient American life, wherein figure the business man's lunch, the dictagraph, the telegraph, the telephone, the automobile, and the railway "limited." It has achieved high art, yet conforms to the modern demand that our literature—since it must be read with despatch, if read at all—be compact and compelling. Moreover, the short story is with us in almost overwhelming numbers, and is probably here to stay. Indeed, our boys and girls are somewhat appalled at the quantity of material from which they must select their reading, and welcome any instruction that enables them to know the good from the bad. It is certain, therefore, that, whatever else they may throw into the educational discard when they leave the high school, they will keep and use anything they may have learned about this form of literature which has become so powerful a factor in our daily life.

This book does not attempt to select the greatest stories of the time. What tribunal would dare make such a choice? Nor does it attempt to trace the evolution of the short story or to point out natural types and differences. These topics are better suited to college classes. Its object is threefold: to supply interesting reading belonging to the student's own time, to help him to see that there is no divorce between classic and modern literature, and, by offering him material structurally good and typical of the qualities represented, to assist him in discriminating between the artistic and the inartistic. The stories have been carefully selected, because in the period of adolescence "nothing read fails to leave its mark";[1] they have also been carefully arranged with a view to the needs of the adolescent boy and girl. Stories of the type loved by primitive man, and therefore easily approached and understood, have been placed first. Those which appealed in periods of higher development follow, roughly in the order of their increasing difficulty. It is hoped, moreover, that this arrangement will help the student to understand and appreciate the development of the story. He begins with the simple tale of adventure and the simple story of character. As he advances he sees the story develop in plot, in character analysis, and in setting, until he ends with the psychological study of *Markheim*, remarkable for its complexity of motives and its great spiritual problem. Both the selection and the arrangement have been made with this further purpose in view—"to keep the heart warm, reinforcing all its good motives, preforming choices, universalizing sympathies."[2]

[1] G. Stanley Hall, *Adolescence*, vol. II.
[2] *Ibid.*

It is a pleasure to acknowledge, in this connection, the suggestions and the criticism of Mr. William N. Otto, Head of the Department of English in Shortridge High School, Indianapolis; and the courtesies of the publishers who have permitted the use of their material.

INTRODUCTION

I

REQUIREMENTS OF THE SHORT STORY

CRITICS have agreed that the short story must conform to certain conditions. First of all, the writer must strive to make one and only one impression. His time is too limited, his space is too confined, his risk of dividing the attention of the reader is too great, to admit of more than this one impression. He therefore selects some moment of action or some phase of character or some particular scene, and focuses attention upon that. Life not infrequently gives such brief, clear-cut impressions. At the railway station we see two young people hurry to a train as if fearful of being detained, and we get the impression of romantic adventure. We pass on the street corner two men talking, and from a chance sentence or two we form a strong impression of the character of one or both. Sometimes we travel through a scene so desolate and depressing or so lovely and uplifting that the effect is never forgotten. Such glimpses of life and scene are as vivid as the vignettes revealed by the searchlight, when its arm slowly explores a mountain-side or the shore of a lake and brings objects for a brief moment into high light. To secure this single strong impression, the writer must decide which of the three essentials—plot, character, or setting—is to have first place.

As action appeals strongly to most people, and very adequately reveals character, the short-story writer may decide to make plot pre-eminent. He accordingly chooses his incidents carefully. Any that do not really aid in developing the story must be cast aside, no matter how interesting or attractive they may be in themselves. This does not mean that an incident which is detached from the train of events may not be used. But such an incident must have proper relations provided for it. Thus the writer may wish to use incidents that belong to two separate stories, because he knows that by relating them he can produce a single effect. Shakespeare does this in *Macbeth*. Finding in the lives of the historic Macbeth and the historic King Duff incidents that he wished to use, he combined them. But he saw to it that they had the right relation, that they fitted into the chain of cause and effect. The reader will insist, as the writer knows, that the story be logical, that incident 1 shall be the cause of incident 2, incident 2 of incident 3, and so on to the end. The triangle used by Freytag to illustrate the plot of a play may make this clear.

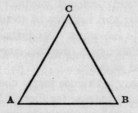

AC is the line of rising action along which the story climbs, incident by incident, to the point C; C is the turning point, the crisis, or the climax; CB is the line of falling action along which the story descends incident by incident to its logical resolution. Nothing may be left to luck or chance. In life the element of chance does sometimes seem to figure, but in the story it has no place. If the ending is not the logical outcome of events, the reader feels cheated. He does not want the situation to be too obvious, for he likes the thrill of suspense. But he wants the hints and foreshadowings to be sincere, so that he may safely draw his conclusions from them. This does not condemn, however, the "surprise" ending, so admirably used by O. Henry. The reader, in this case, admits that the writer has "played fair" throughout, and that the ending which has so surprised and tickled his fancy is as logical as that he had forecast.

To aid in securing the element of suspense, the author often makes use of what Carl H. Grabo, in his *The Art of the Short Story*, calls the "negative" or "hostile" incident. Incidents, as he points out, are of two kinds—positive and negative. The first openly help to untangle the situation; the second seem to delay the straightening out of the threads or even to make the tangle worse. He illustrates this by the story of Cinderella. The appearance of the fairy and her use of the magic wand are positive, or openly helpful incidents, in rescuing Cinderella from her lonely and neglected state. But her forgetfulness of the hour and her loss of the glass slipper are negative or hostile incidents. Nevertheless, we see how these are really blessings in disguise, since they cause the prince to seek and woo her.

The novelist may introduce many characters, because he has time and space to care for them. Not so the short-story writer: he must employ only one main character and a few supporting characters. However, when the plot is the main thing, the characters need not be remarkable in any way. Indeed, as Brander Matthews has said, the heroine may be "a woman," the hero "a man," not any woman or any man in particular. Thus, in *The Lady or the Tiger?* the author leaves the princess without definite traits of character, because his problem is not "what this particular woman would do, but what *a* woman would do." Sometimes, after reading a story of thrilling plot, we find that we do not readily recall the appearance or the names of the characters; we recall only what happened to them. This is true of the women of James Fenimore Cooper's stories. They have no substantiality, but move like veiled figures through the most exciting adventures.

Setting may or may not be an important factor in the story of incident. What is meant by setting? It is an inclusive term. Time, place, local conditions, and sometimes descriptions of nature and of people are parts of it. When these are well cared for, we get an effect called "atmosphere." We know the effect the atmosphere has upon objects. Any one who has observed distant mountains knows that, while they remain practically unchanged, they never look the same on two successive days. Sometimes they stand out hard and clear, sometimes they are soft and alluring, sometimes they look unreal and almost melt into the sky behind them. So the atmosphere of a story may envelop people and events and produce a subtle effect upon the reader. Sometimes the plot material is such as to require little setting. The incidents might have happened anywhere. We hardly notice the absence of setting in our hurry to see what happens. This is true of many of the stories we enjoyed when we were children. For instance, in *The Three Bears* the incidents took place, of course, in the woods, but our imagination really supplied the setting. Most stories, however, whatever their character, use setting as carefully and as effectively as possible. Time and place are often given with exactness. Thus Bret Harte says: "As Mr. John Oakhurst, gambler, stepped into the main street of Poker Flat on the morning of the twenty-

third of November, 1850, he was conscious of a change
in its moral atmosphere since the preceding night." This
definite mention of time and place gives an air of reality
to the story. As to descriptions, the writer sifts them in,
for he knows that few will bother to read whole para-
graphs of description. He often uses local color, by
which we mean the employment of epithets, phrases,
and other expressions that impart a "feeling" for the
place. This use of local color must not be confused with
that intended to produce what is called an "impressionistic" effect. In the latter case the writer subordinates everything to this effect of scene. This use of
local color is discussed elsewhere.

Perhaps the writer wishes to make character the
dominant element. Then he subordinates plot and setting to this purpose and makes them contribute to it.
In selecting the character he wishes to reveal he has
wide choice. "Human nature is the same, wherever
you find it," we are fond of saying. So he may choose
a character that is quite common, some one he knows;
and, having made much of some one trait and ignored
or subordinated others, bring him before us at some
moment of decision or in some strange, perhaps hostile,
environment. Or the author may take some character
quite out of the ordinary: the village miser, the recluse,
or a person with a peculiar mental or moral twist. But,
whatever his choice, it is not enough that the character
be actually drawn from real life. Indeed, such fidelity
to what literally exists may be a hinderance to the writer.
The original character may have done strange things
and suffered strange things that cannot be accounted
for. But, in the story, inconsistencies must be removed,
and the conduct of the characters must be logical. Life
seems inconsistent to all of us at times, but it is probably
less so than it seems. People puzzle us by their apparent

inconsistencies, when to themselves their actions seem perfectly logical. But, as Mr. Grabo points out, "In life we expect inconsistencies; in a story we depend upon their elimination." The law of cause and effect, which we found so indispensable in the story of plot, we find of equal importance in the story of character. There must be no sudden and unaccountable changes in the behavior or sentiments of the people in the story. On the contrary, there must be reason in all they say and do.

Another demand of the character story is that the characters be lifelike. In the plot story, or in the impressionistic story, we may accept the flat figures on the canvas; our interest is elsewhere. But in the character story we must have real people whose motives and conduct we discuss pro and con with as much interest as if we knew them in the flesh. A character of this convincing type is Hamlet. About him controversy has always raged. It is impossible to think of him as other than a real man. Whenever the writer finds that the characters in his story have caused the reader to wax eloquent over their conduct, he may rest easy: he has made his people lifelike.

Setting in the character story is important, for it is in this that the chief actor moves and has his being. His environment is continually causing him to speak and act. The incidents selected, even though some of them may seem trivial in themselves, must reveal depth after depth in his soul. Whatever the means by which the author reveals the character—whether by setting, conduct, analysis, dialogue, or soliloquy—his task is a hard one. In *Markheim* we have practically all of these used, with the result that the character is unmistakable and convincing.

Stories of scenes are neither so numerous nor so easy to produce successfully as those of plot and character.

But sometimes a place so profoundly impresses a writer that its demands may not be disregarded. Robert Louis Stevenson strongly felt the influence of certain places. "Certain dank gardens cry aloud for murder; certain old houses demand to be haunted; certain coasts are set apart for shipwreck. Other spots seem to abide their destiny, suggestive and impenetrable." Perhaps all of us have seen some place of which we have exclaimed: "It is like a story!" When, then, scene is to furnish the dominant interest, plot and character become relatively insignificant and shadowy. "The pressure of the atmosphere," says Brander Matthews, holds our attention. *The Fall of the House of Usher*, by Edgar Allan Poe, is a story of this kind. It is the scene that affects us with dread and horror; we have no peace until we see the house swallowed up by the tarn, and have fled out of sight of the tarn itself. The plot is extremely slight, and the Lady Madeline and her unhappy brother hardly more than shadows.

It must not be supposed from the foregoing explanation that the three essentials of the short story are ever really divorced. They are happily blended in many of our finest stories. Nevertheless, analysis of any one of these will show that in the mind of the writer one purpose was pre-eminent. On this point Robert Louis Stevenson thus speaks: "There are, so far as I know, three ways and three only of writing a story. You may take a plot and fit characters to it, or you may take a character and choose incidents and situations to develop it, or, lastly, you may take a certain atmosphere and get actions and persons to express and realize it." When to this clear conception of his limitations and privileges the author adds an imagination that clearly visualizes events and the "verbal magic" by which good style is secured, he produces the short story that is a masterpiece.

II

HOW THIS BOOK MAY BE USED

THIS book may be used in four ways. First, it may serve as an appetizer. Even the casual reading of good literature has a tendency to create a demand for more. Second, it may be made the basis for discussion and comparison. By using these stories, the works of recognized authors, as standards, the student may determine the value of such stories as come into his home. Third, these selections may be studied in a regular short-story course, such as many high schools have, to illustrate the requirements and the types of this form of narration. The chapter on "The Requirements of the Short Story" will be found useful both in this connection and in the comparative study of stories. Fourth, the student will better appreciate and understand the short story if he attempts to tell or to write one. This does not mean that we intend to train him for the literary market. Our object is entirely different. No form of literature brings more real joy to the child than the story. Not only does he like to hear stories; he likes to tell them. And where the short-story course is rightly used, he likes to write them. He finds that the pleasure of exercising creative power more than offsets the drudgery inevitable in composition. A plan that has been satisfactorily carried out in the classroom is here briefly outlined.

The teacher reads with the class a story in which plot furnishes the main interest. This type is chosen because it is more easily analyzed by beginners. The class discusses this, applying the tests of the short story given elsewhere in this book. Then a number of short stories of different types are read and compared. Next, each member of the class selects from some recent book or magazine a short story he enjoys. This he outlines and reports to the class. If this report is not satisfactory, the class insists that either the author or the reporter be exonerated. The story is accordingly read to the class, or is read and reported on by another member. The class is then usually able to decide whether the story is faulty or the first report inadequate.

Next the class gives orally incidents that might or might not be expanded into short stories. The students soon discover that some of these require the lengthy treatment of a novel, that others are good as simple incidents but nothing more, and that still others might develop into satisfactory short stories. The class is now asked to develop original plots. Since plots cannot be produced on demand, but require time for the mind to act subconsciously, the class practises, during the "period of incubation," the writing of dialogue. For these the teacher suggests a list of topics, although any student is free to substitute one of his own. Among the topics that have been used are: "Johnny goes with his mother to church for the first time," "Mrs. Hennessy is annoyed by the chickens of Mrs. Jones," "Albert applies for a summer job." Sometimes the teacher relates an incident, and has the class reproduce it in dialogue. By comparing their work with dialogue by recognized writers the youthful authors soon learn how to punctuate and paragraph conversation, and where to place necessary comment and explanation. They also discover that dialogue must either reveal character or advance the story; and that it must be in keeping with the theme and maintain the tone used at the beginning. A commonplace dialogue must not suddenly become romantic in tone, and dialect must not lapse into ordinary English.

The original plots the class offers later may have been suggested in many ways. Newspaper accounts, court reports, historical incidents, family traditions—all may contribute. Sometimes the student proudly declares of his plot, "I made it out of my own head." These plots are arranged in outline form to show how incident 1 developed incident 2, that incident 3, and so on to the conclusion. The class points out the weak places in these plots and offers helpful suggestions. This co-operation often produces surprisingly good results. A solution that the troubled originator of the plot never thought of may come almost as an inspiration from the class. Criticism throughout is largely constructive. After the student has developed several plots in outline, he usually finds among them one that he wishes to use for his story. This is worked out in some detail, submitted to the class, and later in a revised form to the teacher. The story when complete is corrected and sometimes re-written.

Most of the class prefer to write stories of plot, but some insist upon trying stories of character or of setting. These pupils are shown the difficulties in their way, but are allowed to try their hand if they insist. Sometimes the results are good; more often the writer, after an honest effort, admits that he cannot handle his subject well and substitutes a story of plot.

In any case the final draft is sure to leave much to be desired; but even so, the gain has been great. The pupil writer has constantly been measuring his work by standards of recognized excellence in form and in creative power; as a result he has learned to appreciate the short story from the art side. Moreover, he has had a large freedom in his work that has relieved it of drudgery. And, best of all, he has been doing original work with plastic material; and to work with plastic material is always a source of joy, whether it be the mud that the child makes into pies, the clay that the artist moulds into forms of beauty, or the facts of life that the creative imagination of the writer shapes into literature.

THE FIRST CHRISTMAS TREE

A STORY OF THE FOREST

BY

HENRY VAN DYKE

This story is placed first because it is of the type that first delighted man. It is the story of high adventure, of a struggle with the forces of nature, barbarous men, and heathen gods. The hero is " a hunter of demons, a subduer of the wilderness, a woodman of the faith." He seeks hardships and conquers them. The setting is the illimitable forest in the remote past. The forest, like the sea, makes an irresistible appeal to the imagination. Either may be the scene of the marvellous and the thrilling. Quite unlike the earliest tales, this story is enriched with description and exposition; nevertheless, it has their simplicity and dignity. It reminds us of certain of the great Biblical narratives, such as the contest between Elijah and the prophets of Baal and the victory of Daniel over the jealous presidents and princes of Darius. In " The First Christmas Tree," as in many others of these stories, a third person is the narrator. But the hero may tell his own adventures. " I did this. I did that. Thus I felt at the conclusion." Instances are Defoe's " Robinson Crusoe " and Stevenson's " Kidnapped." But whether in the first or third person, the story holds us by the magic of adventure.

THE FIRST CHRISTMAS TREE*

I

THE CALL OF THE WOODSMAN

The day before Christmas, in the year of our Lord 722.

Broad snow-meadows glistening white along the banks of the river Moselle; pallid hill-sides blooming with mystic roses where the glow of the setting sun still lingered upon them; an arch of clearest, faintest azure bending overhead; in the centre of the aerial landscape the massive walls of the cloister of Pfalzel, gray to the east, purple to the west; silence over all,—a gentle, eager, conscious stillness, diffused through the air like perfume, as if earth and sky were hushing themselves to hear the voice of the river faintly murmuring down the valley.

In the cloister, too, there was silence at the sunset hour. All day long there had been a strange and joyful stir among the nuns. A breeze of curiosity and excitement had swept along the corridors and through every quiet cell.

The elder sisters,—the provost, the deaconess, the stewardess, the portress with her huge bunch of keys jingling at her girdle,—had been hurrying to and fro, busied with household cares. In the huge kitchen there was a bustle of hospitable preparation. The little bandy-legged dogs that kept the spits turning before the fires had been trotting steadily for many an hour, until their

* From "The First Christmas Tree," by Henry Van Dyke. Copyright, 1897, by Charles Scribner's Sons.

tongues hung out for want of breath. The big black pots swinging from the cranes had bubbled and gurgled and shaken and sent out puffs of appetizing steam.

St. Martha was in her element. It was a field-day for her virtues.

The younger sisters, the pupils of the convent, had forsaken their Latin books and their embroidery-frames, their manuscripts and their miniatures, and fluttered through the halls in little flocks like merry snow-birds, all in black and white, chattering and whispering together. This was no day for tedious task-work, no day for grammar or arithmetic, no day for picking out illuminated letters in red and gold on stiff parchment, or patiently chasing intricate patterns over thick cloth with the slow needle. It was a holiday. A famous visitor had come to the convent.

It was Winfried of England, whose name in the Roman tongue was Boniface, and whom men called the Apostle of Germany. A great preacher; a wonderful scholar; he had written a Latin grammar himself,— think of it,—and he could hardly sleep without a book under his pillow; but, more than all, a great and daring traveller, a venturesome pilgrim, a high-priest of romance.

He had left his home and his fair estate in Wessex; he would not stay in the rich monastery of Nutescelle, even though they had chosen him as the abbot ; he had refused a bishopric at the court of King Karl. Nothing would content him but to go out into the wild woods and preach to the heathen.

Up and down through the forests of Hesse and Thuringia, and along the borders of Saxony, he had wandered for years, with a handful of companions, sleeping under the trees, crossing mountains and marshes, now here, now there, never satisfied with ease and comfort, always in love with hardship and danger.

What a man he was! Fair and slight, but straight as a spear and strong as an oaken staff. His face was still young; the smooth skin was bronzed by wind and sun. His gray eyes, clear and kind, flashed like fire when he spoke of his adventures, and of the evil deeds of the false priests with whom he contended.

What tales he had told that day! Not of miracles wrought by sacred relics; not of courts and councils and splendid cathedrals; though he knew much of these things, and had been at Rome and received the Pope's blessing. But to-day he had spoken of long journeyings by sea and land; of perils by fire and flood; of wolves and bears and fierce snowstorms and black nights in the lonely forest; of dark altars of heathen gods, and weird, bloody sacrifices, and narrow escapes from murderous bands of wandering savages.

The little novices had gathered around him, and their faces had grown pale and their eyes bright as they listened with parted lips, entranced in admiration, twining their arms about one another's shoulders and holding closely together, half in fear, half in delight. The older nuns had turned from their tasks and paused, in passing by, to hear the pilgrim's story. Too well· they knew the truth of what he spoke. Many a one among them had seen the smoke rising from the ruins of her father's roof. Many a one had a brother far away in the wild country to whom her heart went out night and day, wondering if he were still among the living.

But now the excitements of that wonderful day were over; the hour of the evening meal had come; the inmates of the cloister were assembled in the refectory.

On the daïs sat the stately Abbess Addula, daughter

of King Dagobert, looking a princess indeed, in her violet tunic, with the hood and cuffs of her long white robe trimmed with fur, and a snowy veil resting like a crown on her snowy hair. At her right hand was the honored guest, and at her left hand her grandson, the young Prince Gregor, a big, manly boy, just returned from the high school.

The long, shadowy hall, with its dark-brown rafters and beams; the double rows of nuns, with their pure veils and fair faces; the ruddy glow of the slanting sunbeams striking upwards through the tops of the windows and painting a pink glow high up on the walls,—it was all as beautiful as a picture, and as silent. For this was the rule of the cloister, that at the table all should sit in stillness for a little while, and then one should read aloud, while the rest listened.

" It is the turn of my grandson to read to-day," said the abbess to Winfried; " we shall see how much he has learned in the school. Read, Gregor; the place in the book is marked."

The tall lad rose from his seat and turned the pages of the manuscript. It was a copy of Jerome's version of the Scriptures in Latin, and the marked place was in the letter of St. Paul to the Ephesians,—the passage where he describes the preparation of the Christian as the arming of a warrior for glorious battle. The young voice rang out clearly, rolling the sonorous words, without slip or stumbling, to the end of the chapter.

Winfried listened smiling. " My son," said he, as the reader paused, " that was bravely read. Understandest thou what thou readest? "

" Surely, father," answered the boy; " it was taught me by the masters at Treves; and we have read this epistle clear through, from beginning to end, so that I almost know it by heart."

Then he began again to repeat the passage, turning away from the page as if to show his skill.

But Winfried stopped him with a friendly lifting of the hand.

" Not so, my son; that was not my meaning. When we pray, we speak to God; when we read, it is God who speaks to us. I ask whether thou hast heard what He has said to thee, in thine own words, in the common speech. Come, give us again the message of the warrior and his armor and his battle, in the mother-tongue, so that all can understand it."

The boy hesitated, blushed, stammered; then he came around to Winfried's seat, bringing the book. " Take the book, my father," he cried, " and read it for me. I cannot see the meaning plain, though I love the sound of the words. Religion I know, and the doctrines of our faith, and the life of priests and nuns in the cloister, for which my grandmother designs me, though it likes me little. And fighting I know, and the life of warriors and heroes, for I have read of it in Virgil and the ancients, and heard a bit from the soldiers at Treves; and I would fain taste more of it, for it likes me much. But how the two lives fit together, or what need there is of armor for a clerk in holy orders, I can never see. Tell me the meaning, for if there is a man in all the world that knows it, I am sure it is none other than thou."

So Winfried took the book and closed it, clasping the boy's hand with his own.

" Let us first dismiss the others to their vespers," said he, " lest they should be weary."

A sign from the abbess; a chanted benediction; a murmuring of sweet voices and a soft rustling of many feet over the rushes on the floor; the gentle tide of noise flowed out through the doors and ebbed away down the corridors; the three at the head of the table were left alone in the darkening room.

Then Winfried began to translate the parable of the soldier into the realities of life.

At every turn he knew how to flash a new light into the picture out of his own experience. He spoke of the combat with self, and of the wrestling with dark spirits in solitude. He spoke of the demons that men had worshipped for centuries in the wilderness, and whose malice they invoked against the stranger who ventured into the gloomy forest. Gods, they called them, and told strange tales of their dwelling among the impenetrable branches of the oldest trees and in the caverns of the shaggy hills; of their riding on the wind-horses and hurling spears of lightning against their foes. Gods they were not, but foul spirits of the air, rulers of the darkness. Was there not glory and honor in fighting with them, in daring their anger under the shield of faith, in putting them to flight with the sword of truth? What better adventure could a brave man ask than to go forth against them, and wrestle with them, and conquer them?

" Look you, my friends," said Winfried, " how sweet and peaceful is this convent to-night, on the eve of the nativity of the Prince of Peace! It is a garden full of flowers in the heart of winter; a nest among the branches of a great tree shaken by the winds; a still haven on the edge of a tempestuous sea. And this is what religion means for those who are chosen and called to quietude and prayer and meditation.

" But out yonder in the wide forest, who knows what storms are raving to-night in the hearts of men, though all the woods are still? who knows what haunts of wrath and cruelty and fear are closed to-night against the advent of the Prince of Peace? And shall I tell you what religion means to those who are called and chosen to dare and to fight, and to conquer the world for Christ? It means to launch out into the deep. It means to go against the strongholds of the adversary. It means to struggle to win an entrance for their Master everywhere. What helmet is strong enough for this strife save the helmet of salvation? What breastplate can guard a man against these fiery darts but the breastplate of righteousness? What shoes can stand the wear of these journeys but the preparation of the gospel of peace?''

"Shoes?" he cried again, and laughed as if a sudden thought had struck him. He thrust out his foot, covered with a heavy cowhide boot, laced high about his leg with thongs of skin.

"See here,—how a fighting man of the cross is shod! I have seen the boots of the Bishop of Tours,—white kid, broidered with silk; a day in the bogs would tear them to shreds. I have seen the sandals that the monks use on the highroads,—yes, and worn them; ten pair of them have I worn out and thrown away in a single journey. Now I shoe my feet with the toughest hides, hard as iron; no rock can cut them, no branches can tear them. Yet more than one pair of these have I outworn, and many more shall I outwear ere my journeys are ended. And I think, if God is gracious to me, that I shall die wearing them. Better so than in a soft bed with silken coverings. The boots of a warrior, a hunter, a woodsman,—these are my preparation of the gospel of peace.''

"Come, Gregor," he said, laying his brown hand on the youth's shoulder, "come, wear the forester's boots with me. This is the life to which we are called. Be strong in the Lord, a hunter of the demons, a subduer of the wilderness, a woodsman of the faith. Come!''

The boy's eyes sparkled. He turned to his grandmother. She shook her head vigorously.

"Nay, father," she said, "draw not the lad away

from my side with these wild words. I need him to help me with my labors, to cheer my old age."

"Do you need him more than the Master does?" asked Winfried; "and will you take the wood that is fit for a bow to make a distaff?"

"But I fear for the child. Thy life is too hard for him. He will perish with hunger in the woods."

"Once," said Winfried, smiling, "we were camped by the bank of the river Ohru. The table was spread for the morning meal, but my comrades cried that it was empty; the provisions were exhausted; we must go without breakfast, and perhaps starve before we could escape from the wilderness. While they complained, a fish-hawk flew up from the river with flapping wings, and let fall a great pike in the midst of the camp. There was food enough and to spare. Never have I seen the righteous forsaken, nor his seed begging bread."

"But the fierce pagans of the forest," cried the abbess,—"they may pierce the boy with their arrows, or dash out his brains with their axes. He is but a child, too young for the dangers of strife."

"A child in years," replied Winfried, "but a man in spirit. And if the hero must fall early in the battle, he wears the brighter crown, not a leaf withered, not a flower fallen."

The aged princess trembled a little. She drew Gregor close to her side, and laid her hand gently on his brown hair.

"I am not sure that he wants to leave me yet. Besides, there is no horse in the stable to give him, now, and he cannot go as befits the grandson of a king."

Gregor looked straight into her eyes.

"Grandmother," said he, "dear grandmother, if thou wilt not give me a horse to ride with this man of God, I will go with him afoot."

II

THE TRAIL THROUGH THE FOREST

Two years had passed, to a day, almost to an hour, since that Christmas eve in the cloister of Pfalzel. A little company of pilgrims, less than a score of men, were creeping slowly northward through the wide forest that rolled over the hills of central Germany.

At the head of the band marched Winfried, clad in a tunic of fur, with his long black robe girt high about his waist, so that it might not hinder his stride. His hunter's boots were crusted with snow. Drops of ice sparkled like jewels along the thongs that bound his legs. There was no other ornament to his dress except the bishop's cross hanging on his breast, and the broad silver clasp that fastened his cloak about his neck. He carried a strong, tall staff in his hand, fashioned at the top into the form of a cross.

Close beside him, keeping step like a familiar comrade, was the young Prince Gregor. Long marches through the wilderness had stretched his limbs and broadened his back, and made a man of him in stature as well as in spirit. His jacket and cap were of wolf-skin, and on his shoulder he carried an axe, with broad, shining blade. He was a mighty woodsman now, and could make a spray of chips fly around him as he hewed his way through the trunk of spruce-tree.

Behind these leaders followed a pair of teamsters, guiding a rude sledge, loaded with food and the equipage of the camp, and drawn by two big, shaggy horses, blowing thick clouds of steam from their frosty nostrils. Tiny icicles hung from the hairs on their lips. Their flanks were smoking. They sank above the fetlocks at every step in the soft snow.

Last of all came the rear guard, armed with bows and javelins. It was no child's play, in those days, to cross Europe afoot.

The weird woodland, sombre and illimitable, covered hill and vale, tableland and mountain-peak. There were wide moors where the wolves hunted in packs as if the devil drove them, and tangled thickets where the lynx and the boar made their lairs. Fierce bears lurked among the rocky passes, and had not yet learned to fear the face of man. The gloomy recesses of the forest gave shelter to inhabitants who were still more cruel and dangerous than beasts of prey,—outlaws and sturdy robbers and mad were-wolves and bands of wandering pillagers.

The pilgrim who would pass from the mouth of the Tiber to the mouth of the Rhine must travel with a little army of retainers, or else trust in God and keep his arrows loose in the quiver.

The travellers were surrounded by an ocean of trees, so vast, so full of endless billows, that it seemed to be pressing on every side to overwhelm them. Gnarled oaks, with branches twisted and knotted as if in rage, rose in groves like tidal waves. Smooth forests of beech-trees, round and gray, swept over the knolls and slopes of land in a mighty ground-swell. But most of all, the multitude of pines and firs, innumerable and monotonous, with straight, stark trunks, and branches woven together in an unbroken flood of darkest green, crowded through the valleys and over the hills, rising on the highest ridges into ragged crests, like the foaming edge of breakers.

Through this sea of shadows ran a narrow stream of shining whiteness,—an ancient Roman road, covered with snow. It was as if some great ship had ploughed through the green ocean long ago, and left behind it a thick, smooth wake of foam. Along this open track the travellers held their way,—heavily, for the drifts were deep; warily, for the hard winter had driven many packs of wolves down from the moors.

The steps of the pilgrims were noiseless; but the sledges creaked over the dry snow, and the panting of the horses throbbed through the still, cold air. The pale-blue shadows on the western side of the road grew longer. The sun, declining through its shallow arch, dropped behind the tree-tops. Darkness followed swiftly, as if it had been a bird of prey waiting for this sign to swoop down upon the world.

" Father," said Gregor to the leader, " surely this day's march is done. It is time to rest, and eat, and sleep. If we press onward now, we cannot see our steps; and will not that be against the word of the psalmist David, who bids us not to put confidence in the legs of a man?"

Winfried laughed. " Nay, my son Gregor," said he, " thou hast tripped, even now, upon thy text. For David said only, ' I take no pleasure in the legs of a man.' And so say I, for I am not minded to spare thy legs or mine, until we come farther on our way, and do what must be done this night. Draw the belt tighter, my son, and hew me out this tree that is fallen across the road, for our camp-ground is not here."

The youth obeyed; two of the foresters sprang to help him; and while the soft fir-wood yielded to the stroke of the axes, and the snow flew from the bending branches, Winfried turned and spoke to his followers in a cheerful voice, that refreshed them like wine.

" Courage, brothers, and forward yet a little! The moon will light us presently, and the path is plain. Well know I that the journey is weary; and my own heart wearies also for the home in England, where those I

love are keeping feast this Christmas eve. But we have
work to do before we feast to-night. For this is the
Yuletide, and the heathen people of the forest have
gathered at the thunder-oak of Geismar to worship their
god, Thor. Strange things will be seen there, and deeds
which make the soul black. But we are sent to lighten
their darkness; and we will teach our kinsmen to keep a
Christmas with us such as the woodland has never known.
Forward, then, and let us stiffen up our feeble knees!"

A murmur of assent came from the men. Even the
horses seemed to take fresh heart. They flattened their
backs to draw the heavy loads, and blew the frost from
their nostrils as they pushed ahead.

The night grew broader and less oppressive. A gate
of brightness was opened secretly somewhere in the
sky; higher and higher swelled the clear moon-flood, until it poured over the eastern wall of forest into the
road. A drove of wolves howled faintly in the distance,
but they were receding, and the sound soon died away.
The stars sparkled merrily through the stringent air;
the small, round moon shone like silver; little breaths of
the dreaming wind wandered whispering across the
pointed fir-tops, as the pilgrims toiled bravely onward,
following their clue of light through a labyrinth of
darkness.

After a while the road began to open out a little.
There were spaces of meadow-land, fringed with alders,
behind which a boisterous river ran, clashing through
spears of ice.

Rude houses of hewn logs appeared in the openings,
each one casting a patch of inky blackness upon the
snow. Then the travellers passed a larger group of
dwellings, all silent and unlighted; and beyond, they
saw a great house, with many outbuildings and enclosed
courtyards, from which the hounds bayed furiously, and

a noise of stamping horses came from the stalls. But there was no other sound of life. The fields around lay bare to the moon. They saw no man, except that once, on a path that skirted the farther edge of a meadow, three dark figures passed by, running very swiftly.

Then the road plunged again into a dense thicket, traversed it, and climbing to the left, emerged suddenly upon a glade, round and level except at the northern side, where a swelling hillock was crowned with a huge oak-tree. It towered above the heath, a giant with contorted arms, beckoning to the host of lesser trees. " Here," cried Winfried, as his eyes flashed and his hand lifted his heavy staff, " here is the thunder-oak; and here the cross of Christ shall break the hammer of the false god Thor."

III

THE SHADOW OF THE THUNDER-OAK

Withered leaves still clung to the branches of the oak: torn and faded banners of the departed summer. The bright crimson of autumn had long since disappeared, bleached away by the storms and the cold. But to-night these tattered remnants of glory were red again: ancient blood-stains against the dark-blue sky. For an immense fire had been kindled in front of the tree. Tongues of ruddy flame, fountains of ruby sparks, ascended through the spreading limbs and flung a fierce illumination upward and around. The pale, pure moonlight that bathed the surrounding forests was quenched and eclipsed here. Not a beam of it sifted downward through the branches of the oak. It stood like a pillar of cloud between the still light of heaven and the crackling, flashing fire of earth.

But the fire itself was invisible to Winfried and his companions. A great throng of people were gathered around it in a half-circle, their backs to the open glade, their faces towards the oak. Seen against that glowing background, it was but the silhouette of a crowd, vague, black, formless, mysterious.

The travellers paused for a moment at the edge of the thicket, and took counsel together.

" It is the assembly of the tribe," said one of the foresters, " the great night of the council. I heard of it three days ago, as we passed through one of the villages. All who swear by the old gods have been summoned. They will sacrifice a steed to the god of war, and drink blood, and eat horse-flesh to make them strong. It will be at the peril of our lives if we approach them. At least we must hide the cross, if we would escape death."

" Hide me no cross," cried Winfried, lifting his staff, " for I have come to show it, and to make these blind folk see its power. There is more to be done here to-night than the slaying of a steed, and a greater evil to be stayed than the shameful eating of meat sacrificed to idols. I have seen it in a dream. Here the cross must stand and be our rede."

At his command the sledge was left in the border of the wood, with two of the men to guard it, and the rest of the company moved forward across the open ground. They approached unnoticed, for all the multitude were looking intently towards the fire at the foot of the oak.

Then Winfried's voice rang out, " Hail, ye sons of the forest! A stranger claims the warmth of your fire in the winter night."

Swiftly, and as with a single motion, a thousand eyes were bent upon the speaker. The semicircle opened silently in the middle; Winfried entered with his followers; it closed again behind them.

Then, as they looked round the curving ranks, they saw that the hue of the assemblage was not black, but white,—dazzling, radiant, solemn. White, the robes of the women clustered together at the points of the wide crescent; white, the glittering byrnies of the warriors standing in close ranks; white, the fur mantles of the aged men who held the central place in the circle; white, with the shimmer of silver ornaments and the purity of lamb's-wool, the raiment of a little group of children who stood close by the fire; white, with awe and fear, the faces of all who looked at them; and over all the flickering, dancing radiance of the flames played and glimmered like a faint, vanishing tinge of blood on snow.

The only figure untouched by the glow was the old priest, Hunrad, with his long, spectral robe, flowing hair and beard, and dead-pale face, who stood with his back to the fire and advanced slowly to meet the strangers.

" Who are you? Whence come you, and what seek you here? " His voice was heavy and toneless as a muffled bell.

" Your kinsman am I, of the German brotherhood," answered Winfried, " and from England, beyond the sea, have I come to bring you a greeting from that land, and a message from the All-Father, whose servant I am."

" Welcome, then," said Hunrad, " welcome, kinsman, and be silent; for what passes here is too high to wait, and must be done before the moon crosses the middle heaven, unless, indeed, thou hast some sign or token from the gods. Canst thou work miracles? "

The question came sharply, as if a sudden gleam of hope had flashed through the tangle of the old priest's mind. But Winfried's voice sank lower and a cloud of disappointment passed over his face as he replied: " Nay, miracles have I never wrought, though I have

heard of many; but the All-Father has given no power
to my hands save such as belongs to common man."

"Stand still, then, thou common man," said Hunrad,
scornfully, "and behold what the gods have called us
hither to do. This night is the death-night of the sun-
god, Baldur the Beautiful, beloved of gods and men.
This night is the hour of darkness and the power of
winter, of sacrifice and mighty fear. This night the
great Thor, the god of thunder and war, to whom this
oak is sacred, is grieved for the death of Baldur, and
angry with this people because they have forsaken his
worship. Long is it since an offering has been laid upon
his altar, long since the roots of his holy tree have been
fed with blood. Therefore its leaves have withered before the time, and its boughs are heavy with death.
Therefore the Slavs and the Wends have beaten us in
battle. Therefore the harvests have failed, and the wolf-
hordes have ravaged the folds, and the strength has
departed from the bow, and the wood of the spear has
broken, and the wild boar has slain the huntsman.
Therefore the plague has fallen on our dwellings, and
the dead are more than the living in all our villages.
Answer me, ye people, are not these things true?"

A hoarse sound of approval ran through the circle. A
chant, in which the voices of the men and women
blended, like the shrill wind in the pine-trees above the
rumbling thunder of a waterfall, rose and fell in rude
cadences.

> "O Thor, the Thunderer,
> Mighty and merciless,
> Spare us from smiting!
> Heave not thy hammer,
> Angry, against us;
> Plague not thy people.
> Take from our treasure
> Richest of ransom.

Silver we send thee,
Jewels and javelins,
Goodliest garments,
All our possessions,
Priceless, we proffer.
Sheep will we slaughter,
Steeds will we sacrifice;
Bright blood shall bathe thee,
O tree of Thunder,
Life-floods shall lave thee,
Strong wood of wonder.
Mighty, have mercy,
Smite us no more,
Spare us and save us,
Spare us, Thor! Thor!"

With two great shouts the song ended, and a stillness followed so intense that the crackling of the fire was heard distinctly. The old priest stood silent for a moment. His shaggy brows swept down over his eyes like ashes quenching flame. Then he lifted his face and spoke.

"None of these things will please the god. More costly is the offering that shall cleanse your sin, more precious the crimson dew that shall send new life into this holy tree of blood. Thor claims your dearest and your noblest gift."

Hunrad moved nearer to the handful of children who stood watching the red mines in the fire and the swarms of spark-serpents darting upward. They had heeded none of the priest's words, and did not notice now that he approached them, so eager were they to see which fiery snake would go highest among the oak branches. Foremost among them, and most intent on the pretty game, was a boy like a sunbeam, slender and quick, with blithe brown eyes and laughing lips. The priest's hand was laid upon his shoulder. The boy turned and looked up in his face.

" Here," said the old man, with his voice vibrating as when a thick rope is strained by a ship swinging from her moorings, " here is the chosen one, the eldest son of the Chief, the darling of the people. Hearken, Bernhard, wilt thou go to Valhalla, where the heroes dwell with the gods, to bear a message to Thor ? "

The boy answered, swift and clear :

" Yes, priest, I will go if my father bids me. Is it far away ? Shall I run quickly ? Must I take my bow and arrows for the wolves ? "

The boy's father, the Chieftain Gundhar, standing among his bearded warriors, drew his breath deep, and leaned so heavily on the handle of his spear that the wood cracked. And his wife, Irma, bending forward from the ranks of women, pushed the golden hair from her forehead with one hand. The other dragged at the silver chain about her neck until the rough links pierced her flesh, and the red drops fell unheeded on the snow of her breast.

A sigh passed through the crowd, like the murmur of the forest before the storm breaks. Yet no one spoke save Hunrad :

" Yes, my Prince, both bow and spear shalt thou have, for the way is long, and thou art a brave huntsman. But in darkness thou must journey for a little space, and with eyes blindfolded. Fearest thou ? "

" Naught fear I," said the boy, " neither darkness, nor the great bear, nor the were-wolf. For I am Gundhar's son, and the defender of my folk."

Then the priest led the child in his raiment of lamb's-wool to a broad stone in front of the fire. He gave him his little bow tipped with silver, and his spear with shining head of steel. He bound the child's eyes with a white cloth, and bade him kneel beside the stone with his face to the east. Unconsciously the wide arc of

spectators drew inward toward the centre, as the ends
of the bow draw together when the cord is stretched.
Winfried moved noiselessly until he stood close behind
the priest.

The old man stooped to lift a black hammer of stone
from the ground,—the sacred hammer of the god Thor.
Summoning all the strength of his withered arms, he
swung it high in the air. It poised for an instant above
the child's fair head—then turned to fall.

One keen cry shrilled out from where the women
stood: " Me! take me! not Bernhard! "

The flight of the mother towards her child was swift
as the falcon's swoop. But swifter still was the hand of
the deliverer.

Winfried's heavy staff thrust mightily against the
hammer's handle as it fell. Sideways it glanced from
the old man's grasp, and the black stone, striking on the
altar's edge, split in twain. A shout of awe and joy
rolled along the living circle. The branches of the oak
shivered. The flames leaped higher. As the shout died
away the people saw the lady Irma, with her arms
clasped round her child, and above them, on the altar-
stone, Winfried, his face shining like the face of an
angel.

IV

THE FELLING OF THE TREE

A swift mountain-flood rolling down its channel; a
huge rock tumbling from the hill-side and falling in
mid-stream; the baffled waters broken and confused,
pausing in their flow, dash high against the rock, foaming and murmuring, with divided impulse, uncertain
whether to turn to the right or the left.

Even so Winfried's bold deed fell into the midst of

the thoughts and passions of the council. They were at a standstill. Anger and wonder, reverence and joy and confusion surged through the crowd. They knew not which way to move: to resent the intrusion of the stranger as an insult to their gods, or to welcome him as the rescuer of their darling prince.

The old priest crouched by the altar, silent. Conflicting counsels troubled the air. Let the sacrifice go forward; the gods must be appeased. Nay, the boy must not die; bring the chieftain's best horse and slay it in his stead; it will be enough; the holy tree loves the blood of horses. Not so, there is a better counsel yet; seize the stranger whom the gods have led hither as a victim and make his life pay the forfeit of his daring.

The withered leaves on the oak rustled and whispered overhead. The fire flared and sank again. The angry voices clashed against each other and fell like opposing waves. Then the chieftain Gundhar struck the earth with his spear and gave his decision.

" All have spoken, but none are agreed. There is no voice of the council. Keep silence now, and let the stranger speak. His words shall give us judgment, whether he is to live or to die."

Winfried lifted himself high upon the altar, drew a roll of parchment from his bosom, and began to read.

" A letter from the great Bishop of Rome, who sits on a golden throne, to the people of the forest, Hessians and Thuringians, Franks and Saxons. *In nomine Domini, sanctae et individuae trinitatis, amen!* "

A murmur of awe ran through the crowd. " It is the sacred tongue of the Romans: the tongue that is heard and understood by the wise men of every land. There is magic in it. Listen! "

Winfried went on to read the letter, translating it into the speech of the people.

" ' We have sent unto you our Brother Boniface, and appointed him your bishop, that he may teach you the only true faith, and baptize you, and lead you back from the ways of error to the path of salvation. Hearken to him in all things like a father. Bow your hearts to his teaching. He comes not for earthly gain, but for the gain of your souls. Depart from evil works. Worship not the false gods, for they are devils. Offer no more bloody sacrifices, nor eat the flesh of horses, but do as our Brother Boniface commands you. Build a house for him that he may dwell among you, and a church where you may offer your prayers to the only living God, the Almighty King of Heaven.' "

It was a splendid message: proud, strong, peaceful, loving. The dignity of the words imposed mightily upon the hearts of the people. They were quieted, as men who have listened to a lofty strain of music.

" Tell us, then," said Gundhar, " what is the word that thou bringest to us from the Almighty. What is thy counsel for the tribes of the woodland on this night of sacrifice? "

" This is the word, and this is the counsel," answered Winfried. " Not a drop of blood shall fall to-night, save that which pity has drawn from the breast of your princess, in love for her child. Not a life shall be blotted out in the darkness to-night; but the great shadow of the tree which hides you from the light of heaven shall be swept away. For this is the birth-night of the white Christ, son of the All-Father, and Saviour of mankind. Fairer is He than Baldur the Beautiful, greater than Odin the Wise, kinder than Freya the Good. Since He has come to earth the bloody sacrifices must cease. The dark Thor, on whom you vainly call, is dead. Deep in the shades of Niffelheim he is lost forever. His power in the world is broken. Will you serve a helpless god?

See, my brothers, you call this tree his oak. Does he dwell here? Does he protect it?''

A troubled voice of assent rose from the throng. The people stirred uneasily. Women covered their eyes. Hunrad lifted his head and muttered hoarsely, '' Thor! take vengeance! Thor!''

Winfried beckoned to Gregor. '' Bring the axes, thine and one for me. Now, young woodsman, show thy craft! The king-tree of the forest must fall, and swiftly, or all is lost!''

The two men took their places facing each other, one on each side of the oak. Their cloaks were flung aside, their heads bare. Carefully they felt the ground with their feet, seeking a firm grip of the earth. Firmly they grasped the axe-helves and swung the shining blades.

'' Tree-god!'' cried Winfried, '' art thou angry? Thus we smite thee!''

'' Tree-god!'' answered Gregor, '' art thou mighty? Thus we fight thee!''

Clang! clang! the alternate strokes beat time upon the hard, ringing wood. The axe-heads glittered in their rhythmic flight, like fierce eagles circling about their quarry.

The broad flakes of wood flew from the deepening gashes in the sides of the oak. The huge trunk quivered. There was a shuddering in the branches. Then the great wonder of Winfried's life came to pass.

Out of the stillness of the winter night, a mighty rushing noise sounded overhead.

Was it the ancient gods on their white battle-steeds, with their black hounds of wrath and their arrows of lightning, sweeping through the air to destroy their foes?

A strong, whirling wind passed over the tree-tops. It gripped the oak by its branches and tore it from its

roots. Backward it fell, like a ruined tower, groaning
and crashing as it split asunder in four great pieces.

Winfried let his axe drop, and bowed his head for a
moment in the presence of almighty power.

Then he turned to the people, " Here is the timber,"
he cried, " already felled and split for your new building. On this spot shall rise a chapel to the true God
and his servant St. Peter.

" And here," said he, as his eyes fell on a young
fir-tree, standing straight and green, with its top pointing towards the stars, amid the divided ruins of the
fallen oak, " here is the living tree, with no stain of
blood upon it, that shall be the sign of your new worship. See how it points to the sky. Let us call it the
tree of the Christ-child. Take it up and carry it to the
chieftain's hall. You shall go no more into the shadows
of the forest to keep your feasts with secret rites of
shame. You shall keep them at home, with laughter
and song and rites of love. The thunder-oak has fallen,
and I think the day is coming when there shall not be
a home in all Germany where the children are not
gathered around the green fir-tree to rejoice in the
birth-night of Christ."

So they took the little fir from its place, and carried
it in joyous procession to the edge of the glade, and
laid it on the sledge. The horses tossed their heads
and drew their load bravely, as if the new burden had
made it lighter.

When they came to the house of Gundhar, he bade
them throw open the doors of the hall and set the tree
in the midst of it. They kindled lights among the
branches until it seemed to be tangled full of fire-flies.
The children encircled it, wondering, and the sweet odor
of the balsam filled the house.

Then Winfried stood beside the chair of Gundhar, on

the daïs at the end of the hall, and told the story of Bethlehem; of the babe in the manger, of the shepherds on the hills, of the host of angels and their midnight song. All the people listened, charmed into stillness.

But the boy Bernhard, on Irma's knee, folded by her soft arm, grew restless as the story lengthened, and began to prattle softly at his mother's ear.

"Mother," whispered the child, "why did you cry out so loud, when the priest was going to send me to Valhalla?"

"Oh, hush, my child," answered the mother, and pressed him closer to her side.

"Mother," whispered the boy again, laying his finger on the stains upon her breast, "see, your dress is red! What are these stains? Did some one hurt you?"

The mother closed his mouth with a kiss. "Dear, be still, and listen!"

The boy obeyed. His eyes were heavy with sleep. But he heard the last words of Winfried as he spoke of the angelic messengers, flying over the hills of Judea and singing as they flew. The child wondered and dreamed and listened. Suddenly his face grew bright. He put his lips close to Irma's cheek again.

"Oh, mother!" he whispered very low, "do not speak. Do you hear them? Those angels have come back again. They are singing now behind the tree."

And some say that it was true; but others say that it was only Gregor and his companions at the lower end of the hall, chanting their Christmas hymn:

> "'All glory be to God on high,
> And to the earth be peace!
> Good-will, henceforth, from heaven to men
> Begin, and never cease.'"

A FRENCH TAR-BABY

BY

JOEL CHANDLER HARRIS

The fable was one of the first tributaries to the stream of story-telling. Primitive man with a kind of fine democracy claimed kinship with the animals about him. So Hiawatha learned the language and the secrets of birds and beasts,

> "Talked with them whene'er he met them,
> Called them Hiawatha's Brothers."

Out of this intimacy and understanding grew the fable, wherein animals thought, acted, and talked in the terms of human life. This kind of story is illustrated by the "Fables" of Æsop, the animal stories of Ernest Thompson-Seton, the "Jungle Books" of Rudyard Kipling, and the "Uncle Remus" stories of Joel Chandler Harris. The fable is a tale rather than a true short-story.

A FRENCH TAR-BABY *

In the time when there were hobgoblins and fairies, Brother Goat and Brother Rabbit lived in the same neighborhood, not far from each other.

Proud of his long beard and sharp horns, Brother Goat looked on Brother Rabbit with disdain. He would hardly speak to Brother Rabbit when he met him, and his greatest pleasure was to make his little neighbor the victim of his tricks and practical jokes. For instance, he would say:

"Brother Rabbit, here is Mr. Fox," and this would cause Brother Rabbit to run away as hard as he could. Again he would say:

"Brother Rabbit, here is Mr. Wolf," and poor Brother Rabbit would shake and tremble with fear. Sometimes he would cry out:

"Brother Rabbit, here is Mr. Tiger," and then Brother Rabbit would shudder and think that his last hour had come.

Tired of this miserable existence, Brother Rabbit tried to think of some means by which he could change his powerful and terrible neighbor into a friend. After a time he thought he had discovered a way to make Brother Goat his friend, and so he invited him to dinner.

Brother Goat was quick to accept the invitation. The dinner was a fine affair, and there was an abundance of good eating. A great many different dishes were served. Brother Goat licked his mouth and shook his long beard with satisfaction. He had never before been present at such a feast.

* From "Evening Tales," by Joel Chandler Harris. Copyright, 1893, by Charles Scribner's Sons.

"Well, my friend," exclaimed Brother Rabbit, when the dessert was brought in, "how do you like your dinner?"

"I could certainly wish for nothing better," replied Brother Goat, rubbing the tips of his horns against the back of his chair; "but my throat is very dry and a little water would hurt neither the dinner nor me."

"Gracious!" said Brother Rabbit, "I have neither wine-cellar nor water. I am not in the habit of drinking while I am eating."

"Neither have I any water, Brother Rabbit," said Brother Goat. "But I have an idea! If you will go with me over yonder by the big poplar, we will dig a well."

"No, Brother Goat," said Brother Rabbit, who hoped to revenge himself—"no, I do not care to dig a well. At daybreak I drink the dew from the cups of the flowers, and in the heat of the day I milk the cows and drink the cream."

"Well and good," said Brother Goat. "Alone I will dig the well, and alone I will drink out of it."

"Success to you, Brother Goat," said Brother Rabbit.

"Thank you kindly, Brother Rabbit."

Brother Goat then went to the foot of the big poplar and began to dig his well. He dug with his forefeet and with his horns, and the well got deeper and deeper. Soon the water began to bubble up and the well was finished, and then Brother Goat made haste to quench his thirst. He was in such a hurry that his beard got in the water, but he drank and drank until he had his fill.

Brother Rabbit, who had followed him at a little distance, hid himself behind a bush and laughed heartily. He said to himself: "What an innocent creature you are!"

The next day, when Brother Goat, with his big beard
and sharp horns, returned to his well to get some water,
he saw the tracks of Brother Rabbit in the soft earth.
This put him to thinking. He sat down, pulled his
beard, scratched his head, and tapped himself on the
forehead.

" My friend," he exclaimed after a while, " I will
catch you yet."

Then he ran and got his tools (for Brother Goat was
something of a carpenter in those days) and made a
large doll out of laurel wood. When the doll was finished, he spread tar on it here and there, on the right
and on the left, and up and down. He smeared it all
over with the sticky stuff, until it was as black as a
Guinea negro.

This finished, Brother Goat waited quietly until
evening. At sunset he placed the tarred doll near the
well, and ran and hid himself behind the trees and
bushes. The moon had just risen, and the heavens
twinkled with millions of little star-torches.

Brother Rabbit, who was waiting in his house, believed that the time had come for him to get some water,
so he took his bucket and went to Brother Goat's well.
On the way he was very much afraid that something
would catch him. He trembled when the wind shook
the leaves of the trees. He would go a little distance
and then stop and listen; he hid here behind a stone,
and there behind a tuft of grass.

At last he arrived at the well, and there he saw the
little negro. He stopped and looked at it with astonishment. Then he drew back a little way, advanced
again, drew back, advanced a little, and stopped once
more.

" What can that be? " he said to himself. He listened, with his long ears pointed forward, but the trees

could not talk, and the bushes were dumb. He winked his eyes and lowered his head:

" Hey, friend! who are you? " he asked.

The tar-doll didn't move. Brother Rabbit went up a little closer, and asked again:

" Who are you? "

The tar-doll said nothing. Brother Rabbit breathed more at ease. Then he went to the brink of the well, but when he looked in the water the tar-doll seemed to look in too. He could see her reflection in the water. This made Brother Rabbit so mad that he grew red in the face.

" See here! " he exclaimed, " if you look in this well I'll give you a rap on the nose! "

Brother Rabbit leaned over the brink of the well, and saw the tar-doll smiling at him in the water. He raised his right hand and hit her—bam! His hand stuck.

" What's this? " exclaimed Brother Rabbit. " Turn me loose, imp of Satan! If you do not, I will rap you on the eye with my other hand."

Then he hit her—bim! The left hand stuck also. Then Brother Rabbit raised his right foot, saying:

"Mark me well, little Congo! Do you see this foot? I will kick you in the stomach if you do not turn me loose this instant."

No sooner said than done. Brother Rabbit let fly his right foot—vip! The foot stuck, and he raised the other.

" Do you see this foot? " he exclaimed. " If I hit you with it, you will think a thunderbolt has struck you."

Then he kicked her with the left foot, and it also stuck like the other, and Brother Rabbit held fast his Guinea negro.

" Watch out, now! " he cried. " I've already butted a great many people with my head. If I butt you in your ugly face I'll knock it into a jelly. Turn me loose! Oho! you don't answer?" Bap!

"Guinea girl!" exclaimed Brother Rabbit, "are you dead? Gracious goodness! how my head does stick!"

When the sun rose, Brother Goat went to his well to find out something about Brother Rabbit. The result was beyond his expectations.

"Hey, little rogue, big rogue!" exclaimed Brother Goat. "Hey, Brother Rabbit! what are you doing there? I thought you drank the dew from the cups of the flowers, or milk from the cows. Aha, Brother Rabbit! I will punish you for stealing my water."

"I am your friend," said Brother Rabbit; "don't kill me."

"Thief, thief!" cried Brother Goat, and then he ran quickly into the woods, gathered up a pile of dry limbs, and made a great fire. He took Brother Rabbit from the tar-doll, and prepared to burn him alive. As he was passing a thicket of brambles with Brother Rabbit on his shoulders, Brother Goat met his daughter Bélédie, who was walking about in the fields.

"Where are you going, papa, muffled up with such a burden? Come and eat the fresh grass with me, and throw wicked Brother Rabbit in the brambles."

Cunning Brother Rabbit raised his long ears and pretended to be very much frightened.

"Oh, no, Brother Goat!" he cried. "Don't throw me in the brambles. They will tear my flesh, put out my eyes, and pierce my heart. Oh, I pray you, rather throw me in the fire."

"Aha, little rogue, big rogue! Aha, Brother Rabbit!" exclaimed Brother Goat, exultingly, "you don't like the brambles? Well, then, go and laugh in them," and he threw Brother Rabbit in without a feeling of pity.

Brother Rabbit fell in the brambles, leaped to his feet, and began to laugh.

"Ha-ha-ha! Brother Goat, what a simpleton you are!—ha-ha-ha! A better bed I never had! In these brambles I was born!"

Brother Goat was in despair, but he could not help himself. Brother Rabbit was safe.

A long beard is not always a sign of intelligence.

SONNY'S CHRISTENIN'

BY

RUTH McENERY STUART

This is the story of character, in the form of dramatic monologue. There is only one speaker, but we know by his words that another is present and can infer his part in the conversation. This story has the additional values of humor and local color.

SONNY'S CHRISTENIN' *

Yas, sir, wife an' me, we've turned 'Piscopals—all on account o' Sonny. He seemed to prefer that religion, an' of co'se we wouldn't have the family divided, so we're a-goin' to be ez good 'Piscopals ez we can.

I reckon it'll come a little bit awkward at first. Seem like I never will git so thet I can sass back in church 'thout feelin' sort o' impident—but I reckon I'll chirp up an' come to it, in time.

I never was much of a hand to sound the amens, even in our own Methodist meetin's.

Sir? How old is he? Oh, Sonny's purty nigh six— but he showed a pref'ence for the 'Piscopal Church long fo' he could talk.

When he wasn't no mo' 'n three year old we commenced a-takin him round to church wherever they held meetin's,—'Piscopals, Methodists or Presbyterians,—so's he could see an' hear for hisself. I ca'yed him to a baptizin' over to Chinquepin Crik, once-t, when he was three. I thought I'd let him see it done an' maybe it might make a good impression; but no, sir! The Baptists didn't suit him! Cried ever' time one was douced, an' I had to fetch him away. In our Methodist meetin's he seemed to git worked up an' pervoked, some way. An' the Presbyterians, he didn't take no stock in them at all. Ricollect, one Sunday the preacher, he preached a mighty powerful disco'se on the doctrine o' lost infants not 'lected to salvation—an' Sonny? Why, he slep' right thoo it.

* From " Sonny, a Christmas Guest," by Ruth McEnery Stuart. Copyright, 1896, by The Century Co. Reprinted by special permission.

The first any way lively interest he ever seemed to take
in religious services was at the 'Piscopals, Easter Sunday.   When he seen the lilies an' the candles he thess
clapped his little hands, an' time the folks commenced
answerin' back he was tickled all but to death, an'
started answerin' hisself—on'y, of co'se he'd answer
sort o' hit an' miss.

I see then thet Sonny was a natu'al-born 'Piscopal, an'
we might ez well make up our minds to it—an' I told *her*
so, too.   They say some is born so.   But we thought
we'd let him alone an' let nature take its co'se for
a while—not pressin' him one way or another.   He never
had showed no disposition to be christened, an' ever
sence the doctor tried to vaccinate him he seemed to git
the notion that christenin' an' vaccination was mo' or
less the same thing; an' sence that time, he's been mo'
opposed to it than ever.

Sir?   Oh no, sir.   He didn't vaccinate him; he thess
tried to do it; but Sonny, he wouldn't begin to allow it.
We all tried to indoose 'im.   I offered him everything
on the farm ef he'd thess roll up his little sleeve an' let
the doctor look at his arm—promised him thet he
wouldn't tech a needle to it tell he said the word.   But
he wouldn't.   He 'lowed thet me an' his mamma could
git vaccinated ef we wanted to, but he wouldn't.

Then we showed him our marks where we had been
vaccinated when we was little, an' told him how it had
kep' us clair o' havin' the smallpock all our lives.

Well, sir, it didn't make no diff'ence whether we'd
been did befo' or not, he 'lowed thet he wanted to see
us vaccinated ag'in.

An' so, of co'se, thinkin' it might encour'ge him, we
thess had it did over—tryin' to coax him to consent
after each one, an' makin' pertend like we enjoyed it.

Then, nothin' would do but the nigger, Dicey, had

to be did, an' then he 'lowed thet he wanted the cat did, an' I tried to strike a bargain with him thet if Kitty got vaccinated he would. But he wouldn't comp'omise. He thess let on thet Kit had to be did whe'r or no. So I ast the doctor ef it would likely kill the cat, an' he said he reckoned not, though it might sicken her a little. So I told him to go ahead. Well, sir, befo' Sonny got thoo, he had had that cat an' both dogs vaccinated—but let it tech hisself he would not.

I was mighty sorry not to have it did, 'cause they was a nigger thet had the smallpock down to Cedar Branch, fifteen mile away, an' he didn't die, neither. He got well. An' they say when they git well they're more fatal to a neighborhood 'n when they die.

That was fo' months ago now, but to this day ever' time the wind blows from sou'west I feel oneasy, an' try to entice Sonny to play on the far side o' the house.

Well, sir, in about ten days after that we was the down-in-the-mouthest crowd on that farm, man an' beast, thet you ever see. Ever' last one o' them vaccinations took, sir, an' took severe, from the cat up.

But I reckon we're all safe-t guarded now. They ain't nothin' on the place thet can fetch it to Sonny, an' I trust, with care, he may never be exposed.

But I set out to tell you about Sonny's christenin' an' us turnin' 'Piscopal. Ez I said, he never seemed to want baptism, though he had heard us discuss all his life both it an' vaccination ez the two ordeels to be gone thoo with some time, an' we'd speculate ez to whether vaccination would take or not, an' all sech ez that, an' then, ez I said, after he see what the vaccination was, why he was even mo' prejudyced agin' baptism 'n ever, an' we 'lowed to let it run on tell sech a time ez he'd decide what name he'd want to take an' what denomination he'd want to bestow it on him.

Wife, she's got some 'Piscopal relations thet she sort o' looks up to,—though she don't own it,—but she was raised Methodist an' I was raised a true-blue Presbyterian. But when we professed after Sonny come we went up together at Methodist meetin'. What we was after was righteous livin', an' we didn't keer much which denomination helped us to it.

An' so, feelin' friendly all roun' that-a-way, we thought we'd leave Sonny to pick his church when he got ready, an' then they wouldn't be nothin' to undo or do over in case he went over to the 'Piscopals, which has the name of revisin' over any other church's performances—though sence we've turned 'Piscopals we've found out that ain't so.

Of co'se the preachers, they used to talk to us about it once-t in a while,—seemed to think it ought to be did, —'ceptin', of co'se, the Baptists.

Well, sir, it went along so till last week. Sonny ain't but, ez I said, thess not quite six year old, an' ther seemed to be time enough. But last week he had been playin' out o' doors bare-feeted, thess same ez he always does, an' he tramped on a pine splinter some way. Of co'se, pine, it's the safe-t-est splinter a person can run into a foot, on account of its carryin' its own turpentine in with it to heal up things; but any splinter thet dast to push itself up into a little pink foot is a messenger of trouble, an' we know it. An' so, when we see this one, we tried ever' way to coax him to let us take it out, but he wouldn't, of co'se. He never will, an' somehow the Lord seems to give 'em ambition to work their own way out mos' gen'ally.

But, sir, this splinter didn't seem to have no energy in it. It thess lodged there, an' his little foot it commenced to swell, an' it swole an' swole tell his little toes stuck out so thet the little pig thet went to market looked like ez ef it wasn't on speakin' terms with the little pig thet stayed home, an' wife an' me we watched it, an' I reckon she prayed over it consider'ble, an' I read a extry psalm at night befo' I went to bed, all on account o' that little foot. An' night befo' las' it was lookin' mighty angry an' swole, an' he had limped an' " ouched! " consider'ble all day, an' he was mighty fretful bed-time. So, after he went to sleep, wife she come out on the po'ch where I was settin', and she says to me, says she, her face all drawed up an' workin', says she : " Honey," says she, " I reckon we better sen' for him an' have it did." Thess so, she said it. " Sen' for who, wife? " says I, " an' have what did? " " Why, sen' for him, the 'Piscopal preacher," says she, " an' have Sonny christened. Them little toes o' hisn is ez red ez cherry tomatoes. They burnt my lips thess now like a coal o' fire an'—an' lockjaw is goin' roun' tur'ble.

" Seems to me," says she, " when he started to git sleepy, he didn't gap ez wide ez he gen'ly does—an' I'm 'feered he's a-gittin' it now." An', sir, with that, she thess gathered up her apron an' mopped her face in it an' give way. An' ez for me, I didn't seem to have no mo' backbone down my spinal colume 'n a feather bolster has, I was that weak.

I never ast her why she didn't sen' for our own preacher. I knowed then ez well ez ef she'd 'a' told me why she done it—all on account o' Sonny bein' so tickled over the 'Piscopals' meetin's.

It was mos' nine o'clock then, an' a dark night, an' rainin', but I never said a word—they wasn't no room round the edges o' the lump in my throat for words to come out ef they'd 'a' been one surgin' up there to say, which they wasn't—but I thess went out an' saddled my horse an' I rid into town. Stopped first at the doctor's an' sent him out, though I knowed 't wouldn't do

no good; Sonny wouldn't 'low him to tech it; but I sent
him out anyway, to look at it, an', ef possible, console
wife a little. Then I rid on to the rector's an' ast him to
come out immejate an' baptize Sonny. But nex' day
was his turn to preach down at Sandy Crik, an' he
couldn't come that night, but he promised to come right
after services nex' mornin'—which he done—rid the
whole fo'teen mile from Sandy Crik here in the rain, too,
which I think is a evidence o' Christianity, though no
sech acts is put down in my book o' " evidences " where
they ought rightfully to be.

Well, sir, when I got home that night, I found wife
a heap cheerfuler. The doctor had give Sonny a big
apple to eat an' pernounced him free from all symp-
toms o' lockjaw. But when I come the little feller had
crawled 'way back under the bed an' lay there, eatin'
his apple, an' they couldn't git him out. Soon ez the
doctor had teched a poultice to his foot he had woke up
an' put a stop to it, an' then he had went off by hisself
where nothin' couldn't pester him, to enjoy his apple in
peace. An' we never got him out tell he heered us tellin'
the doctor good-night.

I tried ever' way to git him out—even took up a coal
o' fire an' poked it under at him; but he thess laughed at
that an' helt his apple agin' it an' made it sizz. Well,
sir, he seemed so tickled that I helt that coal o' fire for
him tell he cooked a good big spot on one side o' the
apple, an' et it, an' then, when I took it out, he called
for another, but I didn't give it to him. I don't see no
use in over-indulgin' a child. An' when he knowed the
doctor was gone, he come out an' finished roastin' his
apple by the fire—thess what was left of it 'round the
co'e.

Well, sir, we was mightily comforted by the doctor's
visit, but nex' mornin' things looked purty gloomy ag'in.

That little foot seemed a heap worse, an' he was sort o' flushed an' feverish, an' wife she thought she heard a owl hoot, an' Rover made a mighty funny gurgly sound in his th'oat like ez ef he had bad news to tell us, but didn't have the courage to speak it.

An' then, on top o' that, the nigger Dicey, she come in an' 'lowed she had dreamed that night about eatin' spare-ribs, which everybody knows to dream about fresh pork out o' season, which this is July, is considered a shore sign o' death. Of co'se, wife an' me, we don't b'lieve in no sech ez that, but ef you ever come to see yo' little feller's toes stand out the way Sonny's done day befo' yesterday, why, sir, you'll be ready to b'lieve anything. It's so much better now, you can't judge of its looks day befo' yesterday. We never had even so much ez considered it necessary thet little children should be christened to have 'em saved, but when things got on the ticklish edge, like they was then, why, we felt thet the safest side is the wise side, an', of co'se, we want Sonny to have the best of everything. So, we was mighty thankful when we see the rector comin'. But, sir, when I went out to open the gate for him, what on top o' this round hemisp'ere do you reckon Sonny done? Why, sir, he thess took one look at the gate an' then he cut an' run hard ez he could—limped acrost the yard thess like a flash o' zig-zag lightnin'—an' 'fore anybody could stop him, he had clumb to the tip top o' the butter-bean arbor—clumb it thess like a cat—an' there he set, a-swingin' his feet under him, an' laughin', the rain thess a-streakin' his hair all over his face.

That bean arbor is a favoryte place for him to escape to, 'cause it's too high to reach, an' it ain't strong enough to bear no grown-up person's weight.

Well, sir, the rector, he come in an' opened his valise an' 'rayed hisself in his robes an' opened his book, an' while he was turnin' the leaves, he faced 'round an' says he, lookin' at me *direc*', says he:

" Let the child be brought forward for baptism," says he, thess that-a-way.

Well, sir, I looked at wife, an' wife, she looked at me, an' then we both thess looked out at the butter-bean arbor.

I knowed then thet Sonny wasn't never comin' down while the rector was there, an' rector, he seemed sort o' fretted for a minute when he see how things was, an' he did try to do a little settin' fo'th of opinions. He 'lowed, speakin' in a mighty pompious manner, thet holy things wasn't to be trifled with, an' thet he had come to baptize the child accordin' to the rites o' the church.

Well, that sort o' talk, it thess rubbed me the wrong way, an' I up an' told him thet that might be so, but thet the rites o' the church didn't count for nothin', on our farm, to the rights o' the boy!

I reckon it was mighty disrespec'ful o' me to face him that-a-way, an' him adorned in all his robes, too, but I'm thess a plain up-an'-down man an' I hadn't went for him to come an' baptize Sonny to uphold the granjer of no church. I was ready to do that when the time come, but right now we was workin' in Sonny's interests, an' I intended to have it understood that way. An' it was.

Rector, he's a mighty good, kind-hearted man, git down to the man inside the preacher, an' when he see thess how things stood, why, he come 'round friendly, an' he went out on the po'ch an' united with us in tryin' to help coax Sonny down. First started by promisin' him spiritual benefits, but he soon see that wasn't no go, and he tried worldly persuasion; but no, sir, stid o' him comin' down, Sonny started orderin' the rest of us christened thess the way he done about the vaccination. But, of co'se, we had been baptized befo', an' we nachelly helt out agin' that for some time. But d'rec'ly rector, he seemed to have a sudden idee, an' says he, facin' 'round, church-like, to wife an' me, says he:

"Have you both been baptized accordin' to the rites o' the church?"

An' me, thinkin' of co'se he meant the 'Piscopal Church, says: "No, sir," says I, thess so. And then we see that the way was open for us to be did over ag'in ef we wanted to. So, sir, wife an' me we was took into the church, then an' there. We wouldn't 'a' yielded to him, thoo an' thoo, that-a-way ag'in ef his little foot hadn't 'a' been so swole, an' he maybe takin' his death o' cold settin' out in the po'in'-down rain; but things bein' as they was, we went thoo it with all due respects.

Then he commenced callin' for Dicey, an' the dog, an' the cat, to be did, same ez he done befo'; but, of co'se, they's some liberties thet even a innocent child can't take with the waters o' baptism, an' the rector he got sort o' wo'e-out and disgusted an' 'lowed thet 'less'n we could get the child ready for baptism he'd haf to go home.

Well, sir, I knowed we wouldn't never git 'im down, an' I had went for the rector to baptize him, an' I intended to have it did, ef possible. So, says I, turnin' 'round an' facin' him square, says I: "Rector," says I, "why not baptize him where he is? I mean it. The waters o' Heaven are descendin' upon him where he sets, an' seems to me ef he's favo'bly situated for anything it is for baptism." Well, parson, he thess looked at me up an' down for a minute, like ez ef he s'picioned I was wanderin' in my mind, but he didn't faze me. I thess kep' up my argiment. Says I: "Parson," says I, speakin' thess ez ca'm ez I am this minute—"Parson," says I, " his little foot is mighty swole, an' so'e, an' that splinter—thess s'pose he was to take the lockjaw an' die—don't you reckon you might do it where he sets— from where you stand? "

Wife, she was cryin' by this time, an' parson, he claired his th'oat an' coughed, an' then he commenced walkin' up an' down, an' treckly he stopped, an' says he, speakin' mighty reverential an' serious:

" Lookin' at this case speritually, an' as a minister o' the Gospel," says he, " it seems to me thet the question ain't so much a question of *doin'* ez it is a question of *withholdin'*. I don't know," says he, " ez I've got a right to withhold the sacrament of baptism from a child under these circumstances or to deny sech comfort to his parents ez lies in my power to bestow."

An', sir, with that he stepped out to the end o' the po'ch, opened his book ag'in, an' holdin' up his right hand to'ards Sonny, settin' on top o' the bean-arbor in the rain, he commenced to read the service o' baptism, an' we stood proxies—which is a sort o' a dummy substitutes—for whatever godfather an' mother Sonny see fit to choose in after life.

Parson, he looked half like ez ef he'd laugh once-t. When he had thess opened his book and started to speak, a sudden streak o' sunshine shot out an' the rain started to ease up, an' it looked for a minute ez ef he was goin' to lose the baptismal waters. But d'rec'ly it come down stiddy ag'in an' he went thoo the programme entire.

An' Sonny, he behaved mighty purty; set up perfec'ly ca'm an' composed thoo it all, an' took everything in good part, though he didn't p'intedly know who was bein' baptized, 'cause, of co'se, he couldn't hear the words with the rain in his ears.

He didn't rightly sense the situation tell it come to the part where it says: " Name this child," and, of

co'se, I called out to Sonny to name hisself, which it
had always been our intention to let him do.

" Name yo'self, right quick, like a good boy," says I.

Of co'se Sonny had all his life heered me say thet
I was Deuteronomy Jones, Senior, an' thet I hoped
some day when he got christened he'd be the junior.
He knowed that by heart, an' would agree to it or
dispute it, 'cordin' to how the notion took him, and I
sort o' ca'culated thet he'd out with it now. But no,
sir! Not a word! He thess sot up on thet bean-arbor
an' grinned.

An' so, feelin' put to it, with the services suspended
over my head, I spoke up, an' I says: " Parson," says
I, " I reckon ef he was to speak his little heart, he'd
say Deuteronomy Jones, Junior." An' with thet what
does Sonny do but conterdic' me flat! " No, not Junior!
I want to be named Deuteronomy Jones, Senior! " says
he, thess so. An' parson, he looked to'ards me, an' I
bowed my head an' he pronounced thess one single name,
" Deuteronomy," an' I see he wasn't goin' to say no
more an' so I spoke up quick, an' says I: " Parson,"
says I, " he has spoke his heart's desire. He has named
hisself after me entire—Deuteronomy Jones, Senior."

An' so he was obligated to say it, an' so it is writ
in the family record colume in the big Bible, though I
spelt his Senior with a little s, an' writ him down ez
the only son of the Senior with the big S, which it seems
to me fixes it about right for the time bein'.

Well, when the rector had got thoo an' he had wropped
up his robes an' put 'em in his wallet, an' had told us
to prepare for conformation, he pernounced a blessin'
upon us an' went.

Then Sonny seein' it was all over, why, *he come down.*
He was wet ez a drownded rat, but wife rubbed him
off an' give him some hot tea an' he come a-snuggin'

up in my lap, thess ez sweet a child ez you ever see in yo' life, an' I talked to him ez fatherly ez I could, told him we was all 'Piscopals now, an' soon ez his little foot got well I was goin' to take him out to Sunday-school to tote a banner—all his little 'Piscopal friends totes banners—an' thet he could pick out some purty candles for the altar, an' he 'lowed immejate thet he'd buy pink ones. Sonny always was death on pink—showed it from the time he could snatch a pink rose —an' wife she ain't never dressed him in nothin' else. Ever' pair o' little breeches he's got is either pink or pink-trimmed.

Well, I talked along to him till I worked 'round to shamin' him a little for havin' to be christened settin' up on top a bean-arbor, same ez a crow-bird, which I told him the parson he wouldn't 'a' done ef he'd 'a' felt free to 've left it undone. 'Twasn't to indulge him he done it, but to bless him an' to comfort our hearts. Well, after I had reasoned with him severe that-a-way a while, he says, says he, thess ez sweet an' mild, says he, " Daddy, nex' time y'all gits christened, I'll come down an' be christened right—like a good boy."

Th' ain't a sweeter child in'ardly 'n what Sonny is, nowheres, git him to feel right comf'table, and I know it, an' that's why I have patience with his little out'ard ways.

" Yes, sir," says he; " nex' time I'll be christened like a good boy."

Then, of co'se, I explained to him thet it couldn't never be did no mo', 'cause it had been did, an' did 'Piscopal, which is secure. An' then what you reckon the little feller said?

Says he, " Yes, daddy, but *s'pos'in' mine don't take.* How 'bout that? "

An' I didn't try to explain no further. What was

the use? Wife, she had drawed a stool close-t up to my knee, an' set there sortin' out the little yaller rings ez they'd dry out on his head, an' when he said that I thess looked at her an' we both looked at him, an' says I, "Wife," says I, "ef they's anything in heavenly looks an' behavior, I b'lieve that christenin' is started to take on him a'ready."

An' I b'lieve it had.

CHRISTMAS NIGHT WITH SATAN

BY

JOHN FOX, JR.

" All that is literature seeks to communicate power." *
Here the power communicated is that of sympathizing
with God's "lesser children." The humanitarian story
is a long step in advance of the fable. It recognizes
the true relations of the animal world to man, and insists that it be dealt with righteously and sympathetically.

* De Quincey, "Letters to a Young Man."

CHRISTMAS NIGHT WITH SATAN *

No night was this in Hades with solemn-eyed Dante, for Satan was only a woolly little black dog, and surely no dog was ever more absurdly misnamed. When Uncle Carey first heard that name, he asked gravely:

" Why, Dinnie, where in h——," Uncle Carey gulped slightly, " did you get him? " And Dinnie laughed merrily, for she saw the fun of the question, and shook her black curls.

" He didn't come f'um *that place*."

Distinctly Satan had not come from that place. On the contrary, he might by a miracle have dropped straight from some Happy Hunting-Ground, for all the signs he gave of having touched pitch in this or another sphere. Nothing human was ever born that was gentler, merrier, more trusting or more lovable than Satan. That was why Uncle Carey said again gravely that he could hardly tell Satan and his little mistress apart. He rarely saw them apart, and as both had black tangled hair and bright black eyes; as one awoke every morning with a happy smile and the other with a jolly bark; as they played all day like wind-shaken shadows and each won every heart at first sight—the likeness was really rather curious. I have always believed that Satan made the spirit of Dinnie's house, orthodox and severe though it was, almost kindly toward his great namesake. I know I have never been able, since I knew little Satan, to think old Satan as bad as I once painted

* From " Christmas Eve on Lonesome," by John Fox, Jr. Copyright, 1904, by Charles Scribner's Sons.

him, though I am sure the little dog had many pretty
tricks that the " old boy " doubtless has never used in
order to amuse his friends.

" Shut the door, Saty, please," Dinnie would say, precisely as she would say it to Uncle Billy, the butler, and
straightway Satan would launch himself at it—bang!
He never would learn to close it softly, for Satan liked
that—bang!

If you kept tossing a coin or marble in the air, Satan
would keep catching it and putting it back in your
hand for another throw, till you got tired. Then he
would drop it on a piece of rag carpet, snatch the carpet with his teeth, throw the coin across the room, and
rush for it like mad, until he got tired. If you put a
penny on his nose, he would wait until you counted,
one—two—*three!* Then he would toss it up himself
and catch it. Thus, perhaps, Satan grew to love Mam-
mon right well, but for another and better reason than
that he liked simply to throw it around—as shall now
be made plain.

A rubber ball with a hole in it was his favorite play-
thing, and he would take it in his mouth and rush around
the house like a child, squeezing it to make it whistle.
When he got a new ball, he would hide his old one
away until the new one was the worse worn of the two,
and then he would bring out the old one again. If
Dinnie gave him a nickel or a dime, when they went
down-town, Satan would rush into a store, rear up
on the counter where the rubber balls were kept, drop
the coin, and get a ball for himself. Thus, Satan learned
finance. He began to hoard his pennies, and one day
Uncle Carey found a pile of seventeen under a corner
of the carpet. Usually he carried to Dinnie all coins
that he found in the street, but he showed one day
that he was going into the ball-business for himself.

Uncle Carey had given Dinnie a nickel for some candy, and, as usual, Satan trotted down the street behind her. As usual, Satan stopped before the knick-knack shop.

" Tum on, Saty," said Dinnie. Satan reared against the door as he always did, and Dinnie said again:

" Tum on, Saty." As usual, Satan dropped to his haunches, but what was unusual, he failed to bark. Now Dinnie had got a new ball for Satan only that morning, so Dinnie stamped her foot.

" I tell you to tum on, Saty." Satan never moved. He looked at Dinnie as much as to say:

" I have never disobeyed you before, little mistress, but this time I have an excellent reason for what must seem to you very bad manners——" and being a gentleman withal, Satan rose on his haunches and begged.

" You're des a pig, Saty," said Dinnie, but with a sigh for the candy that was not to be, Dinnie opened the door, and Satan, to her wonder, rushed to the counter, put his forepaws on it, and dropped from his mouth a dime. Satan had found that coin on the street. He didn't bark for change, nor beg for two balls, but he had got it in his woolly little head, somehow, that in that store a coin meant a ball, though never before nor afterward did he try to get a ball for a penny.

Satan slept in Uncle Carey's room, for of all people, after Dinnie, Satan loved Uncle Carey best. Every day at noon he would go to an upstairs window and watch the cars come around the corner, until a very tall, square-shouldered young man swung to the ground, and down Satan would scamper—yelping—to meet him at the gate. If Uncle Carey, after supper and when Dinnie was in bed, started out of the house, still in his business clothes, Satan would leap out before him, knowing that he too might be allowed to go; but if Uncle Carey had put on black clothes that showed a big, dazzling shirt-front, and picked up his high hat, Satan would sit perfectly still and look disconsolate; for as there were no parties or theatres for Dinnie, so there were none for him. But no matter how late it was when Uncle Carey came home, he always saw Satan's little black nose against the window-pane and heard his bark of welcome.

After intelligence, Satan's chief trait was lovableness—nobody ever knew him to fight, to snap at anything, or to get angry; after lovableness, it was politeness. If he wanted something to eat, if he wanted Dinnie to go to bed, if he wanted to get out of the door, he would beg—beg prettily on his haunches, his little red tongue out and his funny little paws hanging loosely. Indeed, it was just because Satan was so little less than human, I suppose, that old Satan began to be afraid he might have a soul. So the wicked old namesake with the Hoofs and Horns laid a trap for little Satan, and, as he is apt to do, he began laying it early—long, indeed, before Christmas.

When Dinnie started to kindergarten that autumn, Satan found that there was one place where he could never go. Like the lamb, he could not go to school; so while Dinnie was away, Satan began to make friends. He would bark, " Howdy-do? " to every dog that passed his gate. Many stopped to rub noses with him through the fence—even Hugo the mastiff, and nearly all, indeed, except one strange-looking dog that appeared every morning at precisely nine o'clock and took his stand on the corner. There he would lie patiently until a funeral came along, and then Satan would see him take his place at the head of the procession; and thus he would march out to the cemetery and back again. Nobody knew where he came from nor where he went, and Uncle Carey called him the " funeral dog " and said he was doubtless looking for his dead master. Satan even made friends with a scrawny little yellow dog that followed an old drunk· ard around—a dog that, when his master fell in the gutter, would go and catch a policeman by the coat-tail, lead the officer to his helpless master, and spend the night with him in jail.

By and by Satan began to slip out of the house at night, and Uncle Billy said he reckoned Satan had " jined de club "; and late one night, when he had not come in, Uncle Billy told Uncle Carey that it was " powerful slippery and he reckoned they'd better send de kerridge after him "—an innocent remark that made Uncle Carey send a boot after the old butler, who fled chuckling down the stairs, and left Uncle Carey chuckling in his room.

Satan had " jined de club "—the big club—and no dog was too lowly in Satan's eyes for admission; for no priest ever preached the brotherhood of man better than Satan lived it—both with man and dog. And thus he lived it that Christmas night—to his sorrow.

Christmas Eve had been gloomy—the gloomiest of Satan's life. Uncle Carey had gone to a neighboring town at noon. Satan had followed him down to the station, and when the train started, Uncle Carey had ordered him to go home. Satan took his time about going home, not knowing it was Christmas Eve. He found strange things happening to dogs that day. The truth was, that policemen were shooting all dogs found that were without a collar and a license, and every now and then a bang and a howl somewhere would stop Satan in his tracks. At a little yellow house on the edge of town he saw half a dozen strange dogs in a kennel, and every now and then a negro would lead a new one up to the house and deliver him to a big man at the door, who, in return, would drop something into the negro's hand. While Satan waited, the old drunkard came along with his little dog at his heels, paused before the door, looked a moment at his faithful follower, and went slowly on. Satan little knew the old drunkard's temptation, for in that yellow house kind-hearted people had offered fifteen cents for each dog brought to them, without a license, that they might mercifully put it to death, and fifteen cents was the precise price for a drink of good whiskey. Just then there was another bang and another howl somewhere, and Satan trotted home to meet a calamity. Dinnie was gone. Her mother had taken her out in the country to Grandmother Dean's to spend Christmas, as was the family custom, and Mrs. Dean would not wait any longer for Satan; so she told Uncle Billy to bring him out after supper.

" Ain't you 'shamed o' yo'self—suh—? " said the old butler; " keeping me from ketchin' Christmas gifts dis day? "

Uncle Billy was indignant, for the negroes begin at four o'clock in the afternoon of Christmas Eve to slip around corners and jump from hiding-places to shout " Christmas Gif'—Christmas Gif' ' "; and the one who shouts first gets a gift. No wonder it was gloomy for Satan—Uncle Carey, Dinnie, and all gone, and not a soul but Uncle Billy in the big house. Every few minutes he would trot on his little black legs upstairs and downstairs, looking for his mistress. As dusk came on, he would every now and then howl plaintively. After begging his supper, and while Uncle Billy was hitching up a horse in the stable, Satan went out in the yard and lay with his nose between the close panels of the fence—quite heart-broken. When he saw his old friend, Hugo the mastiff, trotting into the gaslight, he began to bark his delight frantically. The big mastiff stopped and nosed his sympathy through the fence for a moment and walked slowly on, Satan frisking and barking along inside. At the gate Hugo stopped, and raising one huge paw, playfully struck it. The gate flew open, and with a happy yelp Satan leaped into the street. The noble mastiff hesitated as though this were not quite regular. He did not belong to the club, and he didn't know that Satan had ever been away from home after dark in his life. For a moment he seemed to wait for Dinnie to call him back as she always did, but this time there was no sound, and Hugo walked majestically on, with absurd little Satan running in a circle about him. On the way they met the "funeral dog," who glanced inquiringly at Satan, shied from the mastiff, and trotted on. On the next block the old drunkard's yellow cur ran across the street, and after interchanging the compliments of the season, ran back after his staggering master. As they approached the railroad track a strange dog joined them, to whom Hugo paid no attention. At the crossing another new acquaintance bounded toward them. This one—a half-breed shepherd—was quite friendly, and he received Satan's advances with affable condescension. Then another came and another, and little Satan's head got quite confused. They were a queer-looking lot of curs and half-breeds from the negro settlement at the edge of the woods, and though Satan had little experience, his instincts told him that all was not as it should be, and had he been human he would have wondered very much how they had escaped the carnage that day. Uneasy, he looked around for Hugo; but Hugo had disappeared. Once or twice Hugo had looked around for Satan, and Satan paying no attention, the mastiff trotted on home in disgust. Just then a powerful yellow cur sprang out of the darkness over the railroad track, and Satan sprang to meet him, and so nearly had the life scared out of him by the snarl and flashing fangs of the new-comer that he hardly had the strength to shrink back behind his new friend, the half-breed shepherd.

A strange thing then happened. The other dogs became suddenly quiet, and every eye was on the yellow cur. He sniffed the air once or twice, gave two or three peculiar low growls, and all those dogs except Satan lost the civilization of centuries and went back suddenly to the time when they were wolves and were looking for a leader. The cur was Lobo for that little pack, and after a short parley, he lifted his nose high and started away without looking back, while the other dogs silently trotted after him. With a mystified yelp, Satan ran after them. The cur did not take the turnpike, but jumped the fence into a field, making his way by the rear of houses, from which now and then another dog would slink out and silently join the band. Every one of them Satan nosed most friendlily, and to his great joy the funeral dog, on the edge of town, leaped into their midst. Ten minutes later the cur stopped in the midst of some woods, as though he would inspect his followers. Plainly, he disapproved of Satan, and Satan kept out of his way. Then he sprang into the turnpike and the band trotted down it, under flying black clouds and shifting bands of brilliant moonlight. Once, a buggy swept past them. A familiar odor struck Satan's nose, and he stopped for a moment to smell the horse's tracks; and right he was, too, for out at her grandmother's Dinnie refused to be comforted, and in that buggy was Uncle Billy going back to town after him.

Snow was falling. It was a great lark for Satan. Once or twice, as he trotted along, he had to bark his joy aloud, and each time the big cur gave him such a fierce

growl that he feared thereafter to open his jaws. But
he was happy for all that, to be running out into the
night with such a lot of funny friends and not to know
or care where he was going. He got pretty tired presently, for over hill and down hill they went, at that
unceasing trot, trot, trot! Satan's tongue began to
hang out. Once he stopped to rest, but the loneliness
frightened him and he ran on after them with his heart
almost bursting. He was about to lie right down and
die, when the cur stopped, sniffed the air once or twice,
and with those same low growls, led the marauders
through a rail fence into the woods, and lay quietly
down. How Satan loved that soft, thick grass, all snowy
that it was! It was almost as good as his own bed at
home. And there they lay—how long, Satan never knew,
for he went to sleep and dreamed that he was after a
rat in the barn at home; and he yelped in his sleep,
which made the cur lift his big yellow head and show
his fangs. The moving of the half-breed shepherd and
the funeral dog waked him at last, and Satan got up.
Half crouching, the cur was leading the way toward
the dark, still woods on top of the hill, over which
the Star of Bethlehem was lowly sinking, and under
which lay a flock of the gentle creatures that seemed to
have been almost sacred to the Lord of that Star. They
were in sore need of a watchful shepherd now. Satan
was stiff and chilled, but he was rested and had had
his sleep, and he was just as ready for fun as he always
was. He didn't understand that sneaking. Why they
didn't all jump and race and bark as he wanted to, he
couldn't see; but he was too polite to do otherwise than
as they did, and so he sneaked after them; and one
would have thought he knew, as well as the rest, the
hellish mission on which they were bent.

Out of the woods they went, across a little branch,

and there the big cur lay flat again in the grass. A faint
bleat came from the hill-side beyond, where Satan could
see another woods—and then another bleat, and another. And the cur began to creep again, like a snake
in the grass; and the others crept too, and little Satan
crept, though it was all a sad mystery to him. Again
the cur lay still, but only long enough for Satan to see
curious, fat, white shapes above him—and then, with a
blood-curdling growl, the big brute dashed forward. Oh,
there was fun in them after all! Satan barked joyfully.
Those were some new playmates—those fat, white, hairy
things up there; and Satan was amazed when, with
frightened snorts, they fled in every direction. But this
was a new game, perhaps, of which he knew nothing,
and as did the rest, so did Satan. He picked out one
of the white things and fled barking after it. It was
a little fellow that he was after, but little as he was,
Satan might never have caught up, had not the sheep
got tangled in some brush. Satan danced about him
in mad glee, giving him a playful nip at his wool and
springing back to give him another nip, and then away
again. Plainly, he was not going to bite back, and when
the sheep struggled itself tired and sank down in a
heap, Satan came close and licked him, and as he was
very warm and woolly, he lay down and snuggled up
against him for a while, listening to the turmoil that
was going on around him. And as he listened, he got
frightened.

If this was a new game it was certainly a very peculiar one—the wild rush, the bleats of terror, gasps of
agony, and the fiendish growls of attack and the sounds
of ravenous gluttony. With every hair bristling, Satan
rose and sprang from the woods—and stopped with a
fierce tingling of the nerves that brought him horror
and fascination. One of the white shapes lay still be-

fore him. There was a great steaming red splotch on the snow, and a strange odor in the air that made him dizzy; but only for a moment. Another white shape rushed by. A tawny streak followed, and then, in a patch of moonlight, Satan saw the yellow cur with his teeth fastened in the throat of his moaning playmate. Like lightning Satan sprang at the cur, who tossed him ten feet away and went back to his awful work. Again Satan leaped, but just then a shout rose behind him, and the cur leaped too as though a bolt of lightning had crashed over him, and, no longer noticing Satan or sheep, began to quiver with fright and slink away. Another shout rose from another direction—another from another.

"Drive 'em into the barn-yard!" was the cry.

Now and then there was a fearful bang and a howl of death-agony, as some dog tried to break through the encircling men, who yelled and cursed as they closed in on the trembling brutes that slunk together and crept on; for it is said, every sheep-killing dog knows his fate if caught, and will make little effort to escape. With them went Satan, through the barn-yard gate, where they huddled in a corner—a shamed and terrified group. A tall overseer stood at the gate.

"Ten of 'em!" he said grimly.

He had been on the lookout for just such a tragedy, for there had recently been a sheep-killing raid on several farms in that neighborhood, and for several nights he had had a lantern hung out on the edge of the woods to scare the dogs away; but a drunken farm-hand had neglected his duty that Christmas Eve.

"Yassuh, an' dey's jus' sebenteen dead sheep out dar," said a negro.

"Look at the little one," said a tall boy who looked like the overseer; and Satan knew that he spoke of him.

" Go back to the house, son," said the overseer, " and tell your mother to give you a Christmas present I got for you yesterday." With a glad whoop the boy dashed away, and in a moment dashed back with a brand-new .32 Winchester in his hand.

The dark hour before dawn was just breaking on Christmas Day. It was the hour when Satan usually rushed upstairs to see if his little mistress was asleep. If he were only at home now, and if he only had known how his little mistress was weeping for him amid her playthings and his—two new balls and a brass-studded collar with a silver plate on which was his name, Satan Dean; and if Dinnie could have seen him now, her heart would have broken; for the tall boy raised his gun. There was a jet of smoke, a sharp, clean crack, and the funeral dog started on the right way at last toward his dead master. Another crack, and the yellow cur leaped from the ground and fell kicking. Another crack and another, and with each crack a dog tumbled, until little Satan sat on his haunches amid the writhing pack, alone. His time was now come. As the rifle was raised, he heard up at the big house the cries of children; the popping of fire-crackers; tooting of horns and whistles and loud shouts of " Christmas Gif', Christmas Gif'! " His little heart beat furiously. Perhaps he knew just what he was doing; perhaps it was the accident of habit; most likely Satan simply wanted to go home—but when that gun rose, Satan rose too, on his haunches, his tongue out, his black eyes steady and his funny little paws hanging loosely—and begged! The boy lowered the gun.

" Down, sir! " Satan dropped obediently, but when the gun was lifted again, Satan rose again, and again he begged.

" Down, I tell you! " This time Satan would not down, but sat begging for his life. The boy turned.

"Papa, I can't shoot that dog." Perhaps Satan had reached the stern old overseer's heart. Perhaps he remembered suddenly that it was Christmas. At any rate, he said gruffly:

"Well, let him go."

"Come here, sir!" Satan bounded toward the tall boy, frisking and trustful and begged again.

"Go home, sir!"

Satan needed no second command. Without a sound he fled out the barn-yard, and, as he swept under the front gate, a little girl ran out of the front door of the big house and dashed down the steps, shrieking:

"Saty! Saty! Oh, Saty!" But Satan never heard. On he fled, across the crisp fields, leaped the fence and struck the road, lickety-split! for home, while Dinnie dropped sobbing in the snow.

"Hitch up a horse, quick," said Uncle Carey, rushing after Dinnie and taking her up in his arms. Ten minutes later, Uncle Carey and Dinnie, both warmly bundled up, were after flying Satan. They never caught him until they reached the hill on the outskirts of town, where was the kennel of the kind-hearted people who were giving painless death to Satan's four-footed kind, and where they saw him stop and turn from the road. There was divine providence in Satan's flight for one little dog that Christmas morning; for Uncle Carey saw the old drunkard staggering down the road without his little companion, and a moment later, both he and Dinnie saw Satan nosing a little yellow cur between the palings. Uncle Carey knew the little cur, and while Dinnie was shrieking for Satan, he was saying under his breath:

"Well, I swear!—I swear!—I swear!" And while the big man who came to the door was putting Satan into Dinnie's arms, he said sharply:

" Who brought that yellow dog here? " The man pointed to the old drunkard's figure turning a corner at the foot of the hill.

" I thought so; I thought so. He sold him to you for—for a drink of whiskey."

The man whistled.

" Bring him out. I'll pay his license."

So back went Satan and the little cur to Grandmother Dean's—and Dinnie cried when Uncle Carey told her why he was taking the little cur along. With her own hands she put Satan's old collar on the little brute, took him to the kitchen, and fed him first of all. Then she went into the breakfast-room.

" Uncle Billy," she said severely, " didn't I tell you not to let Saty out? "

" Yes, Miss Dinnie," said the old butler.

" Didn't 1 tell you I was goin' to whoop you if you let Saty out? "

" Yes, Miss Dinnie."

Miss Dinnie pulled forth from her Christmas treasures a toy riding-whip and the old darky's eyes began to roll in mock terror.

" I'm sorry, Uncle Billy, but I des got to whoop you a little."

" Let Uncle Billy off, Dinnie," said Uncle Carey, " this is Christmas."

" All wite," said Dinnie, and she turned to Satan.

In his shining new collar and innocent as a cherub, Satan sat on the hearth begging for his breakfast.

A NEST-EGG

BY

JAMES WHITCOMB RILEY

This is the simple character sketch in which there is romance treated with a fine reserve. It employs the local color so characteristic of Mr. Riley's poems of Indiana.

A NEST-EGG *

But a few miles from the city here, and on the sloping banks of the stream noted more for its plenitude of
" chubs " and " shiners " than the gamier two- and
four-pound bass for which, in season, so many credulous
anglers flock and lie in wait, stands a country residence,
so convenient to the stream, and so inviting in its pleasant exterior and comfortable surroundings—barn, dairy,
and spring-house—that the weary, sunburnt, and dis-
heartened fisherman, out from the dusty town for a
day of recreation, is often wont to seek its hospitality.
The house in style of architecture is something of a departure from the typical farmhouse, being designed
and fashioned with no regard to symmetry or propor-
tion, but rather, as is suggested, built to conform to the
matter-of-fact and most sensible ideas of its owner, who,
if it pleased him, would have small windows where large
ones ought to be, and vice versa, whether they balanced
properly to the eye or not. And chimneys—he would
have as many as he wanted, and no two alike, in either
height or size. And if he wanted the front of the house
turned from all possible view, as though abashed at any
chance of public scrutiny, why, that was his affair and
not the public's; and, with like perverseness, if he chose
to thrust his kitchen under the public's very nose, what
should the generally fagged-out, half-famished representative of that dignified public do but reel in his dead

* From Volume VI of the Biographical Edition of the Complete Works of James Whitcomb Riley, copyright, 1913. Used
by special permission of the publishers, the Bobbs-Merrill Company.

minnow, shoulder his fishing-rod, clamber over the back fence of the old farmhouse and inquire within, or jog back to the city, inwardly anathematizing that very particular locality or the whole rural district in general. That is just the way that farmhouse looked to the writer of this sketch one week ago—so individual it seemed— so liberal, and yet so independent. It wasn't even weather-boarded, but, instead, was covered smoothly with some cement, as though the plasterers had come while the folks were visiting, and so, unable to get at the interior, had just plastered the outside.

I am more than glad that I was hungry enough, and weary enough, and wise enough to take the house at its first suggestion; for, putting away my fishing-tackle for the morning, at least, I went up the sloping bank, crossed the dusty road, and confidently clambered over the fence.

Not even a growling dog to intimate that I was trespassing. All was open—gracious-looking—pastoral. The sward beneath my feet was velvet-like in elasticity, and the scarce visible path I followed through it led promptly to the open kitchen door. From within I heard a woman singing some old ballad in an undertone, while at the threshold a trim, white-spurred rooster stood poised on one foot, curving his glossy neck and cocking his wattled head as though to catch the meaning of the words. I paused. It was a scene I felt restrained from breaking in upon, nor would I, but for the sound of a strong male voice coming around the corner of the house:

" Sir. Howdy ! "

Turning, I saw a rough-looking but kindly featured man of sixty-five, the evident owner of the place.

I returned his salutation with some confusion and much deference. " I must really beg your pardon for this intrusion," I began, " but I have been tiring myself out fishing, and your home here looked so pleasant—and I felt so thirsty—and——"

" Want a drink, I reckon," said the old man, turning abruptly toward the kitchen door, then pausing as suddenly, with a backward motion of his thumb—" jest foller the path here down to the little brick—that's the spring—and you'll find 'at you've come to the right place fer drinkin'-worter! Hold on a minute tel I git you a tumbler—there're nothin' down there but a tin."

" Then don't trouble yourself any further," I said, heartily, " for I'd rather drink from a tin cup than a goblet of pure gold."

" And so'd I," said the old man, reflectively, turning mechanically, and following me down the path. " 'Druther drink out of a tin—er jest a fruit-can with the top knocked off—er—er—er a gourd," he added in a zestful, reminiscent tone of voice, that so heightened my impatient thirst that I reached the spring-house fairly in a run.

" Well-sir! " exclaimed my host, in evident delight, as I stood dipping my nose in the second cupful of the cool, revivifying liquid, and peering in a congratulatory kind of way at the blurred and rubicund reflection of my features in the bottom of the cup, " well-sir, blame-don! ef it don't do a feller good to see you enjoyin' of it that-away! But don't you drink too much o' the worter!— 'cause there're some sweet milk over there in one o' them crocks, maybe; and ef you'll jest, kindo' keerful-like, lift off the led of that third one, say, over there to yer left, and dip you out a tinful er two o' that, w'y, it'll do you good to drink it, and it'll do me good to see you at it—— But hold up!—hold up! " he called, abruptly, as, nowise loath, I bent above the vessel designated. " Hold yer hosses fer a second! Here's Marthy; let her git it fer ye."

If I was at first surprised and confused, meeting the master of the house, I was wholly startled and chagrined in my present position before its mistress. But as I arose, and stammered, in my confusion, some incoherent apology, I was again reassured and put at greater ease by the comprehensive and forgiving smile the woman gave me, as I yielded her my place, and, with lifted hat, awaited her further kindness.

" I came just in time, sir," she said, half laughingly, as with strong, bare arms she reached across the gurgling trough and replaced the lid that I had partially removed.—" I came just in time, I see, to prevent father from having you dip into the ' morning's-milk,' which, of course, has scarcely a veil of cream over the face of it, as yet. But men, as you are doubtless willing to admit," she went on jocularly, " don't know about these things. You must pardon father, as much for his well-meaning ignorance of such matters, as for this cup of cream, which I am sure you will better relish."

She arose, still smiling, with her eyes turned frankly on my own. And I must be excused when I confess that as I bowed my thanks, taking the proffered cup and lifting it to my lips, I stared with an uncommon interest and pleasure at the donor's face.

She was a woman of certainly not less than forty years of age. But the figure, and the rounded grace and fulness of it, together with the features and the eyes, completed as fine a specimen of physical and mental health as ever it has been my fortune to meet; there was something so full of purpose and resolve—something so wholesome, too, about the character—something so womanly— I might almost say manly, and would, but for the petty prejudice maybe occasioned by the trivial fact of a locket having dropped from her bosom as she knelt; and that trinket still dangles in my memory even as it then dangled and dropped back to its concealment in her breast as she arose. But her face, by no means handsome in the common meaning, was marked with a breadth and strength of outline and expression that approached the heroic—a face that once seen is forever fixed in memory—a personage once met one must know more of. And so it was, that an hour later, as I strolled with the old man about his farm, looking, to all intents, with the profoundest interest at his Devonshires, Shorthorns, Jerseys, and the like, I lured from him something of an outline of his daughter's history.

" There're no better girl 'n Marthy! " he said, mechanically answering some ingenious allusion to her worth. " And yit," he went on reflectively, stooping from his seat in the barn door and with his open jack-knife picking up a little chip with the point of the blade—" and yit—you wouldn't believe it—but Marthy was the oldest o' three daughters, and hed—I may say—hed more advantages o' marryin'—and yit, as I was jest goin' to say, she's the very one 'at didn't marry. Hed every advantage—Marthy did. W'y, we even hed her educated— her mother was a-livin' then—and we was well enough fixed to afford the educatin' of her, mother allus contended—and we was—besides, it was Marthy's notion, too, and you know how women is thataway when they git their head set. So we sent Marthy down to Indianop'lus, and got her books and putt her in school there, and paid fer her keepin' and ever'thing; and she jest—well, you may say, lived there stiddy fer better'n four year. O' course she'd git back ever' once-an-a-while, but her visits was allus, some-way-another, onsatisfactory-like, 'cause, you see, Marthy was allus my favorite, and I'd allus laughed and told her 'at the other girls could git married if they wanted, but *she* was goin' to be the ' nest-egg ' of our family, and 'slong as I lived I wanted her at home

with me. And she'd laugh and contend 'at she'd as lif
be an old maid as not, and never expected to marry,
ner didn't want to. But she had me sceart onc't,
though! Come out from the city one time, durin' the
army, with a peart-lookin' young feller in blue clothes
and gilt straps on his shoulders. Young lieutenant he
was—name o' Morris. Was layin' in camp there in the
city somers. I disremember which camp it was now ad-
zackly—but anyway, it 'peared like he had plenty o'
time to go and come, fer from that time on he kep'
on a-comin'—ever' time Marthy 'ud come home, he'd
come, too; and I got to noticin' 'at Marthy come home
a good 'eal more'n she used to afore Morris first brought
her. And blame ef the thing didn't git to worryin' me!
And onc't I spoke to mother about it, and told her ef
I thought the feller wanted to marry Marthy I'd jest
stop his comin' right then and there. But mother she
sorto' smiled and said somepin' 'bout men a-never seein'
through nothin'; and when I ast her what she meant,
w'y, she ups and tells me 'at Morris didn't keer nothin'
fer Marthy, ner Marthy fer Morris, and then went on
to tell me that Morris was kindo' aidgin' up to'rds Annie
—she was next to Marthy, you know, in pint of years
and experience, but ever'body allus said 'at Annie was
the purtiest one o' the whole three of 'em. And so when
mother told me 'at the signs pinted to'rds Annie, w'y, of
course, I hedn't no particular objections to that, 'cause
Morris was of good fambly enough it turned out, and,
in fact, was as stirrin' a young feller as ever I'd want
fer a son-in-law, and so I hed nothin' more to say—ner
they wasn't no occasion to say nothin', 'cause right along
about then I begin to notice 'at Marthy quit comin'
home so much, and Morris kep' a-comin' more. Tel
finally, one time he was out here all by hisself, 'long
about dusk, come out here where I was feedin', and ast

me, all at onc't, and in a straight-for'ard way, ef he couldn't marry Annie; and, some-way-another, blame ef it didn't make me as happy as him when I told him yes! You see that thing proved, pine-blank, 'at he wasn't a-fishin' round fer Marthy. Well-sir, as luck would hev it, Marthy got home about a half-hour later, and I'll give you my word I was never so glad to see the girl in my life! It was foolish in me, I reckon, but when I see her drivin' up the lane—it was purt' nigh dark then, but I could see her through the open winder from where I was settin' at the supper-table, and so I jest quietly excused myself, p'lite-like, as a feller will, you know, when they's comp'ny round, and I slipped off and met her jest as she was about to git out to open the barn gate. ' Hold up, Marthy,' says I; ' set right where you air; I'll open the gate fer you, and I'll do anything else fer you in the world 'at you want me to!'

" ' W'y, what's pleased *you* so? ' she says, laughin', as she druv through slow-like and a-ticklin' my nose with the cracker of the buggy-whip.—' What's pleased *you?* '

" ' Guess,' says I, jerkin' the gate to, and turnin' to lift her out.

" ' The new peanner's come? ' says she, eager-like.

" ' Yer new peanner's come,' says I; ' but that's not it.'

" ' Strawberries fer supper? ' says she.

" ' Strawberries fer supper,' says I; ' but that ain't it.'

" Jest then Morris's hoss whinnied in the barn, and she glanced up quick and smilin' and says, ' Somebody come to see somebody? '

" ' You're a-gittin' warm,' says I.

" ' Somebody come to see *me?* ' she says, anxious-like.

" ' No,' says I, ' and I'm glad of it—fer this one 'at's

come wants to git married, and o' course I wouldn't harber in my house no young feller 'at was a-layin' round fer a chance to steal away the "Nest-egg,"' says I, laughin'.

"Marthy had riz up in the buggy by this time, but as I helt up my hands to her, she sorto' drawed back a minute, and says, all serious-like and kindo' whisperin':

"'Is it *Annie?*'

"I nodded. 'Yes,' says I, 'and what's more, I've give my consent, and mother's give hern—the thing's all settled. Come, jump out and run in and be happy with the rest of us!' and I helt out my hands ag'in, but she didn't 'pear to take no heed. She was kindo' pale, too, I thought, and swallered a time er two like as ef she couldn't speak plain.

"'Who is the man?' she ast.

"'Who—who's the man?' I says, a-gittin' kindo' out o' patience with the girl.—'W'y, you know who it is, o' course.—It's Morris,' says I. 'Come, jump down! Don't you see I'm waitin' fer ye?'

"'Then take me,' she says; and blame-don! ef the girl didn't keel right over in my arms as limber as a rag! Clean fainted away! Honest! Jest the excitement, I reckon, o' breakin' it to her so suddent-like—'cause she liked Annie, I've sometimes thought, better'n even she did her own mother. Didn't go half so hard with her when her other sister married. Yes-sir!" said the old man, by way of sweeping conclusion, as he rose to his feet—"Marthy's the on'y one of 'em 'at never married—both the others is gone—Morris went all through the army and got back safe and sound—'s livin' in Idyho, and doin' fust-rate. Sends me a letter ever' now and then. Got three little chunks o' grandchildren out there, and I' never laid eyes on one of 'em. You see, I'm a-gittin' to be quite a middle-aged man—in fact, a very middle-aged man, you might say. Sence mother died, which has be'n—lem-me-see—mother's be'n dead somers in the neighborhood o' ten year.—Sence mother died I've be'n a-gittin' more and more o' *Marthy's* notion—that is,—you couldn't ever hire *me* to marry nobody! and them has allus be'n and still is the ' Nest-egg's ' views! Listen! That's her a-callin' fer us now. You must sorto' overlook the freedom, but I told Marthy you'd promised to take dinner with us to-day, and it 'ud never do to disappint her now. Come on.'' And, ah! it would have made the soul of you either rapturously glad or madly envious to see how meekly I consented.

I am always thinking that I never tasted coffee till that day; I am always thinking of the crisp and steaming rolls, ored over with the molten gold that hinted of the clover-fields, and the bees that had not yet permitted the honey of the bloom and the white blood of the stalk to be divorced; I am always thinking that the young and tender pullet we happy three discussed was a near and dear relative of the gay patrician rooster that I first caught peering so inquisitively in at the kitchen door; and I am always—always thinking of '' The Nest-egg.''

WEE WILLIE WINKIE

BY

RUDYARD KIPLING

As the sub-title, " An Officer and a Gentleman," indicates, this is a story of character. Mr. Kipling, like Robert Louis Stevenson, James Whitcomb Riley, and Eugene Field, has carried into his maturity an imperishable youth of spirit which makes him an interpreter of children. Here he has shown what our Anglo-Saxon ideals—honor, obedience, and reverence for woman—mean to a little child.

WEE WILLIE WINKIE *

" An officer and a gentleman."

His full name was Percival William Williams, but he picked up the other name in a nursery-book, and that was the end of the christened titles. His mother's *ayah* called him Willie-*Baba*, but as he never paid the faintest attention to anything that the *ayah* said, her wisdom did not help matters.

His father was the Colonel of the 195th, and as soon as Wee Willie Winkie was old enough to understand what Military Discipline meant, Colonel Williams put him under it. There was no other way of managing the child. When he was good for a week, he drew good-conduct pay; and when he was bad, he was deprived of his good-conduct stripe. Generally he was bad, for India offers many chances of going wrong to little six-year-olds.

Children resent familiarity from strangers, and Wee Willie Winkie was a very particular child. Once he accepted an acquaintance, he was graciously pleased to thaw. He accepted Brandis, a subaltern of the 195th, on sight. Brandis was having tea at the Colonel's, and Wee Willie Winkie entered strong in the possession of a good-conduct badge won for not chasing the hens round the compound. He regarded Brandis with gravity for at least ten minutes, and then delivered himself of his opinion.

" I like you," said he slowly, getting off his chair and coming over to Brandis. " I like you. I shall call you

* From " Under the Deodars," by Rudyard Kipling. Copyright, 1899, by Rudyard Kipling. Reprinted by special permission of Doubleday, Page and Company.

Coppy, because of your hair. Do you *mind* being called Coppy? It is because of ve hair, you know."

Here was one of the most embarrassing of Wee Willie Winkie's peculiarities. He would look at a stranger for some time, and then, without warning or explanation, would give him a name. And the name stuck. No regimental penalties could break Wee Willie Winkie of this habit. He lost his good-conduct badge for christening the Commissioner's wife " Pobs "; but nothing that the Colonel could do made the Station forego the nickname, and Mrs. Collen remained " Pobs " till the end of her stay. So Brandis was christened " Coppy," and rose, therefore, in the estimation of the regiment.

If Wee Willie Winkie took an interest in any one, the fortunate man was envied alike by the mess and the rank and file. And in their envy lay no suspicion of self-interest. " The Colonel's son " was idolized on his own merits entirely. Yet Wee Willie Winkie was not lovely. His face was permanently freckled, as his legs were permanently scratched, and in spite of his mother's almost tearful remonstrances he had insisted upon having his long yellow locks cut short in the military fashion. " I want my hair like Sergeant Tummil's," said Wee Willie Winkie, and, his father abetting, the sacrifice was accomplished.

Three weeks after the bestowal of his youthful affections on Lieutenant Brandis—henceforward to be called " Coppy " for the sake of brevity—Wee Willie Winkie was destined to behold strange things and far beyond his comprehension.

Coppy returned his liking with interest. Coppy had let him wear for five rapturous minutes his own big sword—just as tall as Wee Willie Winkie. Coppy had promised him a terrier puppy, and Coppy had permitted him to witness the miraculous operation of shaving.

Nay, more—Coppy had said that even he, Wee Willie
Winkie, would rise in time to the ownership of a box
of shiny knives, a silver soap-box, and a silver-handled
" sputter-brush," as Wee Willie Winkie called it. De-
cidedly, there was no one except his own father, who
could give or take away good-conduct badges at pleasure, half so wise, strong, and valiant as Coppy with
the Afghan and Egyptian medals on his breast. Why,
then, should Coppy be guilty of the unmanly weakness
of kissing—vehemently kissing—a " big girl," Miss
Allardyce to wit? In the course of a morning ride Wee
Willie Winkie had seen Coppy so doing, and, like the
gentleman he was, had promptly wheeled round and cantered back to his groom, lest the groom should also see.

Under ordinary circumstances he would have spoken
to his father, but he felt instinctively that this was a
matter on which Coppy ought first to be consulted.

" Coppy," shouted Wee Willie Winkie, reining up
outside that subaltern's bungalow early one morning—
" I want to see you, Coppy! "

" Come in, young 'un," returned Coppy, who was
at early breakfast in the midst of his dogs. " What mischief have you been getting into now? "

Wee Willie Winkie had done nothing notoriously bad
for three days, and so stood on a pinnacle of virtue.

" *I've* been doing nothing bad," said he, curling himself into a long chair with a studious affectation of the
Colonel's languor after a hot parade. He buried his
freckled nose in a tea-cup and, with eyes staring roundly
over the rim, asked: " I say, Coppy, is it pwoper to kiss
big girls? "

" By Jove! You're beginning early. Who do you
want to kiss? "

" No one. My muvver's always kissing me if I don't
stop her. If it isn't pwoper, how was you kissing

Major Allardyce's big girl last morning, by ve canal?''

Coppy's brow wrinkled. He and Miss Allardyce had with great craft managed to keep their engagement secret for a fortnight. There were urgent and imperative reasons why Major Allardyce should not know how matters stood for at least another month, and this small marplot had discovered a great deal too much.

"I saw you," said Wee Willie Winkie calmly. "But ve *sais* didn't see. I said, '*Hut jao!*'"

"Oh, you had that much sense, you young Rip," groaned poor Coppy, half amused and half angry. "And how many people may you have told about it?''

"Only me myself. You didn't tell when I twied to wide ve buffalo ven my pony was lame; and I fought you wouldn't like."

"Winkie," said Coppy enthusiastically, shaking the small hand, "you're the best of good fellows. Look here, you can't understand all these things. One of these days—hang it, how can I make you see it!—I'm going to marry Miss Allardyce, and then she'll be Mrs. Coppy, as you say. If your young mind is so scandalized at the idea of kissing big girls, go and tell your father."

"What will happen?" said Wee Willie Winkie, who firmly believed that his father was omnipotent.

"I shall get into trouble," said Coppy, playing his trump card with an appealing look at the holder of the ace.

"Ven I won't," said Wee Willie Winkie briefly. "But my faver says it's un-man-ly to be always kissing, and I didn't fink *you'd* do vat, Coppy."

"I'm not always kissing, old chap. It's only now and then, and when you're bigger you'll do it too. Your father meant it's not good for little boys."

" Ah! " said Wee Willie Winkie, now fully enlightened. " It's like ve sputter-brush? "

" Exactly," said Coppy gravely.

" But I don't fink I'll ever want to kiss big girls, nor no one, 'cept my muvver. And I *must* do vat, you know."

There was a long pause, broken by Wee Willie Winkie.

" Are you fond of vis big girl, Coppy? "

" Awfully! " said Coppy.

" Fonder van you are of Bell or ve Butcha—or me? "

" It's in a different way," said Coppy. " You see, one of these days Miss Allerdyce will belong to me, but you'll grow up and command the Regiment and— all sorts of things. It's quite different, you see."

" Very well," said Wee Willie Winkie, rising. " If you're fond of ve big girl, I won't tell any one. I must go now."

Coppy rose and escorted his small guest to the door, adding—" You're the best of little fellows, Winkie. I tell you what. In thirty days from now you can tell if you like—tell any one you like."

Thus the secret of the Brandis-Allardyce engagement was dependent on a little child's word. Coppy, who knew Wee Willie Winkie's idea of truth, was at ease, for he felt that he would not break promises. Wee Willie Winkie betrayed a special and unusual interest in Miss Allardyce, and, slowly revolving round that embarrassed young lady, was used to regard her gravely with unwinking eye. He was trying to discover why Coppy should have kissed her. She was not half so nice as his own mother. On the other hand, she was Coppy's property, and would in time belong to him. Therefore it behooved him to treat her with as much respect as Coppy's big sword or shiny pistol.

The idea that he shared a great secret in common with Coppy kept Wee Willie Winkie unusually virtuous for three weeks. Then the Old Adam broke out, and he made what he called a " camp-fire " at the bottom of the garden. How could he have foreseen that the flying Sparks would have lighted the Colonel's little hay-rick and consumed a week's store for the horses? Sudden and swift was the punishment—deprivation of the good-conduct badge and, most sorrowful of all, two days' confinement to barracks—the house and veranda—coupled with the withdrawal of the light of his father's countenance.

He took the sentence like the man he strove to be, drew himself up with a quivering under-lip, saluted, and, once clear of the room, ran to weep bitterly in his nursery—called by him " my quarters." Coppy came in the afternoon and attempted to console the culprit.

" I'm under awwest," said Wee Willie Winkie mournfully, "and I didn't ought to speak to you."

Very early the next morning he climbed on to the roof of the house—that was not forbidden—and beheld Miss Allardyce going for a ride.

" Where are you going? " cried Wee Willie Winkie.

" Across the river," she answered, and trotted forward.

Now the cantonment in which the 195th lay was bounded on the north by a river—dry in the winter. From his earliest years, Wee Willie Winkie had been forbidden to go across the river, and had noted that even Coppy—the almost almighty Coppy—had never set foot beyond it. Wee Willie Winkie had once been read to, out of a big blue book, the history of the Princess and the Goblins—a most wonderful tale of a land where the Goblins were always warring with the children of men until they were defeated by one Curdie. Ever

since that date it seemed to him that the bare black and
purple hills across the river were inhabited by Goblins,
and, in truth, every one had said that there lived the
Bad Men. Even in his own house the lower halves of
the windows were covered with green paper on account
of the Bad Men who might, if allowed clear view, fire
into peaceful drawing-rooms and comfortable bedrooms.
Certainly, beyond the river, which was the end of all
the Earth, lived the Bad Men. And here was Major
Allardyce's big girl, Coppy's property, preparing to
venture into their borders! What would Coppy say if
anything happened to her? If the Goblins ran off with
her as they did with Curdie's Princess? She must at
all hazards be turned back.

The house was still. Wee Willie Winkie reflected
for a moment on the very terrible wrath of his father;
and then—broke his arrest! It was a crime unspeakable. The low sun threw his shadow, very large and
very black, on the trim garden-paths, as he went down
to the stables and ordered his pony. It seemed to him
in the hush of the dawn that all the big world had
been bidden to stand still and look at Wee Willie Winkie
guilty of mutiny. The drowsy *sais* gave him his mount,
and, since the one great sin made all others insignificant,
Wee Willie Winkie said that he was going to ride over
to Coppy Sahib, and went out at a foot-pace, stepping
on the soft mould of the flower-borders.

The devastating track of the pony's feet was the last
misdeed that cut him off from all sympathy of Humanity. He turned into the road, leaned forward, and rode
as fast as the pony could put foot to the ground in the
direction of the river.

But the liveliest of twelve-two ponies can do little
against the long canter of a Waler. Miss Allardyce was
far ahead, had passed through the crops, beyond the

Police-posts, when all the guards were asleep, and her mount was scattering the pebbles of the river-bed as Wee Willie Winkie left the cantonment and British India behind him. Bowed forward and still flogging, Wee Willie Winkie shot into Afghan territory, and could just see Miss Allardyce a black speck flickering across the stony plain. The reason of her wandering was simple enough. Coppy, in a tone of too-hastily-assumed authority, had told her over night that she must not ride out by the river. And she had gone to prove her own spirit and teach Coppy a lesson.

Almost at the foot of the inhospitable hills, Wee Willie Winkie saw the Waler blunder and come down heavily. Miss Allardyce struggled clear, but her ankle had been severely twisted, and she could not stand. Having fully shown her spirit, she wept, and was surprised by the apparition of a white, wide-eyed child in khaki, on a nearly spent pony.

" Are you badly, badly hurted? " shouted Wee Willie Winkie, as soon as he was within range. " You didn't ought to be here."

" I don't know," said Miss Allardyce ruefully, ignoring the reproof. " Good gracious, child, what are *you* doing here? "

" You said you was going acwoss ve wiver," panted Wee Willie Winkie, throwing himself off his pony. " And nobody—not even Coppy—must go acwoss ve wiver, and I came after you ever so hard, but you wouldn't stop, and now you've hurted yourself, and Coppy will be angwy wiv me, and—I've bwoken my awwest! I've bwoken my awwest! "

The future Colonel of the 195th sat down and sobbed. In spite of the pain in her ankle, the girl was moved.

" Have you ridden all the way from cantonments, little man? What for? "

" You belonged to Coppy. Coppy told me so!"
wailed Wee Willie Winkie disconsolately. " I saw him
kissing you, and he said he was fonder of you van Bell
or ve Butcha or me. And so I came. You must get up
and come back. You didn't ought to be here. Vis is
a bad place, and I've bwoken my awwest."

" I can't move, Winkie," said Miss Allardyce, with a
groan. " I've hurt my foot. What shall I do?"

She showed a readiness to weep anew, which steadied
Wee Willie Winkie, who had been brought up to believe
that tears were the depth of unmanliness. Still, when
one is as great a sinner as Wee Willie Winkie, even a
man may be permitted to break down.

" Winkie," said Miss Allardyce, " when you've rested
a little, ride back and tell them to send out something
to carry me back in. It hurts fearfully."

The child sat still for a little time, and Miss Allardyce closed her eyes; the pain was nearly making her
faint. She was roused by Wee Willie Winkie tying up
the reins on his pony's neck and setting it free with
a vicious cut of his whip that made it whicker. The
little animal headed towards the cantonments.

" Oh, Winkie! What are you doing?"

" Hush!" said Wee Willie Winkie. " Vere's a man
coming—one of ve Bad Men. I must stay wiv you.
My faver says a man must *always* look after a girl.
Jack will go home, and ven vey'll come and look for us.
Vat's why I let him go."

Not one man, but two or three, had appeared from
behind the rocks of the hills, and the heart of Wee
Willie Winkie sank within him, for just in this manner
were the Goblins wont to steal out and vex Curdie's
soul. Thus had they played in Curdie's garden (he
had seen the picture), and thus had they frightened the
Princess's nurse. He heard them talking to each other,

and recognized with joy the bastard Pushto that he had picked up from one of his father's grooms lately dismissed. People who spoke that tongue could not be the Bad Men. They were only natives, after all.

They came up to the boulders on which Miss Allardyce's horse had blundered.

Then rose from the rock Wee Willie Winkie, child of the Dominant Race, aged six and three-quarters, and said briefly and emphatically, " *Jao!* " The pony had crossed the river-bed.

The man laughed, and laughter from natives was the one thing Wee Willie Winkie could not tolerate. He asked them what they wanted and why they did not depart. Other men with most evil faces and crooked-stocked guns crept out of the shadows of the hills, till, soon, Wee Willie Winkie was face to face with an audience some twenty strong. Miss Allardyce screamed.

" Who are you? " said one of the men.

" I am the Colonel Sahib's son, and my order is that you go at once. You black men are frightening the Miss Sahib. One of you must run into cantonments and take the news that the Miss Sahib has hurt herself, and that the Colonel's son is here with her."

" Put our feet into the trap? " was the laughing reply. " Hear this boy's speech! "

" Say that I sent you—I, the Colonel's son. They will give you money."

" What is the use of this talk? Take up the child and the girl, and we can at least ask for the ransom. Ours are the villages on the heights," said a voice in the background.

These *were* the Bad Men—worse than Goblins—and it needed all Wee Willie Winkie's training to prevent him from bursting into tears. But he felt that to cry before a native, excepting only his mother's *ayah,* would be an infamy greater than any mutiny. Moreover, he, as future Colonel of the 195th, had that grim regiment at his back.

" Are you going to carry us away? " said Wee Willie Winkie, very blanched and uncomfortable.

" Yes, my little Sahib Bahadur," said the tallest of the men, " and eat you afterwards."

" That is child's talk," said Wee Willie Winkie. " Men do not eat men."

A yell of laughter interrupted him, but he went on firmly—" And if you do carry us away, I tell you that all my regiment will come up in a day and kill you all without leaving one. Who will take my message to the Colonel Sahib? "

Speech in any vernacular—and Wee Willie Winkie had a colloquial acquaintance with three—was easy to the boy who could not yet manage his " r's " and " th's " aright.

Another man joined the conference, crying, " O foolish men! What this babe says is true. He is the heart's heart of those white troops. For the sake of peace let them go both, for if he be taken, the regiment will break loose and gut the valley. *Our* villages are in the valley, and we shall not escape. That regiment are devils. They broke Khoda Yar's breastbone with kicks when he tried to take the rifles; and if we touch this child they will fire and rape and plunder for a month till nothing remains. Better to send a man back to take the message and get a reward. I say that this child is their God, and that they will spare none of us, nor our women, if we harm him."

It was Din Mahommed, the dismissed groom of the Colonel, who made the diversion, and an angry and heated discussion followed. Wee Willie Winkie, standing over Miss Allardyce, waited the upshot. Surely his

" wegiment," his own " wegiment," would not desert him if they knew of his extremity.

. . . .

The riderless pony brought the news to the 195th, though there had been consternation in the Colonel's household for an hour before. The little beast came in through the parade-ground in front of the main barracks, where the men were settling down to play Spoil-five till the afternoon. Devlin, the Color-Sergeant of E Company, glanced at the empty saddle and tumbled through the barrack-rooms, kicking up each Room Corporal as he passed. " Up, ye beggars! There's something happened to the Colonel's son," he shouted.

" He couldn't fall off! S'help me, 'e *couldn't* fall off," blubbered a drummer-boy. " Go an' hunt acrost the river. He's over there if he's anywhere, an' maybe those Pathans have got 'im. For the love o' Gawd don't look for 'im in the nullahs! Let's go over the river."

" There's sense in Mott yet," said Devlin. " E Company, double out to the river—sharp! "

So E Company, in its shirt-sleeves mainly, doubled for the dear life, and in the rear toiled the perspiring Sergeant, adjuring it to double yet faster. The cantonment was alive with the men of the 195th hunting for Wee Willie Winkie, and the Colonel finally overtook E Company, far too exhausted to swear, struggling in the pebbles of the river-bed.

Up the hill under which Wee Willie Winkie's Bad Men were discussing the wisdom of carrying off the child and the girl, a look-out fired two shots.

" What have I said? " shouted Din Mahommed. " There is the warning! The *pulton* are out already and are coming across the plain! Get away! Let us not be seen with the boy! "

The men waited for an instant, and then, as another

shot was fired, withdrew into the hills, silently as they had appeared.

" The wegiment is coming," said Wee Willie Winkie confidently to Miss Allardyce, " and it's all wight. Don't cwy ! "

He needed the advice himself, for ten minutes later, when his father came up, he was weeping bitterly with his head in Miss Allardyce's lap.

And the men of the 195th carried him home with shouts and rejoicings; and Coppy, who had ridden a horse into a lather, met him, and, to his intense disgust, kissed him openly in the presence of the men.

But there was balm for his dignity. His father assured him that not only would the breaking of arrest be condoned, but that the good-conduct badge would be restored as soon as his mother could sew it on his blouse-sleeve. Miss Allardyce had told the Colonel a story that made him proud of his son.

" She belonged to you, Coppy," said Wee Willie Winkie, indicating Miss Allardyce with a grimy fore-finger. " I *knew* she didn't ought to go acwoss ve wiver, and I knew ve wegiment would come to me if I sent Jack home."

" You're a hero, Winkie," said Coppy—" a *pukka* hero ! "

" I don't know what vat means," said Wee Willie Winkie, " but you mustn't call me Winkie any no more. I'm Percival Will'am Will'ams."

And in this manner did Wee Willie Winkie enter into his manhood.

THE GOLD BUG

BY
EDGAR ALLAN POE

Poe was the first American short-story writer. Others had written stories that were short, but he was the first to recognize the short-story as having a form and an aim all its own. Moreover, he was willing to admit the public to his laboratory and to explain his process, for he discounted inspiration and emphasized craftsmanship. In "The Philosophy of Composition" he declares that every plot "must be elaborated to its dénouement before anything is attempted with the pen. It is only with the dénouement constantly in view that we can give a plot its indispensable air of consequence, or causation, by making the incidents and especially the tone, at all points, tend to the development of the intention." He also tells us that he prefers beginning with an effect. Having chosen, in the first place, an effect that is both novel and vivid, he decides "whether it can be best wrought by incident or tone," and afterward looks about "for such combinations of events, or tone, as shall best aid . . . in the construction of the effect."

In view of such explanations, it is interesting to study "The Gold Bug" and to see how well the plot has been worked out and the tone established. It is doubtful whether in this story the plot meant to the writer what it means to the reader. The latter likes the adventure with its ingeniously fitted parts, each so necessary to the whole. But after the gold has been found—and that is the point of greatest interest—the story goes on and on to explain the cryptogram. This, no doubt, was to Poe the most interesting thing about the story, the tracing of the steps by which the scrap of parchment was deciphered and reasoned upon and made to yield up its secret. As to the time and place, the strange conduct and character of Legrand, the fears and superstitions of Jupiter, and the puzzled solicitude of the narrator—all these aid materially in establishing and maintaining the tone.

THE GOLD BUG *

"What ho! what ho! this fellow is dancing mad!
He hath been bitten by the Tarantula."
—*All in the Wrong.*

Many years ago, I contracted an intimacy with a Mr.
William Legrand. He was of an ancient Huguenot
family, and had once been wealthy; but a series of
misfortunes had reduced him to want. To avoid the
mortification consequent upon his disasters, he left New
Orleans, the city of his forefathers, and took up his
residence at Sullivan's Island, near Charleston, South
Carolina.

This island is a very singular one. It consists of
little else than the sea sand, and is about three miles
long. Its breadth at no point exceeds a quarter of a
mile. It is separated from the mainland by a scarcely
perceptible creek, oozing its way through a wilderness
of reeds and slime, a favorite resort of the marsh-hen.
The vegetation, as might be supposed, is scant, or at
least dwarfish. No trees of any magnitude are to be
seen. Near the western extremity, where Fort Moultrie
stands, and where are some miserable frame buildings,
tenanted during summer by the fugitives from Charleston dust and fever, may be found, indeed, the bristly
palmetto; but the whole island, with the exception of
this western point, and a line of hard white beach on
the seacoast, is covered with a dense undergrowth of
the sweet myrtle, so much prized by the horticulturists

* From "The Works of Edgar Allan Poe," published by Charles
Scribner's Sons.

of England. The shrub here often attains the height of fifteen or twenty feet, and forms an almost impenetrable coppice, burdening the air with its fragrance.

In the utmost recesses of this coppice, not far from the eastern or more remote end of the island, Legrand had built himself a small hut, which he occupied when I first, by mere accident, made his acquaintance. This soon ripened into friendship—for there was much in the recluse to excite interest and esteem. I found him well educated, with unusual powers of mind, but infected with misanthropy, and subject to perverse moods of alternate enthusiasm and melancholy. He had with him many books, but rarely employed them. His chief amusements were gunning and fishing, or sauntering along the beach and through the myrtles, in quest of shells or entomological specimens;—his collection of the latter might have been envied by a Swammerdamm. In these excursions he was usually accompanied by an old negro, called Jupiter, who had been manumitted before the reverses of the family, but who could be induced, neither by threats nor by promises, to abandon what he considered his right of attendance upon the footsteps of his young "Massa Will." It is not improbable that the relatives of Legrand, conceiving him to be somewhat unsettled in intellect, had contrived to instil this obstinacy into Jupiter, with a view to the supervision and guardianship of the wanderer.

The winters in the latitude of Sullivan's Island are seldom very severe, and in the fall of the year it is a rare event indeed when a fire is considered necessary. About the middle of October, 18—, there occurred, however, a day of remarkable chilliness. Just before sunset I scrambled my way through the evergreens to the hut of my friend, whom I had not visited for several weeks— my residence being at that time in Charleston, a distance of nine miles from the island, while the facilities of passage and re-passage were very far behind those of the present day. Upon reaching the hut I rapped, as was my custom, and, getting no reply, sought for the key where I knew it was secreted, unlocked the door and went in. A fine fire was blazing upon the hearth. It was a novelty, and by no means an ungrateful one. I threw off an overcoat, took an armchair by the crackling logs, and awaited patiently the arrival of my hosts.

Soon after dark they arrived, and gave me a most cordial welcome. Jupiter, grinning from ear to ear, bustled about to prepare some marsh-hens for supper. Legrand was in one of his fits—how else shall I term them?—of enthusiasm. He had found an unknown bivalve, forming a new genus, and, more than this, he had hunted down and secured, with Jupiter's assistance, a *scarabæus* which he believed to be totally new, but in respect to which he wished to have my opinion on the morrow.

"And why not to-night?" I asked, rubbing my hands over the blaze, and wishing the whole tribe of *scarabæi* at the devil.

"Ah, if I had only known you were here!" said Legrand, "but it's so long since I saw you; and how could I foresee that you would pay me a visit this very night of all others? As I was coming home I met Lieutenant G——, from the fort, and, very foolishly, I lent him the bug; so it will be impossible for you to see it until the morning. Stay here to-night, and I will send Jup down for it at sunrise. It is the loveliest thing in creation!"

"What?—sunrise?"

"Nonsense! no!—the bug. It is of a brilliant gold color—about the size of a large hickory-nut—with two jet black spots near one extremity of the back, and

another, somewhat longer, at the other. The *antennæ*
are——"

" Dey aint *no* tin in him, Massa Will, I keep a-tellin'
on you," here interrupted Jupiter; " de bug is a goole-
bug, solid, ebery bit of him, inside and all, sep him
wing—neber feel half so hebby a bug in my life."

" Well, suppose it is, Jup," replied Legrand, somewhat more earnestly, it seemed to me, than the case
demanded, " is that any reason for your letting the
birds burn? The color "—here he turned to me—" is
really almost enough to warrant Jupiter's idea. You
never saw a more brilliant metallic lustre than the scales
emit—but of this you cannot judge till to-morrow. In
the mean time I can give you some idea of the shape."
Saying this, he seated himself at a small table, on which
were a pen and ink, but no paper. He looked for some
in a drawer, but found none.

" Never mind," said he at length, " this will answer; "
and he drew from his waistcoat pocket a scrap of what I
took to be very dirty foolscap, and made upon it a
rough drawing with the pen. While he did this, I retained my seat by the fire, for I was still chilly. When
the design was complete, he handed it to me without
rising. As I received it, a low growl was heard, succeeded by a scratching at the door. Jupiter opened it,
and a large Newfoundland, belonging to Legrand, rushed
in, leaped upon my shoulders, and loaded me with
caresses; for I had shown him much attention during
previous visits. When his gambols were over, I looked
at the paper, and, to speak the truth, found myself not
a little puzzled at what my friend had depicted.

" Well! " I said, after contemplating it for some
minutes, " this *is* a strange *scarabæus*, I must confess;
new to me: never saw anything like it before—unless
it was a skull, or a death's-head, which it more nearly

resembles than anything else that has come under *my* observation.''

'' A death's-head!'' echoed Legrand—'' Oh—yes—well, it has something of that appearance upon paper, no doubt. The two upper black spots look like eyes, eh? and the longer one at the bottom like a mouth—and then the shape of the whole is oval.''

'' Perhaps so,'' said I; '' but, Legrand, I fear you are no artist. I must wait until I see the beetle itself, if I am to form any idea of its personal appearance.''

'' Well, I don't know,'' said he, a little nettled, '' I draw tolerably—*should* do it at least—have had good masters, and flatter myself that I am not quite a block-head.''

'' But, my dear fellow, you are joking then,'' said I, '' this is a very passable *skull*,—indeed, I may say that it is a very *excellent* skull, according to the vulgar notions about such specimens of physiology—and your *scarabæus* must be the queerest *scarabæus* in the world if it resembles it. Why, we may get up a very thrilling bit of superstition upon this hint. I presume you will call the bug *scarabæus caput hominis,* or something of that kind—there are many similar titles in the Natural Histories. But where are the *antennæ* you spoke of?''

'' The *antennæ!*'' said Legrand, who seemed to be getting unaccountably warm upon the subject; '' I am sure you must see the *antennæ.* I made them as distinct as they are in the original insect, and I presume that is sufficient.''

'' Well, well,'' I said, '' perhaps you have—still I don't see them;'' and I handed him the paper without additional remark, not wishing to ruffle his temper; but I was much surprised at the turn affairs had taken; his ill humor puzzled me—and, as for the drawing of

the beetle, there were positively *no antennæ* visible, and
the whole *did* bear a very close resemblance to the ordinary cuts of a death's-head.

He received the paper very peevishly, and was about
to crumple it, apparently to throw it in the fire, when a
casual glance at the design seemed suddenly to rivet
his attention. In an instant his face grew violently red
—in another as excessively pale. For some minutes he
continued to scrutinize the drawing minutely where he
sat. At length he arose, took a candle from the table,
and proceeded to seat himself upon a sea-chest in the
farthest corner of the room. Here again he made an
anxious examination of the paper; turning it in all
directions. He said nothing, however, and his conduct
greatly astonished me; yet I thought it prudent not
to exacerbate the growing moodiness of his temper by
any comment. Presently he took from his coat pocket
a wallet, placed the paper carefully in it, and deposited
both in a writing-desk, which he locked. He now grew
more composed in his demeanor; but his original air
of enthusiasm had quite disappeared. Yet he seemed
not so much sulky as abstracted. As the evening wore
away he became more and more absorbed in revery,
from which no sallies of mine could arouse him. It had
been my intention to pass the night at the hut, as I
had frequently done before, but, seeing my host in this
mood, I deemed it proper to take leave. He did not
press me to remain, but, as I departed, he shook my hand
with even more than his usual cordiality.

It was about a month after this (and during the
interval I had seen nothing of Legrand) when I received a visit, at Charleston, from his man, Jupiter. I
had never seen the good old negro look so dispirited, and
I feared that some serious disaster had befallen my
friend.

" Well, Jup," said I, " what is the matter now?—
how is your master?"

" Why, to speak de troof, massa, him not so berry
well as mought be."

" Not well! I am truly sorry to hear it. What does
he complain of?"

" Dar! dat's it!—him neber plain of notin—but him
berry sick for all dat."

" *Very* sick, Jupiter!—why didn't you say so at once?
Is he confined to bed?"

" No, dat he aint!—he aint find nowhar—dat's just
whar de shoe pinch—my mind is got to be berry hebby
bout poor Massa Will."

" Jupiter, I should like to understand what it is you
are talking about. You say your master is sick. Hasn't
he told you what ails him?"

" Why, massa, taint worf while for to git mad bout
de matter—Massa Will say noffin at all aint de matter
wid him—but den what make him go about looking dis
here way, wid he head down and he soldiers up, and as
white as a gose? And den he keep a syphon all de
time——"

" Keeps a what, Jupiter?"

" Keeps a syphon wid de figgurs on de slate—de
queerest figgurs I ebber did see. Ise gittin to be skeered,
I tell you. Hab for to keep mighty tight eye pon him
noovers. Todder day he gib me slip fore de sun up
and was gone de whole ob de blessed day. I had a big
stick ready cut for to gib him d——d good beating when
he did come—but Ise sich a fool dat I hadn't de heart
arter all—he look so berry poorly."

" Eh?—what?—ah yes!—upon the whole I think you
had better not be too severe with the poor fellow—don't
flog him, Jupiter—he can't very well stand it—but can
you form no idea of what has occasioned this illness, or

rather this change of conduct? Has anything unpleasant happened since I saw you?"

"No, massa, dey aint bin noffin onpleasant *since* den —'twas *fore* den I'm feared—'twas de berry day you was dare."

"How? what do you mean?"

"Why, massa, I mean de bug—dare now."

"The what?"

"De bug—I'm berry sartain dat Massa Will bin bit somewhere bout de head by dat goole-bug."

"And what cause have you, Jupiter, for such a supposition?"

"Claws enuff, massa, and mouff too. I nebber did see sich a d——d bug—he kick and he bite ebery ting what cum near him. Massa Will cotch him fuss, but had for to let him go gin mighty quick, I tell you— den was de time he must ha got de bite. I didn't like de look ob de bug mouff, myself, no how, so I wouldn't take hold ob him wid my finger, but I cotch him wid a piece ob paper dat I found. I rap him up in de paper and stuff piece ob it in he mouff—dat was de way."

"And you think, then, that your master was really bitten by the beetle, and that the bite made him sick?"

"I don't tink noffin about it—I nose it. What make him dream bout de goole so much, if taint cause he bit by de goole-bug? Ise heerd bout dem goole-bugs fore dis."

"But how do you know he dreams about gold?"

"How I know? why cause he talk about it in he sleep—dat's how I nose."

"Well, Jup, perhaps you are right; but to what fortunate circumstance am I to attribute the honor of a visit from you to-day?"

"What de matter, massa?"

"Did you bring any message from Mr. Legrand?"

" No, massa, I bring dis here pissel; " and here
Jupiter handed me a note which ran thus:

" MY DEAR ——, Why have I not seen you for so long a time?
I hope you have not been so foolish as to take offence at any little
brusquerie of mine; but no, that is improbable.

" Since I saw you I have had great cause for anxiety. I have
something to tell you, yet scarcely know how to tell it, or whether
I should tell it at all.

" I have not been quite well for some days past, and poor old
Jup annoys me, almost beyond endurance, by his well-meant atten-
tions. Would you believe it?—he had prepared a huge stick,
the other day, with which to chastise me for giving him the slip,
and spending the day, *solus*, among the hills on the mainland. I
verily believe that my ill looks alone saved me a flogging.

" I have made no addition to my cabinet since we met.

" If you can, in any way, make it convenient, come over with
Jupiter. *Do* come. I wish to see you *to-night*, upon business of
importance. I assure you that it is of the *highest* importance.

" Ever yours,
" WILLIAM LEGRAND."

There was something in the tone of this note which
gave me great uneasiness. Its whole style differed materially from that of Legrand. What could he be dreaming of? What new crotchet possessed his excitable
brain? What " business of the highest importance "
could *he* possibly have to transact? Jupiter's account
of him boded no good. I dreaded lest the continued
pressure of misfortune had, at length, fairly unsettled
the reason of my friend. Without a moment's hesitation, therefore, I prepared to accompany the negro.

Upon reaching the wharf, I noticed a scythe and
three spades, all apparently new, lying in the bottom
of the boat in which we were to embark.

" What is the meaning of all this, Jup? " I inquired.

" Him syfe, massa, and spade."

" Very true; but what are they doing here? "

" Him de syfe and de spade what Massa Will sis pon
my buying for him in de town, and de debbil's own lot
of money I had to gib for 'em.''

" But what, in the name of all that is mysterious, is
your ' Massa Will ' going to do with scythes and
spades ? ''

" Dat's more dan *I* know, and debbil take me if I
don't blieve 't is more dan he know, too. But it's all
cum ob de bug.''

Finding that no satisfaction was to be obtained of
Jupiter, whose whole intellect seemed to be absorbed by
" de bug,'' I now stepped into the boat and made sail.
With a fair and strong breeze we soon ran into the
little cove to the northward of Fort Moultrie, and a walk
of some two miles brought us to the hut. It was about
three in the afternoon when we arrived. Legrand had
been awaiting us in eager expectation. He grasped my
hand with a nervous *empressement*, which alarmed me
and strengthened the suspicions already entertained.
His countenance was pale even to ghastliness, and his
deep-set eyes glared with unnatural lustre. After some
inquiries respecting his health, I asked him, not knowing what better to say, if he had yet obtained the
scarabæus from Lieutenant G——.

" Oh, yes,'' he replied, coloring violently, " I got it
from him the next morning. Nothing should tempt me
to part with that *scarabæus*. Do you know that Jupiter
is quite right about it ? '

" In what way ? '' I asked, with a sad foreboding at
heart.

" In supposing it to be a bug of *real gold*.'' He said
this with an air of profound seriousness, and I felt inexpressibly shocked.

" This bug is to make my fortune,'' he continued,
with a triumphant smile, " to reinstate me in my family

possessions. Is it any wonder, then, that I prize it? Since Fortune has thought fit to bestow it upon me, I have only to use it properly and I shall arrive at the gold of which it is the index. Jupiter, bring me that *scarabæus!* "

"What! de bug, massa? I'd rudder not go fer trubble dat bug—you mus git him for your own self." Hereupon Legrand arose, with a grave and stately air. and brought me the beetle from a glass case in which it was enclosed. It was a beautiful *scarabæus,* and, at that time, unknown to naturalists—of course a great prize in a scientific point of view. There were two round, black spots near one extremity of the back, and a long one near the other. The scales were exceedingly hard and glossy, with all the appearance of burnished gold. The weight of the insect was very remarkable, and, taking all things into consideration, I could hardly blame Jupiter for his opinion respecting it; but what to make of Legrand's agreement with that opinion, I could not, for the life of me, tell.

"I sent for you," said he, in a grandiloquent tone, when I had completed my examination of the beetle, "I sent for you, that I might have your counsel and assistance in furthering the views of Fate and of the bug——"

"My dear Legrand," I cried, interrupting him, "you are certainly unwell, and had better use some little precautions. You shall go to bed, and I will remain with you a few days, until you get over this. You are feverish and——"

"Feel my pulse," said he.

I felt it, and, to say the truth, found not the slightest indication of fever.

"But you may be ill, and yet have no fever. Allow me this once to prescribe for you. In the first place, go to bed. In the next——"

" You are mistaken," he interposed, " I am as well as I can expect to be under the excitement which I suffer. If you really wish me well, you will relieve this excitement."

" And how is this to be done? "

" Very easily. Jupiter and myself are going upon an expedition into the hills, upon the mainland, and, in this expedition, we shall need the aid of some person in whom we can confide. You are the only one we can trust. Whether we succeed or fail, the excitement which you now perceive in me will be equally allayed."

" I am anxious to oblige you in any way," I replied; " but do you mean to say that this infernal beetle has any connection with your expedition into the hills? "

" It has."

" Then, Legrand, I can become a party to no such absurd proceeding."

" I am sorry—very sorry—for we shall have to try it by ourselves."

" Try it by yourselves! The man is surely mad!— but stay—how long do you propose to be absent? "

" Probably all night. We shall start immediately, and be back, at all events, by sunrise."

" And will you promise me, upon your honor, that when this freak of yours is over, and the bug business (good God!) settled to your satisfaction, you will then return home and follow my advice implicitly, as that of your physician? "

" Yes; I promise; and now let us be off, for we have no time to lose."

With a heavy heart I accompanied my friend. We started about four o'clock—Legrand, Jupiter, the dog, and myself. Jupiter had with him the scythe and spades—the whole of which he insisted upon carrying,

more through fear, it seemed to me, of trusting either
of the implements within reach of his master, than
from any excess of industry or complaisance. His demeanor was dogged in the extreme, and " dat d——d
bug " were the sole words which escaped his lips during the journey. For my own part, I had charge of a
couple of dark lanterns, while Legrand contented himself with the *scarabæus*, which he carried attached to
the end of a bit of whip-cord; twirling it to and fro, with
the air of a conjurer, as he went. When I observed this
last, plain evidence of my friend's aberration of mind, I
could scarcely refrain from tears. I thought it best,
however, to humor his fancy, at least for the present, or
until I could adopt some more energetic measures with
a chance of success. In the mean time I endeavored,
but all in vain, to sound him in regard to the object of
the expedition. Having succeeded in inducing me to
accompany him, he seemed unwilling to hold conversation upon any topic of minor importance, and to all
my questions vouchsafed no other reply than " we shall
see! "

We crossed the creek at the head of the island by
means of a skiff, and, ascending the high grounds on
the shore of the mainland, proceeded in a northwesterly
direction, through a tract of country excessively wild
and desolate, where no trace of a human footstep was to
be seen. Legrand led the way with decision; pausing
only for an instant, here and there, to consult what
appeared to be certain landmarks of his own contrivance
upon a former occasion.

In this manner we journeyed for about two hours,
and the sun was just setting when we entered a region
infinitely more dreary than any yet seen. It was a
species of tableland, near the summit of an almost inac-
cessible hill, densely wooded from base to pinnacle, and

interspersed with huge crags that appeared to lie loosely upon the soil, and in many cases were prevented from precipitating themselves into the valleys below merely by the support of the trees against which they reclined. Deep ravines, in various directions, gave an air of still sterner solemnity to the scene.

The natural platform to which we had clambered was thickly overgrown with brambles, through which we soon discovered that it would have been impossible to force our way but for the scythe; and Jupiter, by direction of his master, proceeded to clear for us a path to the foot of an enormously tall tulip-tree, which stood, with some eight or ten oaks, upon the level, and far surpassed them all, and all other trees which I had then ever seen, in the beauty of its foliage and form, in the wide spread of its branches, and in the general majesty of its appearance. When we reached this tree, Legrand turned to Jupiter, and asked him if he thought he could climb it. The old man seemed a little staggered by the question, and for some moments made no reply. At length he approached the huge trunk, walked slowly around it, and examined it with minute attention. When he had completed his scrutiny, he merely said:

" Yes, massa, Jup climb any tree he ebber see in he life."

" Then up with you as soon as possible, for it will soon be too dark to see what we are about."

" How far mus go up, massa? " inquired Jupiter.

" Get up the main trunk first, and then I will tell you which way to go—and here—stop! take this beetle with you."

" De bug, Massa Will!—de goole-bug! " cried the negro, drawing back in dismay—" what for mus tote de bug way up de tree?—d——n if I do! "

" If you are afraid, Jup, a great big negro like you,

to take hold of a harmless little dead beetle, why, you
can carry it up by this string—but, if you do not take
it up with you in some way, I shall be under the necessity of breaking your head with this shovel.''

" What de matter now, massa? " said Jup, evidently
shamed into compliance; " always want fur to raise fuss
wid old nigger. Was only funnin anyhow. *Me* feered
de bug! what I keer for de bug? " Here he took
cautiously hold of the extreme end of the string, and,
maintaining the insect as far from his person as circumstances would permit, prepared to ascend the tree.

In youth, the tulip-tree, or *Liriodendron Tulipifera*,
the most magnificent of American foresters, has a trunk
peculiarly smooth, and often rises to a great height
without lateral branches; but, in its riper age, the bark
becomes gnarled and uneven, while many short limbs
make their appearance on the stem. Thus the difficulty
of ascension, in the present case, lay more in semblance
than in reality. Embracing the huge cylinder, as closely
as possible, with his arms and knees, seizing with his
hands some projections, and resting his naked toes upon
others, Jupiter, after one or two narrow escapes from
falling, at length wriggled himself into the first great
fork, and seemed to consider the whole business as virtually accomplished. The *risk* of the achievement was,
in fact, now over, although the climber was some sixty
or seventy feet from the ground.

" Which way mus go now, Massa Will? " he asked.

" Keep up the largest branch,—the one on this side,''
said Legrand. The negro obeyed him promptly, and apparently with but little trouble, ascending higher and
higher, until no glimpse of his squat figure could be
obtained through the dense foliage which enveloped it.
Presently his voice was heard in a sort of halloo.

" How much fudder is got for go? "

"How high up are you?" asked Legrand.

"Ebber so fur," replied the negro; "can see de sky fru de top ob de tree."

"Never mind the sky, but attend to what I say. Look down the trunk and count the limbs below you on this side. How many limbs have you passed?"

"One, two, tree, four, fibe—I done pass fibe big limb, massa, pon dis side."

"Then go one limb higher."

In a few minutes the voice was heard again, announcing that the seventh limb was attained.

"Now, Jup," cried Legrand, evidently much excited, "I want you to work your way out upon that limb as far as you can. If you see anything strange, let me know."

By this time what little doubt I might have entertained of my poor friend's insanity was put finally at rest. I had no alternative but to conclude him stricken with lunacy, and I became seriously anxious about getting him home. While I was pondering upon what was best to be done, Jupiter's voice was again heard.

"Mos feerd for to ventur pon dis limb berry far— 'tis dead limb putty much all de way."

"Did you say it was a *dead* limb, Jupiter?" cried Legrand in a quavering voice.

"Yes, massa, him dead as de door-nail—done up for sartain—done departed dis here life."

"What in the name of heaven shall I do?" asked Legrand, seemingly in the greatest distress.

"Do!" said I, glad of an opportunity to interpose a word, "why come home and go to bed. Come now!— that's a fine fellow. It's getting late, and, besides, you remember your promise."

"Jupiter," cried he, without heeding me in the least, "do you hear me?"

" Yes, Massa Will, hear you ebber so plain."

" Try the wood well, then, with your knife, and see if you think it *very* rotten."

" Him rotten, massa, sure nuff," replied the negro in a few moments, "but not so berry rotten as mought be. Mought ventur out leetle way pon de limb by myself, dat's true."

" By yourself!—what do you mean? "

" Why, I mean de bug. 'Tis *berry* hebby bug. Spose I drop him down fuss, and den de limb won't break wid just de weight ob one nigger."

" You infernal scoundrel! " cried Legrand, apparently much relieved, " what do you mean by telling me such nonsense as that? As sure as you let that beetle fall, I'll break your neck. Look here, Jupiter! do you hear me? "

" Yes, massa, needn't hollo at poor nigger dat style."

" Well! now listen!—if you will venture out on the limb as far as you think safe, and not let go the beetle, I'll make you a present of a silver dollar as soon as you get down."

" I'm gwine, Massa Will—deed I is," replied the negro very promptly—" mos out to the eend now."

" *Out to the end!* " here fairly screamed Legrand, " do you say you are out to the end of that limb? "

" Soon be to de eend, massa,—o-o-o-o-oh! Lord-gol-a-marcy! what *is* dis here pon de tree? "

" Well! " cried Legrand, highly delighted, " what is it? "

" Why taint noffin but a skull—somebody bin lef him head up de tree, and de crows done gobble ebery bit ob de meat off."

" A skull, you say!—very well!—how is it fastened to the limb?—what holds it on? "

" Sure nuff, massa; mus look. Why, dis berry curous

sarcumstance, pon my word—dare's a great big nail in de skull, what fastens ob it on to de tree.''

'' Well now, Jupiter, do exactly as I tell you—do you hear? ''

'' Yes, massa.''

'' Pay attention, then!—find the left eye of the skull.''

'' Hum! hoo! dat's good! why, dar aint no eye lef at all.''

'' Curse your stupidity! do you know your right hand from your left? ''

'' Yes, I nose dat—nose all bout dat—'tis my lef hand what I chops de wood wid.''

'' To be sure! you are left-handed; and your left eye is on the same side as your left hand. Now, I suppose, you can find the left eye of the skull, or the place where the left eye has been. Have you found it? ''

Here was a long pause. At length the negro asked,

'' Is de lef eye of de skull pon de same side as de lef hand of de skull, too?—cause de skull aint got not a bit ob a hand at all—nebber mind! I got de lef eye now—here de lef eye! what must do wid it? ''

'' Let the beetle drop through it, as far as the string will reach—but be careful and not let go your hold of the string.''

'' All dat done, Massa Will; mighty easy ting for to put de bug fru de hole—look for him dar below! ''

During this colloquy no portion of Jupiter's person could be seen; but the beetle, which he had suffered to descend, was now visible at the end of the string, and glistened, like a globe of burnished gold, in the last rays of the setting sun, some of which still faintly illumined the eminence upon which we stood. The *scarabæus* hung quite clear of any branches, and, if allowed to fall, would have fallen at our feet. Legrand immediately took the scythe, and cleared with it a circular space, three or four yards in diameter, just beneath the insect, and, having accomplished this, ordered Jupiter to let go the string and come down from the tree.

Driving a peg, with great nicety, into the ground, at the precise spot where the beetle fell, my friend now produced from his pocket a tape-measure. Fastening one end of this at that point of the trunk of the tree which was nearest the peg, he unrolled it till it reached the peg, and thence farther unrolled it, in the direction already established by the two points of the tree and the peg, for the distance of fifty feet—Jupiter clearing away the brambles with the scythe. At the spot thus attained a second peg was driven, and about this, as a centre, a rude circle, about four feet in diameter, described. Taking now a spade himself, and giving one to Jupiter and one to me, Legrand begged us to set about digging as quickly as possible.

To speak the truth, I had no especial relish for such amusement at any time, and, at that particular moment, would most willingly have declined it; for the night was coming on, and I felt much fatigued with the exercise already taken; but I saw no mode of escape, and was fearful of disturbing my poor friend's equanimity by a refusal. Could I have depended, indeed, upon Jupiter's aid, I would have had no hesitation in attempting to get the lunatic home by force; but I was too well assured of the old negro's disposition to hope that he would assist me, under any circumstances, in a personal contest with his master. I made no doubt that the latter had been infected with some of the innumerable Southern superstitions about money buried, and that his fantasy had received confirmation by the finding of the *scarabæus*, or, perhaps, by Jupiter's obstinacy in maintaining it to be "a bug of real gold." A mind disposed to lunacy would readily be led away by such suggestions, especially if chiming in with favorite preconceived ideas; and then I called to mind the poor fellow's speech about the beetle's being "the index of his fortune." Upon the whole, I was sadly vexed and puzzled, but at length I concluded to make a virtue of necessity—to dig with a good will, and thus the sooner to convince the visionary, by ocular demonstration, of the fallacy of the opinions he entertained.

The lanterns having been lit, we all fell to work with a zeal worthy a more rational cause; and, as the glare fell upon our persons and implements, I could not help thinking how picturesque a group we composed, and how strange and suspicious our labors must have appeared to any interloper who, by chance, might have stumbled upon our whereabouts.

We dug very steadily for two hours. Little was said; and our chief embarrassment lay in the yelpings of the dog, who took exceeding interest in our proceedings. He, at length, became so obstreperous that we grew fearful of his giving the alarm to some stragglers in the vicinity; or, rather, this was the apprehension of Legrand; for myself, I should have rejoiced at any interruption which might have enabled me to get the wanderer home. The noise was, at length, very effectually silenced by Jupiter, who, getting out of the hole with a dogged air of deliberation, tied the brute's mouth up with one of his suspenders, and then returned, with a grave chuckle, to his task.

When the time mentioned had expired, we had reached a depth of five feet, and yet no signs of any treasure became manifest. A general pause ensued, and I began to hope that the farce was at an end. Legrand, however, although evidently much disconcerted, wiped his brow thoughtfully and recommenced. We had excavated the entire circle of four feet diameter, and now we slightly enlarged the limit, and went to the farther depth of two feet. Still nothing appeared. The gold-seeker, whom I sincerely pitied, at length clambered from the pit, with the bitterest disappointment imprinted upon every feature, and proceeded, slowly and reluctantly, to put on his coat, which he had thrown off at the beginning of his labor. In the mean time I made no remark. Jupiter, at a signal from his master, began to gather up his tools. This done, and the dog having been unmuzzled, we turned in profound silence towards home.

We had taken, perhaps, a dozen steps in this direction, when, with a loud oath, Legrand strode up to Jupiter, and seized him by the collar. The astonished negro opened his eyes and mouth to the fullest extent, let fall the spades, and fell upon his knees.

"You scoundrel," said Legrand, hissing out the syllables from between his clenched teeth—"you infernal black villain!—speak, I tell you!—answer me this instant, without prevarication!—which—which is your left eye?"

"Oh, my golly, Massa Will! aint dis here my lef eye for sartain?" roared the terrified Jupiter, placing his hand upon his *right* organ of vision, and holding it there with a desperate pertinacity, as if in immediate dread of his master's attempt at a gouge.

"I thought so!—I knew it! hurrah!" vociferated Legrand, letting the negro go, and executing a series of curvets and caracoles, much to the astonishment of his valet, who, arising from his knees, looked mutely from his master to myself, and then from myself to his master.

"Come! we must go back," said the latter, "the game's not up yet;" and he again led the way to the tulip-tree.

"Jupiter," said he, when we reached its foot, "come

here! was the skull nailed to the limb with the face outward, or with the face to the limb?''

'' De face was out, massa, so dat de crows could get
at de eyes good, widout any trouble.''

'' Well, then, was it this eye or that through which
you dropped the beetle?''—here Legrand touched each
of Jupiter's eyes.

'' 'Twas dis eye, massa—de lef eye—jis as you tell
me,'' and here it was his right eye that the negro indicated.

'' That will do—we must try it again.''

Here my friend, about whose madness I now saw,
or fancied that I saw, certain indications of method,
removed the peg which marked the spot where the
beetle fell, to a spot about three inches to the westward of its former position. Taking, now, the tape-
measure from the nearest point of the trunk to the
peg, as before, and continuing the extension in a straight
line to the distance of fifty feet, a spot was indicated,
removed, by several yards, from the point at which
we had been digging.

Around the new position a circle, somewhat larger
than in the former instance, was now described, and we
again set to work with the spades. I was dreadfully
weary, but, scarcely understanding what had occasioned
the change in my thoughts, I felt no longer any great
aversion from the labor imposed. I had become most
unaccountably interested—nay, even excited. Perhaps
there was something, amid all the extravagant demeanor
of Legrand—some air of forethought, or of deliberation—which impressed me. I dug eagerly, and now
and then caught myself actually looking, with something that very much resembled expectation, for the
fancied treasure, the vision of which had demented my
unfortunate companion. At a period when such vagaries

of thought most fully possessed me, and when we had been at work perhaps an hour and a half, we were again interrupted by the violent howlings of the dog. His uneasiness, in the first instance, had been evidently but the result of playfulness or caprice, but he now assumed a bitter and serious tone. Upon Jupiter's again attempting to muzzle him, he made furious resistance, and, leaping into the hole, tore up the mould frantically with his claws. In a few seconds he had uncovered a mass of human bones, forming two complete skeletons, intermingled with several buttons of metal, and what appeared to be the dust of decayed woollen. One or two strokes of a spade upturned the blade of a large Spanish knife, and, as we dug farther, three or four loose pieces of gold and silver coin came to light.

At sight of these the joy of Jupiter could scarcely be restrained, but the countenance of his master wore an air of extreme disappointment. He urged us, however, to continue our exertions, and the words were hardly uttered when I stumbled and fell forward, having caught the toe of my boot in a large ring of iron that lay half buried in the loose earth.

We now worked in earnest, and never did I pass ten minutes of more intense excitement. During this interval we had fairly unearthed an oblong chest of wood, which, from its perfect preservation and wonderful hardness, had plainly been subjected to some mineralizing process—perhaps that of the bichloride of mercury. This box was three feet and a half long, three feet broad, and two and a half feet deep. It was firmly secured by bands of wrought iron, riveted, and forming a kind of trellis-work over the whole. On each side of the chest, near the top, were three rings of iron—six in all—by means of which a firm hold could be obtained by six persons. Our utmost united endeavors served only to disturb the coffer very slightly in its bed. We at once saw the impossibility of removing so great a weight. Luckily, the sole fastenings of the lid consisted of two sliding bolts. These we drew back—trembling and panting with anxiety. In an instant, a treasure of incalculable value lay gleaming before us. As the rays of the lanterns fell within the pit, there flashed upwards, from a confused heap of gold and of jewels, a glow and a glare that absolutely dazzled our eyes.

I shall not pretend to describe the feelings with which I gazed. Amazement was, of course, predominant. Legrand appeared exhausted with excitement, and spoke very few words. Jupiter's countenance wore, for some minutes, as deadly a pallor as it is possible, in the nature of things, for any negro's visage to assume. He seemed stupefied—thunderstricken. Presently he fell upon his knees in the pit, and, burying his naked arms up to the elbows in gold, let them there remain, as if enjoying the luxury of a bath. At length, with a deep sigh, he exclaimed, as if in a soliloquy:

"And dis all cum ob de goole-bug! de putty goole-bug! de poor little goole-bug, what I boosed in dat sabage kind ob style! Aint you shamed ob yourself, nigger?—answer me dat!"

It became necessary, at last, that I should arouse both master and valet to the expediency of removing the treasure. It was growing late, and it behooved us to make exertion, that we might get everything housed before daylight. It was difficult to say what should be done, and much time was spent in deliberation—so confused were the ideas of all. We finally lightened the box by removing two-thirds of its contents, when we were enabled, with some trouble, to raise it from the hole. The articles taken out were deposited among the brambles, and the dog left to guard them, with strict orders from Jupiter neither, upon any pretence, to stir from the spot, nor to open his mouth until our return. We then hurriedly made for home with the chest; reaching the hut in safety, but after excessive toil, at one o'clock in the morning. Worn out as we were, it was not in human nature to do more just now. We rested until two, and had supper; starting for the hills immediately afterwards, armed with three stout sacks, which by good luck were upon the premises. A little before four we arrived at the pit, divided the remainder of the booty, as equally as might be, among us, and, leaving the holes unfilled, again set out for the hut, at which, for the second time, we deposited our golden burdens, just as the first streaks of the dawn gleamed from over the tree-tops in the East.

We were now thoroughly broken down; but the intense excitement of the time denied us repose. After an unquiet slumber of some three or four hours' duration, we arose, as if by pre-concert, to make examination of our treasure.

The chest had been full to the brim, and we spent the whole day, and the greater part of the next night, in a scrutiny of its contents. There had been nothing like order or arrangement. Everything had been heaped in promiscuously. Having assorted all with care, we found ourselves possessed of even vaster wealth than we had at first supposed. In coin there was rather more than four hundred and fifty thousand dollars: estimating the value of the pieces, as accurately as we could, by the tables of the period. There was not a particle of silver. All was gold of antique date and of great variety: French, Spanish, and German money, with a few English guineas, and some counters, of which we had never seen specimens before. There were several very large and heavy coins, so worn that we could make nothing of their inscriptions. There was no American money. The value of the jewels we found more difficulty in estimating. There were diamonds—some of them exceedingly large and fine—a hundred and ten in all, and not one of them small; eighteen rubies of remarkable brilliancy; three hundred and ten emeralds, all very beautiful; and twenty-one sapphires, with an opal. These stones had all been broken from their settings and thrown loose in the chest. The settings themselves, which we picked out from among the other gold, appeared to have been beaten up with hammers, as if to prevent identification. Besides all this, there was a vast quantity of solid gold ornaments: nearly two hundred massive finger and ear rings; rich chains—thirty of these, if I remember; eighty-three very large and heavy crucifixes; five gold censers of great value; a prodigious golden punch-bowl, ornamented with richly chased vine-leaves and Bacchanalian figures; with two sword handles exquisitely embossed, and many other smaller articles which I cannot recollect. The weight of these valuables exceeded three hundred and fifty pounds avoirdupois; and in this estimate I have not included one hundred and ninety-seven superb gold watches; three of the number being worth each five hundred dollars, if one. Many of them were very old, and as time-keepers valueless, the works having suffered more or less from corrosion; but all were richly jewelled and in cases of great worth. We estimated the entire contents of the chest, that night, at a million and a half of dollars; and, upon the subsequent disposal of the trinkets and jewels (a few being retained for our own use), it was found that we had greatly undervalued the treasure.

When, at length, we had concluded our examination, and the intense excitement of the time had in some measure subsided, Legrand, who saw that I was dying with impatience for a solution of this most extraordinary riddle, entered into a full detail of all the circumstances connected with it.

" You remember," said he, " the night when I handed you the rough sketch I had made of the *scarabæus*. You recollect also, that I became quite vexed at you for insisting that my drawing resembled a death's-head. When you first made this assertion I thought you were jesting; but afterwards I called to mind the peculiar spots on the back of the insect, and admitted to myself that your remark had some little foundation in fact. Still, the sneer at my graphic powers irritated me— for I am considered a good artist—and, therefore, when you handed me the scrap of parchment, I was about to crumple it up and throw it angrily into the fire."

" The scrap of paper, you mean," said I.

" No: it had much of the appearance of paper, and at first I supposed it to be such, but when I came to draw upon it, I discovered it, at once, to be a piece of very thin parchment. It was quite dirty, you remember. Well, as I was in the very act of crumpling it up, my glance fell upon the sketch at which you had been looking, and you may imagine my astonishment when I perceived, in fact, the figure of a death's-head just where, it seemed to me, I had made the drawing of the beetle. For a moment I was too much amazed to think with accuracy. I knew that my design was very different in detail from this—although there was a certain similarity in general outline. Presently I took a candle and, seating myself at the other end of the room, proceeded to scrutinize the parchment more closely. Upon turning it over, I saw my own sketch upon the reverse, just as I had made it. My first idea, now, was mere surprise at the really remarkable similarity of outline—at the singular coincidence involved in the fact that, unknown to me, there should have been a skull upon the other side of the parchment, immediately beneath my figure of the *scarabœus*, and that this skull, not only in outline, but in size, should so closely resemble my drawing. I say the singularity of this coincidence absolutely stupefied me for a time. This is the usual effect of such coincidences. The mind struggles to establish a connection—a sequence of cause and effect—and, being unable to do so, suffers a species of temporary paralysis. But, when I recovered from this stupor, there dawned upon me gradually a conviction which startled me even far more than the coincidence. I began distinctly, positively, to remember that there had been *no* drawing on the parchment when I made my sketch of the *scarabœus*. I became perfectly certain of this; for I recollected turning up first one side and then the other, in search of the cleanest spot. Had the skull been then there, of course I could not have failed to notice it. Here was indeed a mystery which I felt it impossible to explain; but, even at that early moment, there seemed to glimmer, faintly, within the most remote and secret chambers of my intellect, a glowworm-like conception of that truth which last night's adventure brought to so magnificent a demonstration. I arose at once, and, putting the parchment securely away, dismissed all farther reflection until I should be alone.

" When you had gone, and when Jupiter was fast asleep, I betook myself to a more methodical investigation of the affair. In the first place I considered the manner in which the parchment had come into my possession. The spot where we discovered the *scarabœus*

was on the coast of the mainland, about a mile east-
ward of the island, and but a short distance above high-
water mark. Upon my taking hold of it, it gave me a
sharp bite, which caused me to let it drop. Jupiter,
with his accustomed caution, before seizing the insect,
which had flown towards him, looked about him for a
leaf, or something of that nature, by which to take hold
of it. It was at this moment that his eyes, and mine
also, fell upon the scrap of parchment, which I then
supposed to be paper. It was lying half buried in
the sand, a corner sticking up. Near the spot where
we found it, I observed the remnants of the hull of
what appeared to have been a ship's long boat. The
wreck seemed to have been there for a very great while;
for the resemblance to boat timbers could scarcely be
traced.

"Well, Jupiter picked up the parchment, wrapped
the beetle in it, and gave it to me. Soon afterwards
we turned to go home, and on the way met Lieutenant
G——. I showed him the insect, and he begged me to
let him take it to the fort. On my consenting, he thrust
it forthwith into his waistcoat pocket, without the parchment in which it had been wrapped, and which I had
continued to hold in my hand during his inspection.
Perhaps he dreaded my changing my mind, and thought
it best to make sure of the prize at once—you know how
enthusiastic he is on all subjects connected with Natural
History. At the same time, without being conscious of
it, I must have deposited the parchment in my own
pocket.

"You remember that when I went to the table, for
the purpose of making a sketch of the beetle, I found
no paper where it was usually kept. I looked in the
drawer, and found none there. I searched my pockets,
hoping to find an old letter, and then my hand fell

upon the parchment. I thus detail the precise mode in which it came into my possession; for the circumstances impressed me with peculiar force.

"No doubt you will think me fanciful—but I had already established a kind of *connection*. I had put together two links of a great chain. There was a boat lying on a seacoast, and not far from the boat was a parchment—*not a paper*—with a skull depicted on it. You will, of course, ask 'where is the connection?' I reply that the skull, or death's-head, is the well-known emblem of the pirate. The flag of the death's-head is hoisted in all engagements.

"I have said that the scrap was parchment, and not paper. Parchment is durable—almost imperishable. Matters of little moment are rarely consigned to parchment; since, for the mere ordinary purposes of drawing or writing, it is not nearly so well adapted as paper. This reflection suggested some meaning—some relevancy —in the death's-head. I did not fail to observe, also, the *form* of the parchment. Although one of its corners had been, by some accident, destroyed, it could be seen that the original form was oblong. It was just such a slip, indeed, as might have been chosen for a memorandum—for a record of something to be long remembered and carefully preserved."

"But," I interposed, "you say that the skull was *not* upon the parchment when you made the drawing of the beetle. How then do you trace any connection between the boat and the skull—since this latter, according to your own admission, must have been designed (God only knows how or by whom) at some period subsequent to your sketching the *scarabœus?* "

"Ah, hereupon turns the whole mystery; although the secret, at this point, I had comparatively little difficulty in solving. My steps were sure, and could afford

but a single result. I reasoned, for example, thus:
When I drew the *scarabæus*, there was no skull apparent on the parchment. When I had completed the drawing I gave it to you, and observed you narrowly until
you returned it. *You*, therefore, did not design the
skull, and no one else was present to do it. Then it was
not done by human agency. And nevertheless it was
done.

" At this stage of my reflections I endeavored to
remember, and *did* remember, with entire distinctness,
every incident which occurred about the period in question. The weather was chilly (O rare and happy accident!), and a fire was blazing on the hearth. I was
heated with exercise and sat near the table. You, however, had drawn a chair close to the chimney. Just
as I placed the parchment in your hand, and as you were
in the act of inspecting it, Wolf, the Newfoundland,
entered, and leaped upon your shoulders. With your
left hand you caressed him and kept him off, while your
right, holding the parchment, was permitted to fall
listlessly between your knees, and in close proximity
to the fire. At one moment I thought the blaze had
caught it, and was about to caution you, but, before
I could speak, you had withdrawn it, and were engaged
in its examination. When I considered all these par-
ticulars, I doubted not for a moment that *heat* had been
the agent in bringing to light, on the parchment, the
skull which I saw designed on it. You are well aware
that chemical preparations exist, and have existed time
out of mind, by means of which it is possible to write
on either paper or vellum, so that the characters shall
become visible only when subjected to the action of fire.
Zaffre, digested in *aqua regia*, and diluted with four
times its weight of water, is sometimes employed; a
green tint results. The regulus of cobalt, dissolved in

spirit of nitre, gives a red. These colors disappear at longer or shorter intervals after the material written upon cools, but again become apparent upon the re-application of heat.

"I now scrutinized the death's-head with care. Its outer edges—the edges of the drawing nearest the edge of the vellum—were far more *distinct* than the others. It was clear that the action of the caloric had been imperfect or unequal. I immediately kindled a fire, and subjected every portion of the parchment to a glow-ing heat. At first, the only effect was the strengthening of the faint lines in the skull; but, on persevering in the experiment, there became visible at the corner of the slip, diagonally opposite to the spot in which the death's-head was delineated, the figure of what I at first sup-posed to be a goat. A closer scrutiny, however, satis-fied me that it was intended for a kid."

"Ha! ha!" said I, "to be sure I have no right to laugh at you—a million and a half of money is too serious a matter for mirth—but you are not about to establish a third link in your chain: you will not find any especial connection between your pirates and a goat; pirates, you know, have nothing to do with goats; they appertain to the farming interest."

"But I have just said that the figure was *not* that of a goat."

"Well, a kid, then—pretty much the same thing."

"Pretty much, but not altogether," said Legrand. "You may have heard of one *Captain* Kidd. I at once looked on the figure of the animal as a kind of punning or hieroglyphical signature. I say signature; because its position on the vellum suggested this idea. The death's-head at the corner diagonally opposite had, in the same manner, the air of a stamp, or seal. But I was sorely put out by the absence of all else—of the body to my imagined instrument—of the text for my context.''

'' I presume you expected to find a letter between the stamp and the signature.''

'' Something of that kind. The fact is, I felt irresistibly impressed with a presentiment of some vast good fortune impending. I can scarcely say why. Perhaps, after all, it was rather a desire than an actual belief;— but do you know that Jupiter's silly words, about the bug being of solid gold, had a remarkable effect on my fancy? And then the series of accidents and coincidences—these were so *very* extraordinary. Do you observe how mere an accident it was that these events should have occurred on the *sole* day of all the year in which it has been, or may be, sufficiently cool for fire, and that without the fire, or without the intervention of the dog at the precise moment in which he appeared, I should never have become aware of the death's-head, and so never the possessor of the treasure? ''

'' But proceed—I am all impatience.''

'' Well; you have heard, of course, the many stories current—the thousand vague rumors afloat about money buried, somewhere on the Atlantic coast, by Kidd and his associates. These rumors must have had some foundation in fact. And that the rumors have existed so long and so continuously, could have resulted, it appeared to me, only from the circumstance of the buried treasure still *remaining* entombed. Had Kidd concealed his plunder for a time, and afterwards reclaimed it, the rumors would scarcely have reached us in their present unvarying form. You will observe that the stories told are all about money-seekers, not about money-finders. Had the pirate recovered his money, there the affair would have dropped. It seemed to me that some accident—say the loss of a memorandum indicating its locality—had deprived him of the means of recovering it, and that this accident had become known to his followers, who otherwise might never have heard that treasure had been concealed at all, and, who, busying themselves in vain, because unguided, attempts to regain it, had given first birth, and then universal currency, to the reports which are now so common. Have you ever heard of any important treasure being unearthed along the coast?''

'' Never.''

'' But that Kidd's accumulations were immense is well known. I took it for granted, therefore, that the earth still held them; and you will scarcely be surprised when I tell you that I felt a hope, nearly amounting to certainty, that the parchment so strangely found involved a lost record of the place of deposit.''

'' But how did you proceed?''

'' I held the vellum again to the fire, after increasing the heat, but nothing appeared. I now thought it possible that the coating of dirt might have something to do with the failure; so I carefully rinsed the parchment by pouring warm water over it, and, having done this, I placed it in a tin pan, with the skull downwards, and put the pan upon a furnace of lighted charcoal. In a few minutes, the pan having become thoroughly heated, I removed the slip, and, to my inexpressible joy, found it spotted, in several places, with what appeared to be figures arranged in lines. Again I placed it in the pan, and suffered it to remain another minute. Upon taking it off, the whole was just as you see it now.''

Here Legrand, having reheated the parchment, submitted it to my inspection. The following characters were rudely traced, in a red tint, between the death's-head and the goat:—

53‡‡†305))6*;4826)4‡.)4‡) ;806*;48†8¶60))85;;]8*;:
‡*8†83(88)5*†;46(;88*96*?;8)*‡(;485) ;5*†2:*‡(;4956
2(5—4)8¶8*;4069285) ;)6†8)4‡‡;1(‡9;48081;8:8‡1;48
†85;4)485†528806*81(‡9;48;(88;4(‡?34;48)4‡;161;:188
;‡?;

" But," said I, returning him the slip, " I am as much
in the dark as ever. Were all the jewels of Golconda
awaiting me on my solution of this enigma, I am quite
sure that I should be unable to earn them."

" And yet," said Legrand, " the solution is by no
means so difficult as you might be led to imagine from
the first hasty inspection of the characters. These
characters, as any one might readily guess, form a
cipher—that is to say, they convey a meaning; but
then, from what is known of Kidd, I could not suppose him capable of constructing any of the more ab-
struse cryptographs. I made up my mind, at once,
that this was of a simple species—such, however, as
would appear, to the crude intellect of the sailor, absolutely insoluble without the key."

" And you really solved it?"

" Readily; I have solved others of an abstruseness ten
thousand times greater. Circumstances, and a certain
bias of mind, have led me to take interest in such rid-
dles, and it may well be doubted whether human ingenuity can construct an enigma of the kind which
human ingenuity may not, by proper application, resolve. In fact, having once established connected and
legible characters, I scarcely gave a thought to the mere
difficulty of developing their import.

" In the present case—indeed in all cases of secret
writing—the first question regards the *language* of the
cipher; for the principles of solution, so far, especially,
as the more simple ciphers are concerned, depend on,
and are varied by, the genius of the particular idiom.

In general, there is no alternative but experiment (directed by probabilities) of every tongue known to him who attempts the solution, until the true one be attained. But, with the cipher now before us, all difficulty is removed by the signature. The pun upon the word ' Kidd ' is appreciable in no other language than the English. But for this consideration I should have begun my attempts with the Spanish and French, as the tongues in which a secret of this kind would most naturally have been written by a pirate of the Spanish main. As it was, I assumed the cryptograph to be English.

" You observe there are no divisions between the words. Had there been divisions, the task would have been comparatively easy. In such case I should have commenced with a collation and analysis of the shorter words, and, had a word of a single letter occurred, as is most likely (*a* or *I*, for example), I should have considered the solution as assured. But, there being no division, my first step was to ascertain the predominant letters, as well as the least frequent. Counting all, I constructed a table, thus:

" Of the character 8 there are 33

;	"	26
4	"	19
‡)	"	16
*	"	13
5	"	12
6	"	11
†1	"	8
0	"	6
92	"	5
:3	"	4
?	"	3
¶	"	2
]—	"	1

" Now, in English, the letter which most frequently occurs is *e*. Afterwards the succession runs thus: *a o i d h n r s t u y c f g l m w b k p q x z*. *E* predominates, however, so remarkably that an individual sentence of any length is rarely seen, in which it is not the prevailing character.

" Here, then, we have, in the very beginning, the groundwork for something more than a mere guess. The general use which may be made of the table is obvious—but, in this particular cipher, we shall only very partially require its aid. As our predominant character is 8, we will commence by assuming it as the *e* of the natural alphabet. To verify the supposition, let us observe if the 8 be seen often in couples—for *e* is doubled with great frequency in English—in such words, for example, as ' meet,' ' fleet,' ' speed,' ' seen,' ' been,' ' agree,' &c. In the present instance we see it doubled no less than five times, although the cryptograph is brief.

" Let us assume 8, then, as *e*. Now, of all *words* in the language, ' the ' is most usual; let us see, therefore, whether there are not repetitions of any three characters, in the same order of collocation, the last of them being 8. If we discover repetitions of such letters, so arranged, they will most probably represent the word ' the.' On inspection, we find no less than seven such arrangements, the characters being ;48. We may, therefore, assume that the semicolon represents *t*, that 4 represents *h*, and that 8 represents *e*—the last being now well confirmed. Thus a great step has been taken.

" But, having established a single word, we are enabled to establish a vastly important point; that is to say, several commencements and terminations of other words. Let us refer, for example, to the last instance

but one, in which the combination ;48 occurs—not far
from the end of the cipher. We know that the semicolon immediately ensuing is the commencement of a
word, and, of the six characters succeeding this ' the,'
we are cognizant of no less than five. Let us set these
characters down, thus, by the letters we know them
to represent, leaving a space for the unknown—

t eeth.

" Here we are enabled, at once, to discard the ' *th*,'
as forming no portion of the word commencing with
the first *t;* since, by experiment of the entire alphabet
for a letter adapted to the vacancy, we perceive that
no word can be formed of which this *th* can be a part.
We are thus narrowed into

t ee,

and, going through the alphabet, if necessary, as before, we arrive at the word ' tree ' as the sole possible
reading. We thus gain another letter, *r*, represented
by (, with the words ' the tree ' in juxtaposition.
" Looking beyond these words, for a short distance,
we again see the combination ;48, and employ it by way
of *termination* to what immediately precedes. We have
thus this arrangement:

the tree ;4(‡?34 the,

or, substituting the natural letters, where known. it
reads thus:

the tree thr‡?3h the.

" Now, if, in place of the unknown characters, we
leave blank spaces, or substitute dots, we read thus:

the tree thr . . . h the,

when the word '*through*' makes itself evident at once.
But this discovery gives us three new letters, *o, u,* and *g,*
represented by ‡ ? and 3.

" Looking now, narrowly, through the cipher for combinations of known characters, we find, not very far
from the beginning, this arrangement,

83(88, or egree,

which, plainly, is the conclusion of the word ' degree,'
and gives us another letter, *d,* represented by †.

" Four letters beyond the word ' degree,' we perceive the combination

;46(;88*

" Translating the known characters, and representing
the unknown by dots, as before, we read thus:

th . rtee . ,

an arrangement immediately suggestive of the word
' thirteen,' and again furnishing us with two new characters, *i* and *n,* represented by 6 and *.

" Referring, now, to the beginning of the cryptograph, we find the combination,

53‡‡†.

" Translating, as before, we obtain

good,

which assures us that the first letter is *A,* and that the
first two words are ' A good.'

" To avoid confusion, it is now time that we arrange
our key, as far as discovered, in a tabular form. It
will stand thus:

5	represents	a
†	"	d
8	"	e
3	"	g
4	"	h
6	"	i
*	"	n
‡	"	o
(	"	r
;	"	t

" We have, therefore, no less than ten of the most important letters represented, and it will be unnecessary to proceed with the details of the solution. I have said enough to convince you that ciphers of this nature are readily soluble, and to give you some insight into the rationale of their development. But be assured that the specimen before us appertains to the very simplest species of cryptograph. It now only remains to give you the full translation of the characters upon the parchment, as unriddled. Here it is:

" ' *A good glass in the Bishop's hostel in the devil's seat twenty-one degrees and thirteen minutes north-east and by north main branch seventh limb east side shoot from the left eye of the death's-head a bee-line from the tree through the shot fifty feet out.*' "

" But," said I, " the enigma seems still in as bad a condition as ever. How is it possible to extort a meaning from all this jargon about ' devil's seats,' ' death's-heads,' and ' Bishop's hotels '? "

" I confess," replied Legrand, " that the matter still wears a serious aspect, when regarded with a casual glance. My first endeavor was to divide the sentence into the natural division intended by the cryptographist."

" You mean, to punctuate it ? "

" Something of that kind."

" But how was it possible to effect this ? "

" I reflected that it had been a *point* with the writer to run his words together without division, so as to increase the difficulty of solution. Now, a not over-acute man, in pursuing such an object, would be nearly certain to overdo the matter. When, in the course of his composition, he arrived at a break in his subject which would naturally require a pause, or a point, he would be exceedingly apt to run his characters, at this place, more than usually close together. If you will observe the MS., in the present instance, you will easily detect five such cases of unusual crowding. Acting on this hint, I made the division thus :

" ' *A good glass in the Bishop's hostel in the Devil's seat—twenty-one degrees and thirteen minutes—north-east and by north—main branch seventh limb east side—shoot from the left eye of the death's-head—a bee-line from the tree through the shot fifty feet out.*' "

" Even this division," said I, " leaves me still in the dark."

" It left me also in the dark," replied Legrand, " for a few days ; during which I made diligent inquiry, in the neighborhood of Sullivan's Island, for any building which went by the name of the ' Bishop's Hotel '; for, of course, I dropped the obsolete word ' hostel.' Gaining no information on the subject, I was on the point of extending my sphere of search, and proceeding in a more systematic manner, when one morning it entered into my head, quite suddenly, that this ' Bishop's Hostel ' might have some reference to an old family, of the name of Bessop, which, time out of mind, had held possession of an ancient manor-house, about four miles to the northward of the island. I accordingly went over to the plantation, and reinstituted my inquiries among the older negroes of the place. At length one of the most aged of the women said that she had heard of such a place as *Bessop's Castle,* and thought that she could guide me to it, but that it was not a castle, nor a tavern, but a high rock.

" I offered to pay her well for her trouble, and, after some demur, she consented to accompany me to the spot. We found it without much difficulty, when, dismissing her, I proceeded to examine the place. The ' castle ' consisted of an irregular assemblage of cliffs and rocks—one of the latter being quite remarkable for its height as well as for its insulated and artificial appearance. I clambered to its apex, and then felt much at a loss as to what should be next done.

" While I was busied in reflection, my eyes fell on a narrow ledge in the eastern face of the rock, perhaps a yard below the summit upon which I stood. This ledge projected about eighteen inches, and was not more than a foot wide, while a niche in the cliff just above it gave it a rude resemblance to one of the hollow-backed chairs used by our ancestors. I made no doubt that here was the ' devil's seat ' alluded to in the MS., and now I seemed to grasp the full secret of the riddle.

" The ' good glass,' I knew, could have reference to nothing but a telescope; for the word ' glass ' is rarely employed in any other sense by seamen. Now here, I at once saw, was a telescope to be used, and a definite point of view, *admitting no variation,* from which to use it. Nor did I hesitate to believe that the phrases, ' twenty-one degrees and thirteen minutes,' and ' northeast and by north,' were intended as directions for the levelling of the glass. Greatly excited by these discoveries, I hurried home, procured a telescope, and returned to the rock.

"I let myself down the ledge, and found that it was impossible to retain a seat on it unless in one particular position. This fact confirmed my preconceived idea. I proceeded to use the glass. Of course, the 'twenty-one degrees and thirteen minutes' could allude to nothing but elevation above the visible horizon, since the horizontal direction was clearly indicated by the words, 'north-east and by north.' This latter direction I at once established by means of a pocket-compass; then, pointing the glass as nearly at an angle of twenty-one degrees of elevation as I could do it by guess, I moved it cautiously up or down, until my attention was arrested by a circular rift or opening in the foliage of a large tree that overtopped its fellows in the distance. In the centre of this rift I perceived a white spot, but could not, at first, distinguish what it was. Adjusting the focus of the telescope, I again looked, and now made it out to be a human skull.

"On this discovery I was so sanguine as to consider the enigma solved; for the phrase 'main branch, seventh limb, east side,' could refer only to the position of the skull on the tree, while 'shoot from the left eye of the death's-head' admitted, also, of but one interpretation, in regard to a search for buried treasure. I perceived that the design was to drop a bullet from the left eye of the skull, and that a bee-line, or, in other words, a straight line, drawn from the nearest point of the trunk through 'the shot (or the spot where the bullet fell), and thence extended to a distance of fifty feet, would indicate a definite point—and beneath this point I thought it at least *possible* that a deposit of value lay concealed."

"All this," I said, "is exceedingly clear, and, although ingenious, still simple and explicit. When you left the Bishop's Hotel, what then?"

"Why, having carefully taken the bearings of the tree, I turned homewards. The instant that I left ' the devil's seat,' however, the circular rift vanished; nor could I get a glimpse of it afterwards, turn as I would. What seems to me the chief ingenuity in this whole business, is the fact (for repeated experiment has convinced me it *is* a fact) that the circular opening in question is visible from no other attainable point of view than that afforded by the narrow ledge on the face of the rock.

"In this expedition to the ' Bishop's Hotel ' I had been attended by Jupiter, who had no doubt observed, for some weeks past, the abstraction of my demeanor, and took especial care not to leave me alone. But on the next day, getting up very early, I contrived to give him the slip, and went into the hills in search of the tree. After much toil I found it. When I came home at night my valet proposed to give me a flogging. With the rest of the adventure I believe you are as well acquainted as myself."

"I suppose," said I, "you missed the spot, in the first attempt at digging, through Jupiter's stupidity in letting the bug fall through the right instead of through the left eye of the skull."

"Precisely. This mistake made a difference of about two inches and a half in the ' shot '—that is to say, in the position of the peg nearest the tree; and had the treasure been *beneath* the ' shot,' the error would have been of little moment; but ' the shot,' together with the nearest point of the tree, were merely two points for the establishment of a line of direction; of course the error, however trivial in the beginning, increased as we proceeded with the line, and, by the time we had gone fifty feet, threw us quite off the scent. But for my deep-seated convictions that treasure was here somewhere actually buried, we might have had all our labor in vain.''

" I presume the fancy of *the skull*—of letting fall a bullet through the skull's eye—was suggested to Kidd by the piratical flag. No doubt he felt a kind of poetical consistency in recovering his money through this ominous insignium.''

" Perhaps so; still, I cannot help thinking that common-sense had quite as much to do with the matter as poetical consistency. To be visible from the Devil's seat, it was necessary that the object, if small, should be *white;* and there is nothing like your human skull for retaining and even increasing its whiteness under exposure to all vicissitudes of weather.''

" But your grandiloquence, and your conduct in swinging the beetle—how excessively odd! I was sure you were mad. And why did you insist on letting fall the bug, instead of a bullet, from the skull? ''

" Why, to be frank, I felt somewhat annoyed by your evident suspicions touching my sanity, and so resolved to punish you quietly, in my own way, by a little bit of sober mystification. For this reason I swung the beetle, and for this reason I let it fall from the tree. An observation of yours about its great weight suggested the latter idea.''

" Yes, I perceive; and now there is only one point which puzzles me. What are we to make of the skeletons found in the hole? ''

" That is a question I am no more able to answer than yourself. There seems, however, only one plausible way of accounting for them—and yet it is dreadful to believe in such atrocity as my suggestion would imply. It is clear that Kidd—if Kidd indeed secreted this treasure, which I doubt not—it is clear that he must have had assistance in the labor. But, the worst of this labor concluded, he may have thought it expedient to remove all participants in his secret. Perhaps a couple of blows with a mattock were sufficient, while his coadjutors were busy in the pit; perhaps it required a dozen—who shall tell? "

THE RANSOM OF RED CHIEF

BY

O. HENRY

This is a plot-story of the kind in which the American public delights. The reader enjoys the humor due to situation, hyperbole, satire, and astounding verbal liberties to which the writer is given; but he enjoys even more the sharp surprise that awaits him in the plot. He has prepared himself for a certain conclusion and finds himself entirely in the wrong. Nevertheless, he admits that the ending is not illogical nor out of harmony with the general tone. Bill and Sam subscribe themselves " Two Desperate Men," but they are so characterized as to prepare us for their surrender of the boy on the father's own terms.

It is interesting to know that O. Henry himself put slight value upon local color. " People say that I know New York well! " he says. " But change Twenty-third Street to Main Street, rub out the Flatiron Building and put in the Town Hall. Then the story will fit just as truly elsewhere. At least, I hope that is the case with what I write. So long as your story is true to life, the mere change of local color will set it in the East, West, South, or North. The characters in ' The Arabian Nights ' parade up and down Broadway at midday, or Main Street in Dallas, Texas."

THE RANSOM OF RED CHIEF *

It looked like a good thing: but wait till I tell you.
We were down South, in Alabama—Bill Driscoll and
myself—when this kidnapping idea struck us. It was, as
Bill afterward expressed it, " during a moment of temporary mental apparition "; but we didn't find that
out till later.

There was a town down there, as flat as a flannel-
cake, and called Summit, of course. It contained inhabitants of as undeleterious and self-satisfied a class
of peasantry as ever clustered around a Maypole.

Bill and me had a joint capital of about six hundred
dollars, and we needed just two thousand dollars more
to pull off a fraudulent town-lot scheme in Western
Illinois with. We talked it over on the front steps of the
hotel. Philoprogenitiveness, says we, is strong in semi-
rural communities; therefore, and for other reasons, a
kidnapping project ought to do better there than in the
radius of newspapers that send reporters out in plain
clothes to stir up talk about such things. We knew that
Summit couldn't get after us with anything stronger
than constables and, maybe, some lackadaisical blood-
hounds and a diatribe or two in the *Weekly Farmers'
Budget*. So, it looked good.

We selected for our victim the only child of a prominent
citizen named Ebenezer Dorset. The father was respect-
able and tight, a mortgage fancier and a stern, upright
collection-plate passer and forecloser. The kid was a
boy of ten, with bas-relief freckles, and hair the color of

* From " Whirligigs," by O. Henry. Copyright, 1910, by
Doubleday, Page & Company. Reprinted by special permission of
Doubleday, Page & Company.

the cover of the magazine you buy at the news-stand when you want to catch a train. Bill and me figured that Ebenezer would melt down for a ransom of two thousand dollars to a cent. But wait till I tell you.

About two miles from Summit was a little mountain, covered with a dense cedar brake. On the rear elevation of this mountain was a cave. There we stored provisions.

One evening after sundown, we drove in a buggy past old Dorset's house. The kid was in the street, throwing rocks at a kitten on the opposite fence.

" Hey, little boy! " says Bill, " would you like to have a bag of candy and a nice ride? "

The boy catches Bill neatly in the eye with a piece of brick.

" That will cost the old man an extra five hundred dollars, " says Bill, climbing over the wheel.

That boy put up a fight like a welter-weight cinnamon bear; but, at last, we got him down in the bottom of the buggy and drove away. We took him up to the cave, and I hitched the horse in the cedar brake. After dark I drove the buggy to the little village, three miles away, where we had hired it, and walked back to the mountain.

Bill was pasting court-plaster over the scratches and bruises on his features. There was a fire burning behind the big rock at the entrance of the cave, and the boy was watching a pot of boiling coffee, with two buzzard tail-feathers stuck in his red hair. He points a stick at me when I come up, and says:

" Ha! cursed paleface, do you dare to enter the camp of Red Chief, the terror of the plains? "

" He's all right now, " says Bill, rolling up his trousers and examining some bruises on his shins. " We're playing Indian. We're making Buffalo Bill's show look

like magic-lantern views of Palestine in the town hall.
I'm Old Hank, the Trapper, Red Chief's captive, and
I'm to be scalped at daybreak. By Geronimo! that kid
can kick hard.''

Yes, sir, that boy seemed to be having the time of his
life. The fun of camping out in a cave had made him
forget that he was a captive himself. He immediately
christened me Snake-eye, the Spy, and announced that,
when his braves returned from the warpath, I was to be
broiled at the stake at the rising of the sun.

Then we had supper; and he filled his mouth full of
bacon and bread and gravy, and began to talk. He
made a during-dinner speech something like this:

'' I like this fine. I never camped out before; but I
had a pet 'possum once, and I was nine last birthday.
I hate to go to school. Rats ate up sixteen of Jimmy
Talbot's aunt's speckled hen's eggs. Are there any
real Indians in these woods? I want some more gravy.
Does the trees moving make the wind blow? We had
five puppies. What makes your nose so red, Hank?
My father has lots of money. Are the stars hot? I
whipped Ed Walker twice, Saturday. I don't like girls.
You dassent catch toads unless with a string. Do oxen
make any noise? Why are oranges round? Have you
got beds to sleep on in this cave? Amos Murray has
got six toes. A parrot can talk, but a monkey or a fish
can't. How many does it take to make twelve?''

Every few minutes he would remember that he was
a pesky redskin, and pick up his stick rifle and tiptoe to
the mouth of the cave to rubber for the scouts of the
hated paleface. Now and then he would let out a war-
whoop that made Old Hank the Trapper, shiver. That
boy had Bill terrorized from the start.

'' Red Chief,'' says I to the kid, '' would you like
to go home?''

"Aw, what for?" says he. "I don't have any fun at home. I hate to go to school. I like to camp out. You won't take me back home again, Snake-eye, will you?"

"Not right away," says I. "We'll stay here in the cave a while."

"All right!" says he. "That'll be fine. I never had such fun in all my life."

We went to bed about eleven o'clock. We spread down some wide blankets and quilts and put Red Chief between us. We weren't afraid he'd run away. He kept us awake for three hours, jumping up and reaching for his rifle and screeching: "Hist! pard," in mine and Bill's ears, as the fancied crackle of a twig or the rustle of a leaf revealed to his young imagination the stealthy approach of the outlaw band. At last, I fell into a troubled sleep, and dreamed that I had been kidnapped and chained to a tree by a ferocious pirate with red hair.

Just at daybreak, I was awakened by a series of awful screams from Bill. They weren't yells, or howls, or shouts, or whoops, or yawps, such as you'd expect from a manly set of vocal organs—they were simply indecent, terrifying, humiliating screams, such as women emit when they see ghosts or caterpillars. It's an awful thing to hear a strong, desperate, fat man scream incontinently in a cave at daybreak.

I jumped up to see what the matter was. Red Chief was sitting on Bill's chest, with one hand twined in Bill's hair. In the other he had the sharp case-knife we used for slicing bacon; and he was industriously and realistically trying to take Bill's scalp, according to the sentence that had been pronounced upon him the evening before.

I got the knife away from the kid and made him lie down again. But, from that moment, Bill's spirit was broken. He laid down on his side of the bed, but he never closed an eye again in sleep as long as that boy was with us. I dozed off for a while, but along toward sun-up I remembered that Red Chief had said I was to be burned at the stake at the rising of the sun. I wasn't nervous or afraid; but I sat up and lit my pipe and leaned against a rock.

"What you getting up so soon for, Sam?" asked Bill.

"Me?" says I. "Oh, I got a kind of a pain in my shoulder. I thought sitting up would rest it."

"You're a liar!" says Bill. "You're afraid. You was to be burned at sunrise, and you was afraid he'd do it. And he would, too, if he could find a match. Ain't it awful, Sam? Do you think anybody will pay out money to get a little imp like that back home?"

"Sure," said I. "A rowdy kid like that is just the kind that parents dote on. Now, you and the Chief get up and cook breakfast, while I go up on the top of this mountain and reconnoitre."

I went up on the peak of the little mountain and ran my eye over the contiguous vicinity. Over toward Summit I expected to see the sturdy yeomanry of the village armed with scythes and pitchforks beating the country-side for the dastardly kidnappers. But what I saw was a peaceful landscape dotted with one man ploughing with a dun mule. Nobody was dragging the creek; no couriers dashed hither and yon, bringing tidings of no news to the distracted parents. There was a sylvan attitude of somnolent sleepiness pervading that section of the external outward surface of Alabama that lay exposed to my view. "Perhaps," says I to myself, "it has not yet been discovered that the wolves have borne away the tender lambkin from the fold. Heaven help the wolves!'' says I, and I went down the mountain to breakfast.

When I got to the cave I found Bill backed up against the side of it, breathing hard, and the boy threatening to smash him with a rock half as big as a cocoanut.

'' He put a red-hot boiled potato down my back,'' explained Bill, '' and then mashed it with his foot; and I boxed his ears. Have you got a gun about you, Sam?''

I took the rock away from the boy and kind of patched up the argument. '' I'll fix you,'' says the kid to Bill. '' No man ever yet struck the Red Chief but what he got paid for it. You better beware!''

After breakfast the kid takes a piece of leather with strings wrapped around it out of his pocket and goes outside the cave unwinding it.

'' What's he up to now?'' says Bill, anxiously. '' You don't think he'll run away, do you, Sam?''

'' No fear of it,'' says I. '' He don't seem to be much of a home body. But we've got to fix up some plan about the ransom. There don't seem to be much excitement around Summit on account of his disappearance; but maybe they haven't realized yet that he's gone. His folks may think he's spending the night with Aunt Jane or one of the neighbors. Anyhow, he'll be missed to-day. To-night we must get a message to his father demanding the two thousand dollars for his return.''

Just then we heard a kind of war-whoop, such as David might have emitted when he knocked out the champion Goliath. It was a sling that Red Chief had pulled out of his pocket, and he was whirling it around his head.

I dodged, and heard a heavy thud and a kind of a sigh from Bill, like a horse gives out when you take his saddle off. A niggerhead rock the size of an egg had caught Bill just behind his left ear. He loosened himself all over and fell in the fire across the frying pan of hot water for washing the dishes. I dragged him out and poured cold water on his head for half an hour.

By and by, Bill sits up and feels behind his ear and says: " Sam, do you know who my favorite Biblical character is ? "

" Take it easy," says I. " You'll come to your senses presently."

" King Herod," says he. " You won't go away and leave me here alone, will you, Sam ? "

I went out and caught that boy and shook him until his freckles rattled.

" If you don't behave," says I, " I'll take you straight home. Now, are you going to be good, or not ? "

" I was only funning," says he sullenly. " I didn't mean to hurt Old Hank. But what did he hit me for ? I'll behave, Snake-eye, if you won't send me home, and if you'll let me play the Black Scout to-day."

" I don't know the game," says I. " That's for you and Mr. Bill to decide. He's your playmate for the day. I'm going away for a while, on business. Now, you come in and make friends with him and say you are sorry for hurting him, or home you go, at once."

I made him and Bill shake hands, and then I took Bill aside and told him I was going to Poplar Cove, a little village three miles from the cave, and find out what I could about how the kidnapping had been regarded in Summit. Also, I thought it best to send a peremptory letter to old man Dorset that day, demanding the ransom and dictating how it should be paid.

" You know, Sam," says Bill, " I've stood by you without batting an eye in earthquakes, fire, and flood—

in poker games, dynamite outrages, police raids, train robberies, and cyclones. I never lost my nerve yet till we kidnapped that two-legged skyrocket of a kid. He's got me going. You won't leave me long with him, will you, Sam?''

''I'll be back some time this afternoon,'' says I. ''You must keep the boy amused and quiet till I return. And now we'll write the letter to old Dorset.''

Bill and I got paper and pencil and worked on the letter while Red Chief, with a blanket wrapped around him, strutted up and down, guarding the mouth of the cave. Bill begged me tearfully to make the ransom fifteen hundred dollars instead of two thousand. '' I ain't attempting,'' says he, '' to decry the celebrated moral aspect of parental affection, but we're dealing with humans, and it ain't human for anybody to give up two thousand dollars for that forty-pound chunk of freckled wildcat. I'm willing to take a chance at fifteen hundred dollars. You can charge the difference up to me.''

So, to relieve Bill, I acceded, and we collaborated a letter that ran this way:

"*Ebenezer Dorset, Esq.:*

"We have your boy concealed in a place far from Summit. It is useless for you or the most skilful detectives to attempt to find him. Absolutely, the only terms on which you can have him restored to you are these: We demand fifteen hundred dollars in large bills for his return; the money to be left at midnight to-night at the same spot and in the same box as your reply—as hereinafter described. If you agree to these terms, send your answer in writing by a solitary messenger to-night at half-past eight o'clock. After crossing Owl Creek, on the road to Poplar Cove, there are three large trees about a hundred yards apart, close to the fence of the wheat field on the right-hand side. At the bottom of the fence-post, opposite the third tree, will be found a small pasteboard box.

"The messenger will place the answer in this box and return immediately to Summit.

"If you attempt any treachery or fail to comply with our demand as stated, you will never see your boy again.

"If you pay the money as demanded, he will be returned to you safe and well within three hours. These terms are final, and if you do not accede to them no further communication will be attempted.

"TWO DESPERATE MEN."

I addressed this letter to Dorset, and put it in my pocket. As I was about to start, the kid comes up to me and says:

"Aw, Snake-eye, you said I could play the Black Scout while you was gone."

"Play it, of course," says I. "Mr. Bill will play with you. What kind of a game is it?"

"I'm the Black Scout," says Red Chief, "and I have to ride to the stockade to warn the settlers that the Indians are coming. I'm tired of playing Indian myself. I want to be the Black Scout."

"All right," says I. "It sounds harmless to me. I guess Mr. Bill will help you foil the pesky savages."

"What am I to do?" asks Bill, looking at the kid suspiciously.

"You are the hoss," says Black Scout. "Get down on your hands and knees. How can I ride to the stockade without a hoss?"

"You'd better keep him interested," said I, "till we get the scheme going. Loosen up."

Bill gets down on his all fours, and a look comes in his eye like a rabbit's when you catch it in a trap.

"How far is it to the stockade, kid?" he asks, in a husky manner of voice.

"Ninety miles," says the Black Scout. "And you have to hump yourself to get there on time. Whoa, now!"

The Black Scout jumps on Bill's back and digs his heels in his side.

"For Heaven's sake," says Bill, "hurry back, Sam, as soon as you can. I wish we hadn't made the ransom more than a thousand. Say, you quit kicking me or I'll get up and warm you good."

I walked over to Poplar Cove and sat around the post-office and store, talking with the chawbacons that came in to trade. One whiskerando says that he hears Summit is all upset on account of Elder Ebenezer Dorset's boy having been lost or stolen. That was all I wanted to know. I bought some smoking tobacco, referred casually to the price of black-eyed peas, posted my letter surreptitiously, and came away. The postmaster said the mail-carrier would come by in an hour to take the mail on to Summit.

When I got back to the cave Bill and the boy were not to be found. I explored the vicinity of the cave, and risked a yodel or two, but there was no response.

So I lighted my pipe and sat down on a mossy bank to await developments.

In about half an hour I heard the bushes rustle, and Bill wabbled out into the little glade in front of the cave. Behind him was the kid, stepping softly like a scout, with a broad grin on his face. Bill stopped, took off his hat, and wiped his face with a red handkerchief. The kid stopped about eight feet behind him.

"Sam," says Bill, "I suppose you'll think I'm a renegade, but I couldn't help it. I'm a grown person with masculine proclivities and habits of self-defence, but there is a time when all systems of egotism and predominance fail. The boy is gone. I have sent him home. All is off. There was martyrs in old times," goes on Bill, "that suffered death rather than give up the particular graft they enjoyed. None of 'em ever was subjugated to such supernatural tortures as I have been. I tried to be faithful to our articles of depredation; but there came a limit."

" What's the trouble, Bill？ " I asks him.

" I was rode," says Bill, " the ninety miles to the stockade, not barring an inch. Then, when the settlers was rescued, I was given oats. Sand ain't a palatable substitute. And then, for an hour I had to try to explain to him why there was nothin' in holes, how a road can run both ways, and what makes the grass green. I tell you, Sam, a human can only stand so much. I takes him by the neck of his clothes and drags him down the mountain. On the way he kicks my legs black-and-blue from the knees down; and I've got to have two or three bites on my thumb and hand cauterized.

" But he's gone "—continues Bill—" gone home. I showed him the road to Summit and kicked him about eight feet nearer there at one kick. I'm sorry we lose the ransom; but it was either that or Bill Driscoll to the madhouse."

Bill is puffing and blowing, but there is a look of ineffable peace and growing content on his rose-pink features.

" Bill," says I, " there isn't any heart disease in your family, is there？ "

" No," says Bill, " nothing chronic except malaria and accidents. Why？ "

" Then you might turn around," says I, " and have a look behind you."

Bill turns and sees the boy, and loses his complexion and sits down plump on the ground and begins to pluck aimlessly at grass and little sticks. For an hour I was afraid for his mind. And then I told him that my scheme was to put the whole job through immediately and that we would get the ransom and be off with it by midnight if old Dorset fell in with our proposition. So Bill braced up enough to give the kid a weak sort of a smile and a promise to play the Russian in a Japanese war with him as soon as he felt a little better.

I had a scheme for collecting that ransom without danger of being caught by counterplots that ought to commend itself to professional kidnappers. The tree under which the answer was to be left—and the money later on—was close to the road fence with big, bare fields on all sides. If a gang of constables should be watching for any one to come for the note, they could see him a long way off crossing the fields or in the road. But no, sirree! At half-past eight I was up in that tree as well hidden as a tree toad, waiting for the messenger to arrive.

Exactly on time, a half-grown boy rides up the road on a bicycle, locates the pasteboard box at the foot of the fence-post, slips a folded piece of paper into it, and pedals away again back toward Summit.

I waited an hour and then concluded the thing was square. I slid down the tree, got the note, slipped along the fence till I struck the woods, and was back at the cave in another half an hour. I opened the note, got near the lantern, and read it to Bill. It was written with a pen in a crabbed hand, and the sum and substance of it was this:

"*Two Desperate Men.*

"*Gentlemen:* I received your letter to-day by post, in regard to the ransom you ask for the return of my son. I think you are a little high in your demands, and I hereby make you a counter-proposition, which I am inclined to believe you will accept. You bring Johnny home and pay me two hundred and fifty dollars in cash, and I agree to take him off your hands. You had better come at night, for the neighbors believe he is lost, and I couldn't be responsible for what they would do to anybody they saw bringing him back. Very respectfully,

" EBENEZER DORSET."

" Great pirates of Penzance! " says I; " of all the impudent——"

But I glanced at Bill, and hesitated. He had the most appealing look in his eyes I ever saw on the face of a dumb or a talking brute.

" Sam," says he, " what's two hundred and fifty dollars, after all? We've got the money. One more night of this kid will send me to a bed in Bedlam. Besides being a thorough gentleman, I think Mr. Dorset is a spendthrift for making us such a liberal offer. You ain't going to let the chance go, are you? "

" Tell you the truth, Bill," says I, " this little he ewe lamb has somewhat got on my nerves too. We'll take him home, pay the ransom, and make our get-away."

We took him home that night. We got him to go by telling him that his father had bought a silver-mounted rifle and a pair of moccasins for him, and we were going to hunt bears the next day.

It was just twelve o'clock when we knocked at Ebenezer's front door. Just at the moment when I should have been abstracting the fifteen hundred dollars from the box under the tree, according to the original proposition, Bill was counting out two hundred and fifty dollars into Dorset's hand.

When the kid found out we were going to leave him at home he started up a howl like a calliope and fastened himself as tight as a leech to Bill's leg. His father peeled him away gradually, like a porous plaster.

" How long can you hold him? " asks Bill.

" I'm not as strong as I used to be," says old Dorset, " but I think I can promise you ten minutes."

" Enough," says Bill. " In ten minutes I shall cross

the Central, Southern, and Middle Western States, and
be legging it trippingly for the Canadian border.''

And, as dark as it was, and as fat as Bill was, and as
good a runner as I am, he was a good mile and a half
out of Summit before I could catch up with him.

THE FRESHMAN FULL-BACK

BY

RALPH D. PAINE

The chief interest in " The Freshman Full-Back " is that of character. The action has real dramatic quality and is staged with the local color of a college contest. But the great value of the action is ethical, for it shows that one may " wrest victory from defeat " and that it is a shameful thing to be a " coward and a quitter."

THE FRESHMAN FULL-BACK *

The boyish night city editor glanced along the copy-readers' table and petulantly exclaimed:

"Isn't that spread head ready yet, Mr. Seeley? It goes on the front page and we are holding open for it. Whew, but you are slow. You ought to be holding down a job on a quarterly review."

A portly man of middle age dropped his pencil and turned heavily in his chair to face the source of this public humiliation. An angry flush overspread his face and he chewed at a grayish mustache as if fighting down rebellion. His comrades at the long table had looked up from their work and were eyeing the oldest copy-reader with sympathetic uneasiness while they hoped that he would be able to hold himself in hand. The night city editor felt the tension of this brief tableau and awaited the threatened outbreak with a nervous smile. But Seeley jerked his green eyeshade so low that his face was partly in eclipse, and wheeled round to resume his task with a catch of the breath and a tone of surrender in his reply.

"The head will be ready in five minutes, sir. The last pages of the story are just coming in."

A much younger man, at the farther end of the table, whispered to his neighbor:

"That's cheap and nasty, to call down old man Seeley as if he were a cub reporter. He may have 'ost his grip, but he deserves decent treatment for what

* From "College Years," by Ralph D. Paine. Copyright, 1909, by Charles Scribner's Sons.

he has been. Managing editor of this very sheet, London correspondent before that, and the crack man of the staff when most of the rest of us were in short breeches. And now Henry Harding Seeley isn't any too sure of keeping his job on the copy-desk."

" That's what the New York newspaper game can do to you if you stick at it too long," murmured the other. " Back to the farm for mine."

It was long after midnight when these two put on their coats and bade the city editor's desk a perfunctory " Good-night."

They left Henry Harding Seeley still slumped in his chair, writing with dogged industry.

" He's dead tired, you can see that," commented one of the pair as they headed for Broadway, " but, as usual, he is grinding out stuff for the Sunday sheet after hours. He must need the extra coin mighty bad. I came back for my overcoat at four the other morning, after the poker game, and he was still pegging away just like that."

Other belated editors and reporters of the *Chronicle* staff drifted toward the elevator, until the gray-haired copy-reader was left alone in the city room as if marooned. Writing as steadily as if he were a machine warranted to turn out so many words an hour, Seeley urged his pencil until the last page was finished. Then he read and corrected the " story," slipped it through a slit in a door marked " Sunday Editor," and trudged out, while the tower clock was striking three.

Instead of seeking the chop-house, wherein the vivacious and tireless youth of the staff were wont to linger over supper, he turned into a side street and betook himself to a small café as yet unfrequented by the night-owls of journalism. Seeley was a beaten man, and he preferred to nurse his wounds in a morbid isolation.

His gait and aspect were those of one who was stolidly struggling on the defensive, as if hostile circumstances had driven him into a corner where he was making his last stand.

Through the years of his indomitable youth as a reporter of rare ability and resourcefulness, he had never spared himself. Burning the candle at both ends, with a vitality which had seemed inexhaustible, he had won step after step of promotion until, at forty, he was made managing editor of that huge and hard-driven organization, the *New York Chronicle*. For five years of racking responsibility Henry Harding Seeley had been able to maintain the pace demanded of his position.

Then came an error of judgment—a midnight decision demanded of a fagged mind—and his O. K. was scrawled upon the first sheet of a story of embezzlement in Wall Street. By an incredible blunder the name of the fugitive cashier was coupled with that of the wrong bank. Publication of the *Chronicle* story started a terrific run on this innocent institution, which won its libel suit against the newspaper in the amount of one hundred thousand dollars.

The managing editor, two reporters, and the copyreader who had handled the fatal manuscript, were swept out of the building by one cyclonic order from the owner thereof. Henry Seeley accepted his indirect responsibility for the disaster in grim, manly fashion, and straightway sought another berth befitting his journalistic station. But his one costly slip was more than a nine-days' scandal along Park Row, and other canny proprietors were afraid that he might hit them in the very vital regions of their pockets. Worse than this, his confidence in himself had suffered mortal damage. The wear and tear of his earlier years had left him with little reserve power, and he went to pieces in the face of adverse fortune.

"Worked out at forty-five," was the verdict of his friends, and they began to pity him.

The will to succeed had been broken, but Seeley might have rallied had not his wife died during the ebb-tide of his affairs. She had walked hand in hand with him since his early twenties, her faith in him had been his mainstay, and his happiness in her complete and beautiful. Bereft of her when he stood most in need of her, he seemed to have no more fight in him, and, drifting from one newspaper office to another, he finally eddied into his old "shop" as a drudging copy-reader and an object of sympathy to a younger generation.

There was one son, strong, bright, eager, and by dint of driving his eternally wearied brain overtime, the father had been able to send him to Yale, his own alma mater. More or less pious deception had led young Ernest Seeley to believe that his father had regained much of his old-time prestige with the *Chronicle* and that he had a hand in guiding its editorial destinies. The lad was a Freshman, tremendously absorbed in the activities of the autumn term, and his father was content that he should be so hedged about by the interests of the campus world as to have small time or thought for the grizzled, taciturn toiler in New York.

This was the kind of man that trudged heavily into the little German café of an early morning after his long night's slavery at the copy-desk. His mind, embittered and sensitive to slights like a raw nerve, was brooding over the open taunt of the night city editor, who had been an office boy under him in the years gone by. From force of habit he seated himself at a table in the rear of the room, shunning the chance of having

to face an acquaintance. Unfolding a copy of the city
edition, which had been laid on his desk damp from
the press-room, Seeley scanned the front page with
scowling uneasiness, as if fearing to find some blunder
of his own handiwork. Then he turned to the sporting
page and began to read the football news.

His son Ernest had been playing as a substitute
with the university eleven, an achievement which stirred
the father's pride without moving his enthusiasm. And
the boy, chilled by his father's indifference, had said
little about it during his infrequent visits to New York.
But now the elder Seeley sat erect, and his stolid countenance was almost animated as he read, under a New
Haven date line:

"The Yale confidence of winning the game with Princeton to-
morrow has been shattered, and gloom enshrouds the camp of
the Elis to-night. Collins, the great full-back, who has been the
key-stone of Yale's offensive game, was taken to the infirmary
late this afternoon. He complained of feeling ill after the signal
practice yesterday; fever developed overnight, and the consulting
physicians decided that he must be operated on for appendicitis
without delay. His place in the Princeton game will be filled by
Ernest Seeley, the Freshman, who has been playing a phenomenal
game in the back-field, but who is so lacking in experience that
the coaches are all at sea to-night. The loss of Collins has swung
the betting around to even money instead of 5 to 3 on Yale."

The elder Seeley wiped his glasses as if not sure that
he had read aright.

Ernest had seemed to him no more than a sturdy
infant and here he was, on the eve of a championship
football battle, picked to fight for the "old blue." The
father's career at Yale had been a most honorable one.
He, too, had played on the eleven and had helped to
win two desperate contests against Princeton. But all
this belonged to a part of his life which was dead and

done for. He had not achieved in after years what Yale expected of him, and his record there was with his buried memories.

Supper was forgotten while Henry Seeley wondered whether he really wanted to go to New Haven to see his boy play. Many of his old friends and classmates would be there and he did not wish to meet them.

And it stung him to the quick as he reflected:

"I should be very happy to see him win, but—but to see him whipped! I couldn't brace and comfort him. And supposing it breaks his heart to be whipped as it has broken mine? No, I won't let myself think that. I'm a poor Yale man and a worse father, but I couldn't stand going up there to-day."

Even more humiliating was the thought that he would shrink from asking leave of the city editor. Saturday was not his "day off," and he so greatly hated to ask favors at the office, that the possibility of being rebuffed was more than he was willing to face.

Into his unhappy meditations broke a boisterous hail:

"Diogenes Seeley, as I live. Why, you old rascal, I thought you were dead or something. Glad I didn't get foolish and go to bed. Here, waiter, get busy."

Seeley was startled, and he looked much more distressed than rejoiced as he lumbered from his table to grasp the outstretched hand of a classmate. The opera-hat of this Mr. Richard Giddings was cocked at a rakish angle, his blue eye twinkled good cheer and youthful hilarity, and his aspect was utterly care-free.

"How are you, Dick?" said Seeley, with an unusual smile which singularly brightened his face. "You don't look a day older than when I last saw you. Still cutting coupons for a living?"

"Oh, money is the least of my worries," gayly rattled Mr. Giddings. "Been doing the heavy society act to-

night, and on my way home found I needed some
sauerkraut and beer to tone up my jaded system. By
Jove, Harry, you're as gray as a badger. This newspaper game must be bad for the nerves. Lots of fellows have asked me about you. Never see you at the
University Club, nobody sees you anywhere. Remarkable how a man can lose himself right here in New
York. Still running the *Chronicle,* I suppose."

" I'm still in the old shop, Dick," replied Seeley, glad
to be rid of this awkward question. " But I work
nearly all night and sleep most of the day, and am like
a cog in a big machine that never stops grinding."

" Shouldn't do it. Wears a man out," and Mr. Giddings sagely nodded his head. " Course you are going
up to the game to-day. Come along with me. Special
car with a big bunch of your old pals inside. They'll
be tickled to death to find I've dug you out of your hole.
Hello! Is that this morning's paper? Let me look at
the sporting page. Great team at New Haven, they
tell me. What's the latest odds? I put up a thousand
at five to three last week and am looking for some
more easy money."

The alert eye of the volatile Richard Giddings swept
down the New Haven dispatch like lightning.

With a grievous outcry he smote the table and shouted:

" Collins out of the game? Great Scott, Harry, that's
awful news. And a green Freshman going to fill his
shoes at the last minute. I feel like weeping, honest I
do. Who the deuce is this Seeley? Any kin of yours?
I suppose not or you would have bellowed it at me
before this."

" He is my only boy, Dick," and the father held up
his head with a shadow of his old manner. " I didn't
know he had the ghost of a show to make the team until
I saw this dispatch."

" Then, of course, you are coming up with me,"
roared Mr. Giddings. " I hope he's a chip of the old
block. If he has your sand they can't stop him. Jumping Jupiter, they couldn't have stopped you with an
axe when you were playing guard in our time, Harry.
I feel better already to know that it is your kid going
in at full-back to-day."

" No, I'm not going up, Dick," said Seeley slowly.
" For one thing, it is too short notice for me to break
away from the office, and I—I haven't the nerve to
watch the boy go into the game. I'm not feeling very
fit."

" Stuff and nonsense, you need a brain cure," vociferated Richard Giddings. " You, an old Yale guard,
with a pup on the team, and he a Freshman at that!
Throw out your chest, man; tell the office to go to the
devil—where all newspapers belong—and meet me at the
station at ten o'clock sharp. You talk and look like the
oldest living grad with one foot in the grave."

Seeley flushed and bit his lip. His dulled realization
of what Yale had been to him was quickened by this
tormenting comrade of the brave days of old, but he
could not be shaken from his attitude of morbid self-
effacement.

" No, Dick, it's no use," he returned with a tremulous smile. " You can't budge me. But give my love
to the crowd and tell them to cheer for that youngster
of mine until they're blue in the face."

Mr. Richard Giddings eyed him quizzically, and sur-
mised that something or other was gravely wrong with
his grizzled classmate. But Seeley offered no more explanations and the vivacious intruder fell to his task
of demolishing sauerkraut with great gusto, after which
he nimbly vanished into a cruising hansom with a sense
of having been rebuffed.

Seeley watched him depart at great speed and then plodded toward his up-town lodgings. His sleep was distressed with unhappy dreams, and during a wakeful interval he heard a knock at his sitting-room door.

An office boy from the *Chronicle* editorial rooms gave him a note and waited for an answer.

Seeley recognized the handwriting of the managing editor and was worried, for he was always expecting the worst to happen. He sighed with relieved surprise as he read:

" MY DEAR MR. SEELEY:

" Please go to New Haven as soon as possible and do a couple of columns of descriptive introduction of the Yale-Princeton game. The sporting department will cover the technical story, but a big steamboat collision has just happened in North River, two or three hundred drowned and so on, and I need every man in the shop. As an old Yale player I am sure I can depend on you for a good story, and I know you used to do this kind of stuff in fine style."

Seeley fished his watch from under a pillow. It was after ten o'clock and the game would begin at two. While he hurried into his clothes he was conscious of a distinct thrill of excited interest akin to his old-time joy in the day's work. Could he " do this kind of stuff in fine style "? Why, before his brain had begun to be always tired, when he was the star reporter of the *Chronicle*, his football introductions had been classics in Park Row. If there was a spark of the old fire left in him he would try to strike it out, and for the moment he forgot the burden of inertia which had so long crushed him.

" But I don't want to run into Dick Giddings and his crowd," he muttered as he sought his hat and overcoat. " And I'll be up in the press-box away from the mob of old grads. Perhaps my luck has turned."

When Henry Seeley reached the Yale field the eleven had gone to the dressing-rooms in the training house, and he hovered on the edge of the flooding crowds, fairly yearning for a glimpse of the Freshman full-back and a farewell grasp of his hand. The habitual dread lest the son find cause to be ashamed of his father had been shoved into the background by a stronger, more natural emotion. But he well knew that he ought not to invade the training quarters in these last crucial moments. Ernest must not be distraught by a feather's weight of any other interest than the task in hand. The coaches would be delivering their final words of instruction and the old Yale guard could picture to himself the tense absorption of the scene. Like one coming out of a dream, the past was returning to him in vivid, heart-stirring glimpses. Reluctantly he sought his place in the press-box high above the vast amphitheatre.

The preliminary spectacle was movingly familiar: the rippling banks of color which rose on all sides to frame the long carpet of chalked turf; the clamorous outbursts of cheering when an eddy of Yale or Princeton undergraduates swirled and tossed at command of the dancing dervish of a leader at the edge of the field below; the bright, buoyant aspect of the multitude as viewed en masse. Seeley leaned against the railing of his lofty perch and gazed at this pageant until a sporting editor, long in harness, nudged his elbow and said:

"Hello! I haven't seen you at a game in a dozen years. Doing the story or just working the press-badge graft? That namesake of yours will be meat for the Tigers, I'm afraid. Glad he doesn't belong to you, aren't you?"

Seeley stared at him like a man in a trance and replied evasively:

" He may be good enough. It all depends on his sand and nerve. Yes, I am doing the story for a change. Have you the final line-up? "

" Princeton is playing all her regular men," said the sporting editor, giving Seeley his note-book. " The only Yale change is at full-back—and that's a catastrophe."

Seeley copied the lists for reference and his pencil was not steady when he came to " Full-back, Ernest T. Seeley." But he pulled his thoughts away from the eleven and began to jot down notes of the passing incidents which might serve to weave into the fabric of his description. The unwonted stimulus aroused his talent as if it were not dead but dormant. The scene appealed to him with almost as much freshness and color as if he were observing it for the first time.

A roar of cheering rose from a far corner of the field and ran swiftly along the Yale side of the amphitheatre, which blossomed in tossing blue. The Yale eleven scampered into view like colts at pasture, the substitutes veering toward the benches behind the side-line. Without more ado the team scattered in formation for signal practice, paying no heed to the tumult which raged around and above them. Agile, clean-limbed, splendid in their disciplined young manhood, the dark blue of their stockings and the white " Y " gleaming on their sweaters fairly trumpeted their significance to Henry Seeley. And poised behind the rush-line, wearing his hard-won university blue, was the lithe figure of the Freshman full-back, Ernest Seeley.

The youngster, whose fate it was to be called a " forlorn hope," looked fragile beside his comrades of the eleven. Although tall and wiry, he was like a greyhound in a company of mastiffs. His father, looking down at him from so great a height that he could not read his face, muttered to himself while he dug his nails into his palms:

" He is too light for this day's work. But he carries himself like a thoroughbred."

The boy and his fellows seemed singularly remote from the shouting thousands massed so near them. They had become the sole arbiters of their fate, and their impressive isolation struck Henry Seeley anew as the most dramatic feature of this magnificent picture. He must sit idly by and watch his only son battle through the most momentous hour of his young life, as if he were gazing down from another planet.

The staccato cheers of Princeton rocketed along the other side of the field, and the eleven from Old Nassau ran briskly over the turf and wheeled into line for a last rehearsal of their machine-like tactics. Henry Seeley was finding it hard to breathe, just as it had happened in other days when he was waiting for the " kick-off " and facing a straining Princeton line. The minutes were like hours while the officials consulted with the captains in the centre of the field. Then the two elevens ranged themselves across the brown turf, there was breathless silence, and a Princeton toe lifted the ball far down toward the Yale goal. It was the young full-back who waited to receive the opening kick, while his comrades thundered toward him to form a flying screen of interference. But the twisting ball bounded from his too eager arms, and another Yale back fell on it in time to save it from the clutches of a meteoric Princeton end.

" Nervous. Hasn't steadied down yet," exclaimed a reporter behind Henry Seeley. " But he can't afford to give Princeton any more chances like that. Her ends are faster than chain lightning."

The father groaned and wiped the sweat from his eyes. If the team were afraid of this untried full-back, such a beginning would not give them confidence. Then the two lines locked and heaved in the first scrimmage, and a stocky Yale half-back was pulled down in his tracks. Again the headlong Princeton defence held firm and the Yale captain gasped, " Second down and three yards to gain." The Yale interferers sped to circle one end of the line, but they were spilled this way and that and the runner went down a yard short of the needed distance.

The Yale full-back dropped back to punt. Far and true the ball soared into the Princeton field, and the lithe Freshman had somewhat redeemed himself. But now, for their own part, the sons of Old Nassau found themselves unable to make decisive gains against the Yale defence. Greek met Greek in these early clashes, and both teams were forced to punt again and again. Trick-plays were spoiled by alert end-rushers for the blue or the orange and black, fiercely launched assaults at centre were torn asunder, and the longer the contest raged up and down the field the more clearly it was perceived that these ancient rivals were rarely well matched in point of strength and strategy.

The Yale coaches were dismayed at this turn of events. They had hoped to see the ball carried toward the Princeton goal by means of shrewdly devised team-work, instead of which the burden of the game was shifted to one man, the weakest link in the chain, the Freshman at full-back. He was punting with splendid distance, getting the ball away when it seemed as if he must be overwhelmed by the hurtling Tigers. Once or twice, however, a hesitant nervousness almost wrought quick disaster, and the Yale partisans watched him with tormenting apprehension.

The first half of the game was fought into the last few minutes of play and neither eleven had been able to score. Then luck and skill combined to force the struggle far down into Yale territory. Only ten yards more of trampled turf to gain and Princeton would cross the last white line. The indomitable spirit which had placed upon the escutcheon of Yale football the figure of a bulldog rampant, rallied to meet this crisis, and the hard-pressed line held staunch and won possession of the ball on downs. Back to the very shadow of his own goal-posts the Yale full-back ran to punt the ball out of the danger zone. It shot fairly into his grasp from a faultless pass, but his fingers juggled the slippery leather as if it were bewitched. For a frantic, awful instant he fumbled with the ball and wildly dived after it as it caromed off to one side, bounded crazily, and rolled beyond his reach.

The Princeton quarter-back had darted through the line like a bullet. Without slackening speed or veering from his course, he scooped up the ball as he fled toward the Yale goal-line. It was done and over within a twinkling, and while the Yale team stampeded helplessly in his wake the devastating hero was circling behind the goal-posts where he flopped to earth, the precious ball apparently embedded in his stomach. It was a Princeton touchdown fairly won, but made possible by the tragic blunder of one Yale man. While ten thousand Princeton throats were barking their jubilation, as many more loyal friends of Yale sat sad-eyed and sullen and glowered their unspeakable displeasure at the slim figure of the full-back as he limped into line to face the try for goal.

The goal was not scored, however, and the fateful tally stood five to nothing when the first half ended, with the blue banners drooping disconsolate.

Henry Seeley pulled his slouch hat over his eyes and sat with hunched shoulders staring at the Yale team

as it left the field for the intermission. He had forgotten about his story of the game. The old spectre
of failure obsessed him. It was already haunting the
pathway of his boy. Was he also to be beaten by one
colossal blunder? Henry Seeley felt that Ernest's whole
career hung upon his behavior in the second half. How
would the lad " take his medicine "? Would it break
his heart or rouse him to fight more valiantly? As if
the father had been thinking aloud, the sporting editor
at his side observed:

" He may win the game yet. I like the looks of that
boy. But he did make a hideous mess of it, didn't he?
I hope he hasn't got a streak of yellow in him."

Henry Seeley turned on his neighbor with a savage
scowl and could not hold back the quivering retort:

" He belongs to me, I want you to understand, and
we'll say nothing about yellow streaks until he has a
chance to make good next half."

" Whew-w-w, why did you hold it out on me, old
man? " gasped the sporting editor. " No wonder you
kicked me black and blue without knowing it. I hope
he is a chip of the old block. I saw you play here in
your last game."

Seeley grunted something and resumed staring at the
field. He was thinking of the present moment in the
training quarters, of the muddy, weary players sprawled
around the head coach, of his wise, bitter, stinging re-
bukes and admonitions. Perhaps he would take Ernest
out of the game. But Seeley was confident that the
coaches would give the boy a chance to redeem himself
if they believed his heart was in the right place. Presently the two teams trotted on the field, not as nimbly
as at their first appearance, but with dogged resolution
in their demeanor. Henry Seeley saw his son glance up
at the " cheering sections," as if wondering whether

their welcome was meant to include him. One cheer, at least, was intended to greet him, for Henry Seeley stood on his chair, waved his hat, and thundered:

" 'Rah, 'rah, 'rah, for Yale, my boy. Eat 'em alive as your daddy used to do."

The men from Princeton had no intention of being devoured in this summary fashion. They resumed their tireless, whirlwind attack like giants refreshed, and so harried their Yale foemen that they were forced to their utmost to ward off another touchdown. This incessant battering dulled the edges of their offensive tactics, and they seemed unable to set in motion a consistent series of advances. But the joy of Princeton was tempered by the knowledge that this, her dearest enemy, was not beaten until the last play had been signalled.

And somehow the Yale machine of muscle, brains, and power began to find itself when the afternoon shadows were slanting athwart the arena. With the ball on Princeton's forty-yard line the chosen sons of Eli began a heroic advance down the field. It was as if some missing cog had been supplied. " Straight old-fashioned football " it was, eleven minds and bodies working as one and animated by a desperate resolve, which carried the Yale team along for down after down into the heart of Princeton's ground.

Perhaps because he was fresher than the other backs, perhaps because the captain knew his man, the ball was given to the Yale full-back for one swift and battering assault after another. His slim figure pelted at the rush-line, was overwhelmed in an avalanche of striped arms and legs, but somehow twisted, wriggled, dragged itself ahead as if there was no stopping him. The multitude comprehended that this despised and disgraced Freshman was working out his own salva-

tion along with that of his comrades. Once, when the
scrimmage was untangled, he was dragged from beneath a heap of players, unable to regain his feet.
He lay on the grass a huddled heap, blood smearing
his forehead. A surgeon and the trainer doused and
bandaged him, and presently he staggered to his feet and
hobbled to his station, rubbing his hands across his eyes
as if dazed.

When, at length, the stubbornly retreating Princeton
line had been driven deep down into their end of the
field, they, too, showed that they could hold fast in the
last extremity. The Yale attack crumpled against them
as if it had struck a stone wall. Young Seeley seemed
to be so crippled and exhausted that he had been given
a respite from the interlocked, hammering onslaught,
but at the third down the panting quarter-back croaked
out his signal. His comrades managed to rip a semblance of an opening for him, he plunged through,
popped clear of the line, fell to his knees, recovered his
footing by a miracle of agility, and lunged onward,
to be brought down within five yards of the coveted
goal-posts.

He had won the right to make the last momentous
charge. Swaying in his tracks, the full-back awaited
the summons. Then he dived in behind the interference for a circuit of the right end. Two Princeton men
broke through as if they had been shot out of mortars,
but the Yale full-back had turned and was ploughing
straight ahead. Pulled down, dragging the tackler who
clung to his waist, he floundered to earth with most of
the Princeton team piled above him. But the ball lay
beyond the fateful chalk-line, the Yale touchdown was
won, and the game was tied.

The captain clapped Seeley on the shoulder, nodded
at the ball, and the full-back limped on to the field

to kick the goal or lose a victory. There were no more signs of nervousness in his bearing. With grave deliberation he stood waiting for the ball to be placed in front of the goal-posts. The sun had dropped behind the lofty grand-stands. The field lay in a kind of wintry twilight. Thirty thousand men and women gazed in tensest silence at the mud-stained, battered youth who had become the crowning issue of this poignant moment. Up in the press-box a thick-set, grayish man dug his fists in his eyes and could not bear to look at the lonely, reliant figure down yonder on the quiet field. The father found courage to take his hands from his face only when a mighty roar of joy boomed along the Yale side of the amphitheatre, and he saw the ball drop in a long arc behind the goal-posts. The kick had won the game for Yale.

Once clear of the crowds, Henry Seeley hurried toward the training quarters. His head was up, his shoulders squared, and he walked with the free stride of an athlete. Mr. Richard Giddings danced madly across to him:

" Afraid to see him play were you, you silly old fool? He is a chip of the old block. He didn't know when he was licked. Wow, wow, wow, blood will tell! Come along with us, Harry."

" I must shake hands with the youngster, Dick. Glad I changed my mind and came to see him do it."

" All right, see you at Mory's to-night. Tell the boy we're all proud of him."

Seeley resumed his course, saying over and over again, as if he loved the sound of the words, " chip of the old block," " blood will tell."

This verdict was like the ringing call of bugles. It made him feel young, hopeful, resolute, that life were worth having for the sake of its strife. One thing at

least was certain. His son could "take his punishment" and wrest victory from disaster, and he deserved
something better than a coward and a quitter for a
father.

The full-back was sitting on a bench when the elder
Seeley entered the crowded, steaming room of the
training house. The surgeon had removed the muddy,
blood-stained bandage from around his tousled head
and was cleansing an ugly, ragged gash. The boy
scowled and winced but made no complaint, although
his bruised face was very pale.

"Must have made you feel pretty foggy," said the
surgeon. "I shall have to put in a few stitches. It
was a deuce of a thump."

"I couldn't see very well and my legs went queer
for a few minutes, but I'm all right now, thanks," replied the full-back, and then, glancing up, he espied
his father standing near the door. The young hero of
the game beckoned him with a grimy fist. Henry Seeley went over to him, took the fist in his two hands,
and then patted the boy's cheek with awkward and un-
accustomed tenderness.

"Sit still, Ernest. I won't interfere with the doctor's job. I just wanted to let you know that I saw
your bully work. It made me think of—it made me
think of——"

Henry Seeley's voice broke curiously and his lip
quivered. He had not meant to show any emotion.

His son replied with a smile of affectionate admiration:

"It made you think of your own teams, didn't it?
And I was thinking of you in that last half. It helped
my nerve a whole lot to remember that my dad never
knew when he was licked. Why, even the coaches told
me that between the halves. It put more ginger into

me than anything else. We've got to keep up the family record between us.''

The father looked beyond the boy as if he were thinking of a bigger, sterner game than football. There was the light of a resurrected determination in his eyes, and a vibrant earnestness in his voice as he said:

'' I'm not worrying about your keeping the family record bright, Ernest. And, however things may go with me, you will be able to hang fast to the doctrine which helped you to-day, that your father, too, doesn't know when he is whipped.''

GALLEGHER

A NEWSPAPER STORY

BY

RICHARD HARDING DAVIS

This is an illustration of a popular type of the short-story. The movement from beginning to end is swift and urgent; something important is happening all the time. Description is reduced to the minimum, and where it is used does not impede the action. The local color of a great newspaper office in a large city contributes to the impression of orderly activity and haste. Gallegher, moreover, is the kind of character that enlists sympathy by his youth, his daring, and his resourcefulness.

GALLEGHER *

We had had so many office-boys before Gallegher came among us that they had begun to lose the characteristics of individuals, and became merged in a composite photograph of small boys, to whom we applied the generic title of " Here, you "; or " You, boy."

We had had sleepy boys, and lazy boys, and bright, " smart " boys, who became so familiar on so short an acquaintance that we were forced to part with them to save our own self-respect.

They generally graduated into district-messenger boys, and occasionally returned to us in blue coats with nickel-plated buttons, and patronized us.

But Gallegher was something different from anything we had experienced before. Gallegher was short and broad in build, with a solid, muscular broadness, and not a fat and dumpy shortness. He wore perpetually on his face a happy and knowing smile, as if you and the world in general were not impressing him as seriously as you thought you were, and his eyes, which were very black and very bright, snapped intelligently at you like those of a little black-and-tan terrier.

All Gallegher knew had been learnt on the streets; not a very good school in itself, but one that turns out very knowing scholars. And Gallagher had attended both morning and evening sessions. He could not

* From " Gallegher and Other Stories," by Richard Harding Davis. Copyright, 1891, by Charles Scribner's Sons.

tell you who the Pilgrim Fathers were, nor could he
name the thirteen original States, but he knew all the
officers of the twenty-second police district by name,
and he could distinguish the clang of a fire-engine's gong
from that of a patrol-wagon or an ambulance fully two
blocks distant. It was Gallegher who rang the alarm
when the Woolwich Mills caught fire, while the officer
on the beat was asleep, and it was Gallegher who led
the "Black Diamonds" against the "Wharf Rats,"
when they used to stone each other to their hearts'
content on the coal-wharves of Richmond.

I am afraid, now that I see these facts written down,
that Gallegher was not a reputable character; but he
was so very young and so very old for his years that
we all liked him very much nevertheless. He lived in
the extreme northern part of Philadelphia, where the
cotton- and woollen-mills run down to the river, and how
he ever got home after leaving the *Press* building at two
in the morning, was one of the mysteries of the office.
Sometimes he caught a night car, and sometimes he
walked all the way, arriving at the little house, where
his mother and himself lived alone, at four in the morning. Occasionally he was given a ride on an early milk-
cart, or on one of the newspaper delivery wagons, with
its high piles of papers still damp and sticky from the
press. He knew several drivers of "night hawks"—
those cabs that prowl the streets at night looking for
belated passengers—and when it was a very cold morning he would not go home at all, but would crawl into
one of these cabs and sleep, curled upon the cushions,
until daylight.

Besides being quick and cheerful, Gallegher possessed
a power of amusing the *Press's* young men to a degree
seldom attained by the ordinary mortal. His clog-
dancing on the city editor's desk, when that gentleman

was upstairs fighting for two more columns of space, was
always a source of innocent joy to us, and his imita-
tions of the comedians of the variety halls delighted
even the dramatic critic, from whom the comedians themselves failed to force a smile.

But Gallegher's chief characteristic was his love for
that element of news generically classed as " crime."

Not that he ever did anything criminal himself. On
the contrary, his was rather the work of the criminal
specialist, and his morbid interest in the doings of all
queer characters, his knowledge of their methods, their
present whereabouts, and their past deeds of transgres-
sion often rendered him a valuable ally to our police
reporter, whose daily feuilletons were the only portion
of the paper Gallegher deigned to read.

In Gallegher the detective element was abnormally
developed. He had shown this on several occasions, and
to excellent purpose.

Once the paper had sent him into a Home for Destitute Orphans which was believed to be grievously mis-
managed, and Gallegher, while playing the part of a
destitute orphan, kept his eyes open to what was going on around him so faithfully that the story he told
of the treatment meted out to the real orphans was
sufficient to rescue the unhappy little wretches from the
individual who had them in charge, and to have
the individual himself sent to jail.

Gallegher's knowledge of the aliases, terms of impris-
onment, and various misdoings of the leading criminals
in Philadelphia was almost as thorough as that of the
chief of police himself, and he could tell to an hour when
" Dutchy Mack " was to be let out of prison, and could
identify at a glance " Dick Oxford, confidence man,"
as " Gentleman Dan, petty thief."

There were, at this time, only two pieces of news

in any of the papers. The least important of the two was the big fight between the Champion of the United States and the Would-be Champion, arranged to take place near Philadelphia; the second was the Burrbank murder, which was filling space in newspapers all over the world, from New York to Bombay.

Richard F. Burrbank was one of the most prominent of New York's railroad lawyers; he was also, as a matter of course, an owner of much railroad stock, and a very wealthy man. He had been spoken of as a political possibility for many high offices, and, as the counsel for a great railroad, was known even further than the great railroad itself had stretched its system.

At six o'clock one morning he was found by his butler lying at the foot of the hall stairs with two pistol wounds above his heart. He was quite dead. His safe, to which only he and his secretary had the keys, was found open, and $200,000 in bonds, stocks, and money, which had been placed there only the night before, was found missing. The secretary was missing also. His name was Stephen S. Hade, and his name and his description had been telegraphed and cabled to all parts of the world. There was enough circumstantial evidence to show, beyond any question or possibility of mistake, that he was the murderer.

It made an enormous amount of talk, and unhappy individuals were being arrested all over the country, and sent on to New York for identification. Three had been arrested at Liverpool, and one man just as he landed at Sydney, Australia. But so far the murderer had escaped.

We were all talking about it one night, as everybody else was all over the country, in the local room, and the city editor said it was worth a fortune to any one who chanced to run across Hade and succeeded in hand-ing him over to the police. Some of us thought Hade had taken passage from some one of the smaller sea-ports, and others were of the opinion that he had buried himself in some cheap lodging-house in New York, or in one of the smaller towns in New Jersey.

"I shouldn't be surprised to meet him out walking, right here in Philadelphia," said one of the staff. "He'll be disguised, of course, but you could always tell him by the absence of the trigger finger on his right hand. It's missing, you know; shot off when he was a boy."

"You want to look for a man dressed like a tough," said the city editor; "for as this fellow is to all ap-pearances a gentleman, he will try to look as little like a gentleman as possible."

"No, he won't," said Gallegher, with that calm im-pertinence that made him dear to us. "He'll dress just like a gentleman. Toughs don't wear gloves, and you see he's got to wear 'em. The first thing he thought of after doing for Burrbank was of that gone finger, and how he was to hide it. He stuffed the finger of that glove with cotton so's to make it look like a whole finger, and the first time he takes off that glove they've got him—see, and he knows it. So what youse want to do is to look for a man with gloves on. I've been a-doing it for two weeks now, and I can tell you it's hard work, for everybody wears gloves this kind of weather. But if you look long enough you'll find him. And when you think it's him, go up to him and hold out your hand in a friendly way, like a bunco-steerer, and shake his hand; and if you feel that his forefinger ain't real flesh, but just wadded cotton, then grip to it with your right and grab his throat with your left, and holler for help."

There was an appreciative pause.

"I see, gentlemen," said the city editor, drily, "that

Gallegher's reasoning has impressed you; and I also see that before the week is out all of my young men will be under bonds for assaulting innocent pedestrians whose only offence is that they wear gloves in mid-winter.''

.   .   .   .

It was about a week after this that Detective Hefflefinger, of Inspector Byrnes's staff, came over to Philadelphia after a burglar, of whose whereabouts he had been misinformed by telegraph. He brought the warrant, requisition, and other necessary papers with him, but the burglar had flown. One of our reporters had worked on a New York paper, and knew Hefflefinger, and the detective came to the office to see if he could help him in his so far unsuccessful search.

He gave Gallegher his card, and after Gallegher had read it, and had discovered who the visitor was, he became so demoralized that he was absolutely useless.

" One of Byrnes's men " was a much more awe-inspiring individual to Gallegher than a member of the Cabinet. He accordingly seized his hat and overcoat, and leaving his duties to be looked after by others, hastened out after the object of his admiration, who found his suggestions and knowledge of the city so valuable, and his company so entertaining, that they became very intimate, and spent the rest of the day together.

In the meanwhile the managing editor had instructed his subordinates to inform Gallegher, when he condescended to return, that his services were no longer needed. Gallegher had played truant once too often. Unconscious of this, he remained with his new friend until late the same evening, and started the next afternoon toward the *Press* office.

As I have said, Gallegher lived in the most distant part of the city, not many minutes' walk from the Kensington railroad station, where trains ran into the suburbs and on to New York.

It was in front of this station that a smoothly-shaven, well-dressed man brushed past Gallegher and hurried up the steps to the ticket office.

He held a walking-stick in his right hand, and Gallegher, who now patiently scrutinized the hands of every one who wore gloves, saw that while three fingers of the man's hand were closed around the cane, the fourth stood out in almost a straight line with his palm.

Gallegher stopped with a gasp and with a trembling all over his little body, and his brain asked with a throb if it could be possible. But possibilities and probabilities were to be discovered later. Now was the time for action.

He was after the man in a moment, hanging at his heels and his eyes moist with excitement.

He heard the man ask for a ticket to Torresdale, a little station just outside of Philadelphia, and when he was out of hearing, but not out of sight, purchased one for the same place.

The stranger went into the smoking-car, and seated himself at one end toward the door. Gallegher took his place at the opposite end.

He was trembling all over, and suffered from a slight feeling of nausea. He guessed it came from fright, not of any bodily harm that might come to him, but at the probability of failure in his adventure and of its most momentous possibilities.

The stranger pulled his coat collar up around his ears, hiding the lower portion of his face, but not concealing the resemblance in his troubled eyes and close-shut lips to the likenesses of the murderer Hade.

They reached Torresdale in half an hour, and the

stranger, alighting quickly, struck off at a rapid pace down the country road leading to the station.

Gallegher gave him a hundred yards' start, and then followed slowly after. The road ran between fields and past a few frame-houses set far from the road in kitchen gardens.

Once or twice the man looked back over his shoulder, but he saw only a dreary length of road with a small boy splashing through the slush in the midst of it and stopping every now and again to throw snowballs at belated sparrows.

After a ten minutes' walk the stranger turned into a side road which led to only one place, the Eagle Inn, an old roadside hostelry known now as the headquarters for pothunters from the Philadelphia game market and the battle-ground of many a cock-fight.

Gallegher knew the place well. He and his young companions had often stopped there when out chestnutting on holidays in the autumn.

The son of the man who kept it had often accompanied them on their excursions, and though the boys of the city streets considered him a dumb lout, they respected him somewhat owing to his inside knowledge of dog- and cock-fights.

The stranger entered the inn at a side door, and Gallegher, reaching it a few minutes later, let him go for the time being, and set about finding his occasional playmate, young Keppler.

Keppler's offspring was found in the wood-shed.

" 'Tain't hard to guess what brings you out here," said the tavern-keeper's son, with a grin; " it's the fight."

" What fight? " asked Gallegher, unguardedly.

" What fight? Why, *the* fight," returned his companion, with the slow contempt of superior knowledge.

" It's to come off here to-night. You knew that as
well as me; anyway your sportin' editor knows it. He
got the tip last night, but that won't help you any. You
needn't think there's any chance of your getting a peep
at it. Why, tickets is two hundred and fifty apiece! "

" Whew! " whistled Gallegher, " where's it to be? "

" In the barn," whispered Keppler. " I helped 'em
fix the ropes this morning, I did."

" Gosh, but you're in luck," exclaimed Gallegher,
with flattering envy. " Couldn't I jest get a peep at
it? "

" Maybe," said the gratified Keppler. " There's a
winder with a wooden shutter at the back of the barn.
You can get in by it, if you have some one to boost
you up to the sill."

" Sa-a-y," drawled Gallegher, as if something had but
just that moment reminded him. " Who's that gent
who come down the road just a bit ahead of me—him
with the cape-coat! Has he got anything to do with
the fight? "

" Him? " repeated Keppler in tones of sincere disgust. " No-oh, he ain't no sport. He's queer, Dad
thinks. He come here one day last week about ten in
the morning, said his doctor told him to go out 'en the
country for his health. He's stuck up and citified, and
wears gloves, and takes his meals private in his room,
and all that sort of truck. They was saying in the saloon
last night that they thought he was hiding from something, and Dad, just to try him, asks him last night if
he was coming to see the fight. He looked sort of scared,
and said he didn't want to see no fight. And then Dad
says, ' I guess you mean you don't want no fighters
to see you.' Dad didn't mean no harm by it, just
passed it as a joke; but Mr. Carleton, as he calls himself, got white as a ghost an' says, ' I'll go to the fight

willing enough,' and begins to laugh and joke. And this morning he went right into the bar-room, where all the sports were setting, and said he was going in to town to see some friends; and as he starts off he laughs an' says, ' This don't look as if I was afraid of seeing people, does it? ' but Dad says it was just bluff that made him do it, and Dad thinks that if he hadn't said what he did, this Mr. Carleton wouldn't have left his room at all.''

Gallegher had got all he wanted, and much more than he had hoped for—so much more that his walk back to the station was in the nature of a triumphal march.

He had twenty minutes to wait for the next train, and it seemed an hour. While waiting he sent a telegram to Hefflefinger at his hotel. It read: '' Your man is near the Torresdale station, on Pennsylvania Railroad; take cab, and meet me at station. Wait until I come. GALLEGHER.''

With the exception of one at midnight, no other train stopped at Torresdale that evening, hence the direction to take a cab.

The train to the city seemed to Gallegher to drag itself by inches. It stopped and backed at purposeless intervals, waited for an express to precede it, and dallied at stations, and when, at last, it reached the terminus, Gallegher was out before it had stopped and was in the cab and off on his way to the home of the sporting editor.

The sporting editor was at dinner and came out in the hall to see him, with his napkin in his hand. Gallegher explained breathlessly that he had located the murderer for whom the police of two continents were looking, and that he believed, in order to quiet the suspicions of the people with whom he was hiding, that he would be present at the fight that night.

The sporting editor led Gallegher into his library and shut the door. "Now," he said, "go over all that again."

Gallegher went over it again in detail, and added how he had sent for Hefflefinger to make the arrest in order that it might be kept from the knowledge of the local police and from the Philadelphia reporters.

"What I want Hefflefinger to do is to arrest Hade with the warrant he has for the burglar," explained Gallegher; "and to take him on to New York on the owl train that passes Torresdale at one. It don't get to Jersey City until four o'clock, one hour after the morning papers go to press. Of course, we must fix Hefflefinger so's he'll keep quiet and not tell who his prisoner really is."

The sporting editor reached his hand out to pat Gallegher on the head, but changed his mind and shook hands with him instead.

"My boy," he said, "you are an infant phenomenon. If I can pull the rest of this thing off to-night, it will mean the $5,000 reward and fame galore for you and the paper. Now, I'm going to write a note to the managing editor, and you can take it around to him and tell him what you've done and what I am going to do, and he'll take you back on the paper and raise your salary. Perhaps you didn't know you've been discharged?"

"Do you think you ain't a-going to take me with you?" demanded Gallegher.

"Why, certainly not. Why should I? It all lies with the detective and myself now. You've done your share, and done it well. If the man's caught, the reward's yours. But you'd only be in the way now. You'd better go to the office and make your peace with the chief."

"If the paper can get along without me, I can get

along without the old paper,'' said Gallegher, hotly.
'' And if I ain't a-going with you, you ain't neither,
for I know where Hefflefinger is to be, and you don't,
and I won't tell you.''

'' Oh, very well, very well,'' replied the sporting
editor, weakly capitulating. '' I'll send the note by a
messenger; only mind, if you lose your place, don't blame
me.''

Gallegher wondered how this man could value a
week's salary against the excitement of seeing a noted
criminal run down, and of getting the news to the paper, and to that one paper alone.

From that moment the sporting editor sank in Gallegher's estimation.

Mr. Dwyer sat down at his desk and scribbled off
the following note:

> " I have received reliable information that Hade, the Burr-
> bank murderer, will be present at the fight to-night. We have
> arranged it so that he will be arrested quietly and in such a man-
> ner that the fact may be kept from all other papers. I need not
> point out to you that this will be the most important piece of
> news in the country to-morrow.
>
> " Yours, etc.,
> " MICHAEL E. DWYER."

The sporting editor stepped into the waiting cab,
while Gallegher whispered the directions to the driver.
He was told to go first to a district-messenger office,
and from there up to the Ridge Avenue Road, out
Broad Street, and on to the old Eagle Inn, near Torresdale.

It was a miserable night. The rain and snow were
falling together, and freezing as they fell. The sporting editor got out to send his message to the *Press* of-

fice, and then lighting a cigar, and turning up the collar
of his great-coat, curled up in the corner of the cab.

"Wake me when we get there, Gallegher," he said.
He knew he had a long ride, and much rapid work before him, and he was preparing for the strain.

To Gallegher the idea of going to sleep seemed almost
criminal. From the dark corner of the cab his eyes
shone with excitement, and with the awful joy of anticipation. He glanced every now and then to where
the sporting editor's cigar shone in the darkness, and
watched it as it gradually burnt more dimly and went
out. The lights in the shop windows threw a broad
glare across the ice on the pavements, and the lights
from the lamp-posts tossed the distorted shadow of the
cab, and the horse, and the motionless driver, sometimes before and sometimes behind them.

After half an hour Gallegher slipped down to the
bottom of the cab and dragged out a lap-robe, in which
he wrapped himself. It was growing colder, and the
damp, keen wind swept in through the cracks until
the window-frames and woodwork were cold to the
touch.

An hour passed, and the cab was still moving more
slowly over the rough surface of partly paved streets,
and by single rows of new houses standing at different
angles to each other in fields covered with ash-heaps and
brick-kilns. Here and there the gaudy lights of a
drug-store, and the forerunner of suburban civilization,
shone from the end of a new block of houses, and the
rubber cape of an occasional policeman showed in the
light of the lamp-post that he hugged for comfort.

Then even the houses disappeared, and the cab
dragged its way between truck farms, with desolate-
looking, glass-covered beds, and pools of water, half-
caked with ice, and bare trees, and interminable fences.

Once or twice the cab stopped altogether, and Gallegher could hear the driver swearing to himself, or at the horse, or the roads. At last they drew up before the station at Torresdale. It was quite deserted, and only a single light cut a swath in the darkness and showed a portion of the platform, the ties, and the rails glistening in the rain. They walked twice past the light before a figure stepped out of the shadow and greeted them cautiously.

"I am Mr. Dwyer, of the *Press*," said the sporting editor, briskly. "You've heard of me, perhaps. Well, there shouldn't be any difficulty in our making a deal, should there? This boy here has found Hade, and we have reason to believe he will be among the spectators at the fight to-night. We want you to arrest him quietly, and as secretly as possible. You can do it with your papers and your badge easily enough. We want you to pretend that you believe he is this burglar you came over after. If you will do this, and take him away without any one so much as suspecting who he really is, and on the train that passes here at 1.20 for New York, we will give you $500 out of the $5,000 reward. If, however, one other paper, either in New York or Philadelphia, or anywhere else, knows of the arrest, you won't get a cent. Now, what do you say?"

The detective had a great deal to say. He wasn't at all sure the man Gallegher suspected was Hade; he feared he might get himself into trouble by making a false arrest, and if it should be the man, he was afraid the local police would interfere.

"We've no time to argue or debate this matter," said Dwyer, warmly. "We agree to point Hade out to you in the crowd. After the fight is over you arrest him as we have directed, and you get the money and the credit of the arrest. If you don't like this, I will arrest the man myself, and have him driven to town, with a pistol for a warrant."

Hefflefinger considered in silence and then agreed unconditionally. " As you say, Mr. Dwyer," he returned. " I've heard of you for a thoroughbred·sport. I know you'll do what you say you'll do; and as for me I'll do what you say and just as you say, and it's a very pretty piece of work as it stands."

They all stepped back into the cab, and then it was that they were met by a fresh difficulty, how to get the detective into the barn where the fight was to take place, for neither of the two men had $250 to pay for his admittance.

But this was overcome when Gallegher remembered the window of which young Keppler had told him.

In the event of Hade's losing courage and not daring to show himself in the crowd around the ring, it was agreed that Dwyer should come to the barn and warn Hefflefinger; but if he should come, Dwyer was merely to keep near him and to signify by a prearranged gesture which one of the crowd he was.

They drew up before a great black shadow of a house, dark, forbidding, and apparently deserted. But at the sound of the wheels on the gravel the door opened, letting out a stream of warm, cheerful light, and a man's voice said, " Put out those lights. Don't youse know no better than that? " This was Keppler, and he welcomed Mr. Dwyer with effusive courtesy.

The two men showed in the stream of light, and the door closed on them, leaving the house as it was at first, black and silent, save for the dripping of the rain and snow from the eaves.

The detective and Gallegher put out the cab's lamps and led the horse toward a long, low shed in the rear of the yard, which they now noticed was almost filled with teams of many different makes, from the Hobson's choice of a livery stable to the brougham of the man about town.

"No," said Gallegher, as the cabman stopped to hitch the horse beside the others, "we want it nearest that lower gate. When we newspaper men leave this place we'll leave it in a hurry, and the man who is nearest town is likely to get there first. You won't be a-following of no hearse when you make your return trip."

Gallegher tied the horse to the very gate-post itself, leaving the gate open and allowing a clear road and a flying start for the prospective race to Newspaper Row.

The driver disappeared under the shelter of the porch, and Gallegher and the detective moved off cautiously to the rear of the barn. "This must be the window," said Hefflefinger, pointing to a broad wooden shutter some feet from the ground.

"Just you give me a boost once, and I'll get that open in a jiffy," said Gallegher.

The detective placed his hands on his knees, and Gallegher stood upon his shoulders, and with the blade of his knife lifted the wooden button that fastened the window on the inside, and pulled the shutter open.

Then he put one leg inside over the sill, and leaning down helped to draw his fellow-conspirator up to a level with the window. "I feel just like I was burglarizing a house," chuckled Gallegher, as he dropped noiselessly to the floor below and refastened the shutter. The barn was a large one, with a row of stalls on either side in which horses and cows were dozing. There was a haymow over each row of stalls, and at one end of the barn a number of fence-rails had been thrown across from one mow to the other. These rails were covered with hay.

In the middle of the floor was the ring. It was not really a ring, but a square, with wooden posts at its four corners through which ran a heavy rope. The space inclosed by the rope was covered with sawdust.

Gallegher could not resist stepping into the ring, and after stamping the sawdust once or twice, as if to assure himself that he was really there, began dancing around it, and indulging in such a remarkable series of fistic manœuvres with an imaginary adversary that the unimaginative detective precipitately backed into a corner of the barn.

" Now, then," said Gallegher, having apparently vanquished his foe, " you come with me." His companion followed quickly as Gallegher climbed to one of the haymows, and crawling carefully out on the fence-rail, stretched himself at full length, face downward. In this position, by moving the straw a little, he could look down, without being himself seen, upon the heads of whomsoever stood below. " This is better'n a private box, ain't it? " said Gallegher.

The boy from the newspaper office and the detective lay there in silence, biting at straws and tossing anxiously on their comfortable bed.

It seemed fully two hours before they came. Gallegher had listened without breathing, and with every muscle on a strain, at least a dozen times, when some movement in the yard had led him to believe that they were at the door.

And he had numerous doubts and fears. Sometimes it was that the police had learnt of the fight, and had raided Keppler's in his absence, and again it was that the fight had been postponed, or, worst of all, that it would be put off until so late that Mr. Dwyer could not get back in time for the last edition of the paper.

Their coming, when at last they came, was heralded by an advance-guard of two sporting men, who stationed themselves at either side of the big door.

"Hurry up, now, gents," one of the men said with a shiver, "don't keep this door open no longer'n is needful."

It was not a very large crowd, but it was wonderfully well selected. It ran, in the majority of its component parts, to heavy white coats with pearl buttons. The white coats were shouldered by long blue coats with astrakhan fur trimmings, the wearers of which preserved a cliqueness not remarkable when one considers that they believed every one else present to be either a crook or a prize-fighter.

There were well-fed, well-groomed clubmen and brokers in the crowd, a politician or two, a popular comedian with his manager, amateur boxers from the athletic clubs, and quiet, close-mouthed sporting men from every city in the country. Their names if printed in the papers would have been as familiar as the types of the papers themselves.

And among these men, whose only thought was of the brutal sport to come, was Hade, with Dwyer standing at ease at his shoulder,—Hade, white, and visibly in deep anxiety, hiding his pale face beneath a cloth travelling-cap, and with his chin muffled in a woollen scarf. He had dared to come because he feared his danger from the already suspicious Keppler was less than if he stayed away. And so he was there, hovering restlessly on the border of the crowd, feeling his danger and sick with fear.

When Hefflefinger first saw him he started up on his hands and elbows and made a movement forward as if he would leap down then and there and carry off his prisoner single-handed.

" Lie down," growled Gallegher; " an officer of any sort wouldn't live three minutes in that crowd."

The detective drew back slowly and buried himself again in the straw, but never once through the long fight which followed did his eyes leave the person of the murderer. The newspaper men took their places in the foremost row close around the ring, and kept looking at their watches and begging the master of ceremonies to " shake it up, do."

There was a great deal of betting, and all of the men handled the great roll of bills they wagered with a flippant recklessness which could only be accounted for in Gallegher's mind by temporary mental derangement. Some one pulled a box out into the ring and the master of ceremonies mounted it, and pointed out in forcible language that as they were almost all already under bonds to keep the peace, it behooved all to curb their excitement and to maintain a severe silence, unless they wanted to bring the police upon them and have themselves " sent down " for a year or two.

Then two very disreputable-looking persons tossed their respective principals' high hats into the ring, and the crowd, recognizing in this relic of the days when brave knights threw down their gauntlets in the lists as only a sign that the fight was about to begin, cheered tumultuously.

This was followed by a sudden surging forward, and a mutter of admiration much more flattering than the cheers had been, when the principals followed their hats, and slipping out of their great-coats, stood forth in all the physical beauty of the perfect brute.

Their pink skin was as soft and healthy-looking as a baby's, and glowed in the lights of the lanterns like tinted ivory, and underneath this silken covering the great biceps and muscles moved in and out and looked like the coils of a snake around the branch of a tree.

Gentleman and blackguard shouldered each other for a nearer view; the coachmen, whose metal buttons were unpleasantly suggestive of police, put their hands, in the excitement of the moment, on the shoulders of their masters; the perspiration stood out in great drops on the foreheads of the backers, and the newspaper men bit somewhat nervously at the ends of their pencils.

And in the stalls the cows munched contentedly at their cuds and gazed with gentle curiosity at their two fellow-brutes, who stood waiting the signal to fall upon, and kill each other if need be, for the delectation of their brothers.

"Take your places," commanded the master of ceremonies.

In the moment in which the two men faced each other the crowd became so still that, save for the beating of the rain upon the shingled roof and the stamping of a horse in one of the stalls, the place was as silent as a church.

"Time!" shouted the master of ceremonies.

The two men sprang into a posture of defence, which was lost as quickly as it was taken, one great arm shot out like a piston-rod; there was the sound of bare fists beating on naked flesh; there was an exultant indrawn gasp of savage pleasure and relief from the crowd, and the great fight had begun.

How the fortunes of war rose and fell, and changed and rechanged that night, is an old story to those who listen to such stories; and those who do not will be glad to be spared the telling of it. It was, they say, one of the bitterest fights between two men that this country has ever known.

But all that is of interest here is that after an hour of this desperate brutal business the champion ceased to be the favorite; the man whom he had taunted and bullied, and for whom the public had but little sympathy, was proving himself a likely winner, and under his cruel blows, as sharp and clean as those from a cutlass, his opponent was rapidly giving way.

The men about the ropes were past all control now; they drowned Keppler's petitions for silence with oaths and in inarticulate shouts of anger, as if the blows had fallen upon them, and in mad rejoicings. They swept from one end of the ring to the other, with every muscle leaping in unison with those of the man they favored, and when a New York correspondent muttered over his shoulder that this would be the biggest sporting surprise since the Heenan-Sayers fight, Mr. Dwyer nodded his head sympathetically in assent.

In the excitement and tumult it is doubtful if any heard the three quickly repeated blows that fell heavily from the outside upon the big doors of the barn. If they did, it was already too late to mend matters, for the door fell, torn from its hinges, and as it fell a captain of police sprang into the light from out of the storm, with his lieutenants and their men crowding close at his shoulder.

In the panic and stampede that followed, several of the men stood as helplessly immovable as though they had seen a ghost; others made a mad rush into the arms of the officers and were beaten back against the ropes of the ring; others dived headlong into the stalls, among the horses and cattle, and still others shoved the rolls of money they held into the hands of the police and begged like children to be allowed to escape.

The instant the door fell and the raid was declared Hefflefinger slipped over the cross rails on which he had been lying, hung for an instant by his hands, and then dropped into the centre of the fighting mob on the

floor. He was out of it in an instant with the agility of
a pickpocket, was across the room and at Hade's throat
like a dog. The murderer, for the moment, was the
calmer man of the two.

"Here," he panted, "hands off, now. There's no
need for all this violence. There's no great harm in
looking at a fight, is there? There's a hundred-dollar
bill in my right hand; take it and let me slip out of
this. No one is looking. Here."

But the detective only held him the closer.

"I want you for burglary," he whispered under his
breath. "You've got to come with me now, and quick.
The less fuss you make, the better for both of us. If
you don't know who I am, you can feel my badge under
my coat there. I've got the authority. It's all regular, and when we're out of this d——d row I'll show you
the papers."

He took one hand from Hade's throat and pulled a
pair of handcuffs from his pocket.

"It's a mistake. This is an outrage," gasped the
murderer, white and trembling, but dreadfully alive
and desperate for his liberty. "Let me go, I tell you!
Take your hands off of me! Do I look like a burglar,
you fool?"

"I know who you look like," whispered the detective,
with his face close to the face of his prisoner. "Now,
will you go easy as a burglar, or shall I tell these men
who you are and what I *do* want you for? Shall I call
out your real name or not? Shall I tell them? Quick,
speak up; shall I?"

There was something so exultant—something so unnecessarily savage in the officer's face that the man he
held saw that the detective knew him for what he really
was, and the hands that had held his throat slipped
down around his shoulders, or he would have fallen.

The man's eyes opened and closed again, and he swayed weakly backward and forward, and choked as if his throat were dry and burning. Even to such a hardened connoisseur in crime as Gallegher, who stood closely by, drinking it in, there was something so abject in the man's terror that he regarded him with what was almost a touch of pity.

"For God's sake," Hade begged, "let me go. Come with me to my room and I'll give you half the money. I'll divide with you fairly. We can both get away. There's a fortune for both of us there. We both can get away. You'll be rich for life. Do you understand—for life!"

But the detective, to his credit, only shut his lips the tighter.

"That's enough," he whispered, in return. "That's more than I expected. You've sentenced yourself already. Come!"

Two officers in uniform barred their exit at the door, but Hefflefinger smiled easily and showed his badge.

"One of Byrnes's men," he said, in explanation; "came over expressly to take this chap. He's a burglar; 'Arlie' Lane, *alias* Carleton. I've shown the papers to the captain. It's all regular. I'm just going to get his traps at the hotel and walk him over to the station. I guess we'll push right on to New York tonight."

The officers nodded and smiled their admiration for the representative of what is, perhaps, the best detective force in the world, and let him pass.

Then Hefflefinger turned and spoke to Gallegher, who still stood as watchful as a dog at his side. "I'm going to his room to get the bonds and stuff," he whispered; "then I'll march him to the station and take that train. I've done my share; don't forget yours!"

"Oh, you'll get your money right enough," said Gallegher. "And, sa-ay," he added, with the appreciative nod of an expert, "do you know, you did it rather well."

Mr. Dwyer had been writing while the raid was settling down, as he had been writing while waiting for the fight to begin. Now he walked over to where the other correspondents stood in angry conclave.

The newspaper men had informed the officers who hemmed them in that they represented the principal papers of the country, and were expostulating vigorously with the captain, who had planned the raid, and who declared they were under arrest.

"Don't be an ass, Scott," said Mr. Dwyer, who was too excited to be polite or politic. "You know our being here isn't a matter of choice. We came here on business, as you did, and you've no right to hold us."

"If we don't get our stuff on the wire at once," protested a New York man, "we'll be too late for to-morrow's paper, and——"

Captain Scott said he did not care a profanely small amount for to-morrow's paper, and that all he knew was that to the station-house the newspaper men would go. There they would have a hearing, and if the magistrate chose to let them off, that was the magistrate's business, but that his duty was to take them into custody.

"But then it will be too late, don't you understand?" shouted Mr. Dwyer. "You've got to let us go *now*, at once."

"I can't do it, Mr. Dwyer," said the captain, "and that's all there is to it. Why, haven't I just sent the president of the Junior Republican Club to the patrol-wagon, the man that put this coat on me, and do you think I can let you fellows go after that? You were all put under bonds to keep the peace not three days ago, and here you're at it—fighting like badgers. It's worth my place to let one of you off.''

What Mr. Dwyer said next was so uncomplimentary to the gallant Captain Scott that that overwrought individual seized the sporting editor by the shoulder, and shoved him into the hands of two of his men.

This was more than the distinguished Mr. Dwyer could brook, and he excitedly raised his hand in resistance. But before he had time to do anything foolish his wrist was gripped by one strong, little hand, and he was conscious that another was picking the pocket of his great-coat.

He slapped his hands to his sides, and looking down, saw Gallegher standing close behind him and holding him by the wrist. Mr. Dwyer had forgotten the boy's existence, and would have spoken sharply if something in Gallegher's innocent eyes had not stopped him.

Gallegher's hand was still in that pocket, in which Mr. Dwyer had shoved his note-book filled with what he had written of Gallegher's work and Hade's final capture, and with a running descriptive account of the fight. With his eyes fixed on Mr. Dwyer, Gallegher drew it out, and with a quick movement shoved it inside his waistcoat. Mr. Dwyer gave a nod of comprehension. Then glancing at his two guardsmen, and finding that they were still interested in the wordy battle of the correspondents with their chief, and had seen nothing, he stooped and whispered to Gallegher: '' The forms are locked at twenty minutes to three. If you don't get there by that time it will be of no use. but if you're on time you'll beat the town—and the country too.''

Gallegher's eyes flashed significantly, and nodding his head to show he understood, started boldly on a run toward the door. But the officers who guarded it brought him to an abrupt halt, and, much to Mr. Dwyer's astonishment, drew from him what was apparently a torrent of tears.

" Let me go to me father. I want me father," the boy shrieked, hysterically. " They've 'rested father. Oh, daddy, daddy. They're a-goin' to take you to prison."

" Who is your father, sonny? " asked one of the guardians of the gate.

" Keppler's me father," sobbed Gallegher. " They're a-goin' to lock him up, and I'll never see him no more."

" Oh, yes, you will," said the officer, good-naturedly; " he's there in that first patrol-wagon. You can run over and say good-night to him, and then you'd better get to bed. This ain't no place for kids of your age."

" Thank you, sir," sniffed Gallegher, tearfully, as the two officers raised their clubs, and let him pass out into the darkness.

The yard outside was in a tumult, horses were stamping, and plunging, and backing the carriages into one another; lights were flashing from every window of what had been apparently an uninhabited house, and the voices of the prisoners were still raised in angry expostulation.

Three police patrol-wagons were moving about the yard, filled with unwilling passengers, who sat or stood, packed together like sheep, and with no protection from the sleet and rain.

Gallegher stole off into a dark corner, and watched the scene until his eyesight became familiar with the position of the land.

Then with his eyes fixed fearfully on the swinging light of a lantern with which an officer was searching among the carriages, he groped his way between horses' hoofs and behind the wheels of carriages to the cab

which he had himself placed at the furthermost gate.
It was still there, and the horse, as he had left it, with
its head turned toward the city. Gallegher opened the
big gate noiselessly, and worked nervously at the hitching strap. The knot was covered with a thin coating
of ice, and it was several minutes before he could loosen
it. But his teeth finally pulled it apart, and with the
reins in his hands he sprang upon the wheel. And as
he stood so, a shock of fear ran down his back like an
electric current, his breath left him, and he stood immovable, gazing with wide eyes into the darkness.

The officer with the lantern had suddenly loomed up
from behind a carriage not fifty feet distant, and was
standing perfectly still, with his lantern held over his
head, peering so directly toward Gallegher that the boy
felt that he must see him. Gallegher stood with one
foot on the hub of the wheel and with the other on
the box waiting to spring. It seemed a minute before
either of them moved, and then the officer took a step
forward, and demanded sternly, " Who is that? What
are you doing there? "

There was no time for parley then. Gallegher felt
that he had been taken in the act, and that his only
chance lay in open flight. He leaped up on the box,
pulling out the whip as he did so, and with a quick
sweep lashed the horse across the head and back. The
animal sprang forward with a snort, narrowly clearing the gate-post, and plunged off into the darkness.

" Stop! " cried the officer.

So many of Gallegher's acquaintances among the
'longshoremen and mill hands had been challenged in
so much the same manner that Gallegher knew what
would probably follow if the challenge was disregarded.
So he slipped from his seat to the footboard below, and
ducked his head.

The three reports of a pistol, which rang out briskly from behind him, proved that his early training had given him a valuable fund of useful miscellaneous knowledge.

" Don't you be scared," he said, reassuringly, to the horse; " he's firing in the air."

The pistol-shots were answered by the impatient clangor of a patrol-wagon's gong, and glancing over his shoulder Gallegher saw its red and green lanterns tossing from side to side and looking in the darkness like the side-lights of a yacht plunging forward in a storm.

" I hadn't bargained to race you against no patrol-wagons," said Gallegher to his animal; " but if they want a race, we'll give them a tough tussle for it, won't we?"

Philadelphia, lying four miles to the south, sent up a faint yellow glow to the sky. It seemed very far away, and Gallegher's braggadocio grew cold within him at the loneliness of his adventure and the thought of the long ride before him.

It was still bitterly cold.

The rain and sleet beat through his clothes, and struck his skin with a sharp chilling touch that set him trembling.

Even the thought of the overweighted patrol-wagon probably sticking in the mud some safe distance in the rear, failed to cheer him, and the excitement that had so far made him callous to the cold died out and left him weaker and nervous.

But his horse was chilled with the long standing, and now leaped eagerly forward, only too willing to warm the half-frozen blood in its veins.

" You're a good beast," said Gallegher, plaintively. " You've got more nerve than me. Don't you go back on me now. Mr. Dwyer says we've got to beat the town.'' Gallegher had no idea what time it was as he rode through the night, but he knew he would be able to find out from a big clock over a manufactory at a point nearly three-quarters of the distance from Keppler's to the goal.

He was still in the open country and driving recklessly, for he knew the best part of his ride must be made outside the city limits.

He raced between desolate-looking corn-fields with bare stalks and patches of muddy earth rising above the thin covering of snow, truck farms and brick-yards fell behind him on either side. It was very lonely work, and once or twice the dogs ran yelping to the gates and barked after him.

Part of his way lay parallel with the railroad tracks, and he drove for some time beside long lines of freight and coal cars as they stood resting for the night. The fantastic Queen Anne suburban stations were dark and deserted, but in one or two of the block-towers he could see the operators writing at their desks, and the sight in some way comforted him.

Once he thought of stopping to get out the blanket in which he had wrapped himself on the first trip, but he feared to spare the time, and drove on with his teeth chattering and his shoulders shaking with the cold.

He welcomed the first solitary row of darkened houses with a faint cheer of recognition. The scattered lamp-posts lightened his spirits, and even the badly paved streets rang under the beats of his horse's feet like music. Great mills and manufactories, with only a night-watchman's light in the lowest of their many stories, began to take the place of the gloomy farmhouses and gaunt trees that had startled him with their grotesque

shapes. He had been driving nearly an hour, he cal-
culated, and in that time the rain had changed to a wet
snow, that fell heavily and clung to whatever it touched.
He passed block after block of trim workmen's houses,
as still and silent as the sleepers within them, and at last
he turned the horse's head into Broad Street, the city's
great thoroughfare, that stretches from its one end to
the other and cuts it evenly in two.

He was driving noiselessly over the snow and slush
in the street, with his thoughts bent only on the clock-
face he wished so much to see, when a hoarse voice challenged him from the sidewalk. "Hey, you, stop there,
hold up!" said the voice.

Gallegher turned his head, and though he saw that
the voice came from under a policeman's helmet, his
only answer was to hit his horse sharply over the head
with his whip and to urge it into a gallop.

This, on his part, was followed by a sharp, shrill
whistle from the policeman. Another whistle answered
it from a street-corner one block ahead of him.
"Whoa," said Gallegher, pulling on the reins.
"There's one too many of them," he added, in apologetic explanation. The horse stopped, and stood, breathing heavily, with great clouds of steam rising from
its flanks.

"Why in hell didn't you stop when I told you to?"
demanded the voice, now close at the cab's side.

"I didn't hear you," returned Gallegher, sweetly.
"But I heard you whistle, and I heard your partner
whistle, and I thought maybe it was me you wanted to
speak to, so I just stopped."

"You heard me well enough. Why aren't your lights
lit?" demanded the voice.

"Should I have 'em lit?" asked Gallegher, bending
over and regarding them with sudden interest.

"You know you should, and if you don't, you've no right to be driving that cab. I don't believe you're the regular driver, anyway. Where'd you get it?"

"It ain't my cab, of course," said Gallegher, with an easy laugh. "It's Luke McGovern's. He left it outside Cronin's while he went in to get a drink, and he took too much, and me father told me to drive it round to the stable for him. I'm Cronin's son. McGovern ain't in no condition to drive. You can see yourself how he's been misusing the horse. He puts it up at Bachman's livery stable, and I was just going around there now."

Gallegher's knowledge of the local celebrities of the district confused the zealous officer of the peace. He surveyed the boy with a steady stare that would have distressed a less skilful liar, but Gallegher only shrugged his shoulders slightly, as if from the cold, and waited with apparent indifference to what the officer would say next.

In reality his heart was beating heavily against his side, and he felt that if he was kept on a strain much longer he would give way and break down. A second snow-covered form emerged suddenly from the shadow of the houses.

"What is it, Reeder?" it asked.

"Oh, nothing much," replied the first officer. "This kid hadn't any lamps lit, so I called to him to stop and he didn't do it, so I whistled to you. It's all right, though. He's just taking it round to Bachman's. Go ahead," he added, sulkily.

"Get up!" chirped Gallegher. "Good-night," he added, over his shoulder.

Gallegher gave an hysterical little gasp of relief as he trotted away from the two policemen, and poured

bitter maledictions on their heads for two meddling fools
as he went.

"They might as well kill a man as scare him to
death," he said, with an attempt to get back to his
customary flippancy. But the effort was somewhat pitiful, and he felt guiltily conscious that a salt, warm tear
was creeping slowly down his face, and that a lump
that would not keep down was rising in his throat.

"'Tain't no fair thing for the whole police force to
keep worrying at a little boy like me," he said, in shamefaced apology. "I'm not doing nothing wrong, and
I'm half froze to death, and yet they keep a-nagging
at me."

It was so cold that when the boy stamped his feet
against the footboard to keep them warm, sharp pains
shot up through his body, and when he beat his arms
about his shoulders, as he had seen real cabmen do,
the blood in his finger-tips tingled so acutely that he
cried aloud with the pain.

He had often been up that late before, but he had
never felt so sleepy. It was as if some one was pressing a sponge heavy with chloroform near his face, and
he could not fight off the drowsiness that lay hold of
him.

He saw, dimly hanging above his head, a round disc
of light that seemed like a great moon, and which he
finally guessed to be the clock-face for which he had
been on the lookout. He had passed it before he realized
this; but the fact stirred him into wakefulness again,
and when his cab's wheels slipped around the City Hall
corner, he remembered to look up at the other big clock-
face that keeps awake over the railroad station and
measures out the night.

He gave a gasp of consternation when he saw that it
was half-past two, and that there was but ten minutes

left to him. This, and the many electric lights and the sight of the familiar pile of buildings, startled him into a semi-consciousness of where he was and how great was the necessity for haste.

He rose in his seat and called on the horse, and urged it into a reckless gallop over the slippery asphalt. He considered nothing else but speed, and looking neither to the left nor right dashed off down Broad Street into Chestnut, where his course lay straight away to the office, now only seven blocks distant.

Gallegher never knew how it began, but he was suddenly assaulted by shouts on either side, his horse was thrown back on its haunches, and he found two men in cabmen's livery hanging at its head, and patting its sides, and calling it by name. And the other cabmen who have their stand at the corner were swarming about the carriage, all of them talking and swearing at once, and gesticulating wildly with their whips.

They said they knew the cab was McGovern's and they wanted to know where he was, and why he wasn't on it; they wanted to know where Gallegher had stolen it, and why he had been such a fool as to drive it into the arms of its owner's friends; they said that it was about time that a cab-driver could get off his box to take a drink without having his cab run away with, and some of them called loudly for a policeman to take the young thief in charge.

Gallegher felt as if he had been suddenly dragged into consciousness out of a bad dream, and stood for a second like a half-awakened somnambulist.

They had stopped the cab under an electric light, and its glare shone coldly down upon the trampled snow and the faces of the men around him.

Gallegher bent forward, and lashed savagely at the horse with his whip.

" Let me go," he shouted, as he tugged impotently
at the reins. " Let me go, I tell you. I haven't stole
no cab, and you've got no right to stop me. I only want
to take it to the *Press* office," he begged. " They'll send
it back to you all right. They'll pay you for the trip.
I'm not running away with it. The driver's got the collar—he's 'rested—and I'm only a-going to the *Press*
office. Do you hear me? " he cried, his voice rising and
breaking in a shriek of passion and disappointment. " I
tell you to let go those reins. Let me go, or I'll kill you.
Do you hear me? I'll kill you." And leaning forward,
the boy struck savagely with his long whip at the faces
of the men about the horse's head.

Some one in the crowd reached up and caught him
by the ankles, and with a quick jerk pulled him off
the box, and threw him on to the street. But he was
up on his knees in a moment, and caught at the man's
hand.

" Don't let them stop me, mister," he cried, " please
let me go. I didn't steal the cab, sir. S'help me, I
didn't. I'm telling you the truth. Take me to the *Press*
office, and they'll prove it to you. They'll pay you anything you ask 'em. It's only such a little ways now,
and I've come so far, sir. Please don't let them stop
me," he sobbed, clasping the man about the knees. " For
Heaven's sake, mister, let me go! "

.   .   .   .

The managing editor of the *Press* took up the india-
rubber speaking-tube at his side, and answered,
" Not yet " to an inquiry the night editor had already put to him five times within the last twenty
minutes.

Then he snapped the metal top of the tube impa-
tiently, and went upstairs. As he passed the door of
the local room, he noticed that the reporters had not

gone home, but were sitting about on the tables and chairs, waiting. They looked up inquiringly as he passed, and the city editor asked, " Any news yet? " and the managing editor shook his head.

The compositors were standing idle in the composing-room, and their foreman was talking with the night editor.

" Well? " said that gentleman, tentatively.

" Well," returned the managing editor, " I don't think we can wait; do you? "

" It's a half-hour after time now," said the night editor, " and we'll miss the suburban trains if we hold the paper back any longer. We can't afford to wait for a purely hypothetical story. The chances are all against the fight's having taken place or this Hade's having been arrested."

" But if we're beaten on it——" suggested the chief. " But I don't think that is possible. If there were any story to print, Dwyer would have had it here before now."

The managing editor looked steadily down at the floor.

" Very well," he said, slowly, " we won't wait any longer. Go ahead," he added, turning to the foreman with a sigh of reluctance. The foreman whirled himself about, and began to give his orders; but the two editors still looked at each other doubtfully.

As they stood so, there came a sudden shout and the sound of people running to and fro in the reportorial rooms below. There was the tramp of many footsteps on the stairs, and above the confusion they heard the voice of the city editor telling some one to " run to Madden's and get some brandy, quick."

No one in the composing-room said anything; but those compositors who had started to go home began slipping off their overcoats, and every one stood with his eyes fixed on the door.

It was kicked open from the outside, and in the doorway stood a cab-driver and the city editor, supporting between them a pitiful little figure of a boy, wet and miserable, and with the snow melting on his clothes and running in little pools to the floor. "Why, it's Gallegher," said the night editor, in a tone of the keenest disappointment.

Gallegher shook himself free from his supporters, and took an unsteady step forward, his fingers fumbling stiffly with the buttons of his waistcoat.

"Mr. Dwyer, sir," he began faintly, with his eyes fixed fearfully on the managing editor, "he got arrested—and I couldn't get here no sooner, 'cause they kept a-stopping me, and they took me cab from under me—but—" he pulled the note-book from his breast and held it out with its covers damp and limp from the rain, "but we got Hade, and here's Mr. Dwyer's copy."

And then he asked, with a queer note in his voice, partly of dread and partly of hope, "Am I in time, sir?"

The managing editor took the book, and tossed it to the foreman, who ripped out its leaves and dealt them out to his men as rapidly as a gambler deals out cards.

Then the managing editor stooped and picked Gallegher up in his arms, and, sitting down, began to unlace his wet and muddy shoes.

Gallegher made a faint effort to resist this degradation of the managerial dignity; but his protest was a very feeble one, and his head fell back heavily on the managing editor's shoulder.

To Gallegher the incandescent lights began to whirl about in circles, and to burn in different colors; the faces of the reporters kneeling before him and chafing his hands and feet grew dim and unfamiliar, and the roar and rumble of the great presses in the basement sounded far away, like the murmur of the sea.

And then the place and the circumstances of it came back to him again sharply and with sudden vividness.

Gallegher looked up, with a faint smile, into the managing editor's face. " You won't turn me off for running away, will you? " he whispered.

The managing editor did not answer immediately. His head was bent, and he was thinking, for some reason or other, of a little boy of his own, at home in bed. Then he said, quietly, " Not this time, Gallegher."

Gallegher's head sank back comfortably on the older man's shoulder, and he smiled comprehensively at the faces of the young men crowded around him. " You hadn't ought to," he said, with a touch of his old impudence, " 'cause—I beat the town."

THE JUMPING FROG

BY

MARK TWAIN

This is a story typical of American humor. As William Lyon Phelps says, '' The essentially American qualities of common-sense, energy, good-humor, and Philistinism fairly shriek from his [Mark Twain's] pages.''— *Essays on Modern Novelists.*

THE NOTORIOUS JUMPING FROG
OF CALAVERAS * COUNTY †

In compliance with the request of a friend of mine, who wrote me from the East, I called on good-natured, garrulous old Simon Wheeler, and inquired after my friend's friend, Leonidas W. Smiley, as requested to do, and I hereunto append the result. I have a lurking suspicion that *Leonidas W.* Smiley is a myth; that my friend never knew such a personage; and that he only conjectured that if I asked old Wheeler about him, it would remind him of his infamous *Jim* Smiley, and he would go to work and bore me to death with some exasperating reminiscence of him as long and as tedious as it should be useless to me. If that was the design, it succeeded.

I found Simon Wheeler dozing comfortably by the bar-room stove of the dilapidated tavern in the decaying mining camp of Angel's, and I noticed that he was fat and bald-headed, and had an expression of winning gentleness and simplicity upon his tranquil countenance. He roused up, and gave me good-day. I told him a friend of mine had commissioned me to make some inquiries about a cherished companion of his boyhood named *Leonidas W.* Smiley—*Rev. Leonidas W.* Smiley, a young minister of the Gospel, who he had heard was at one time a resident of Angel's Camp. I added that if Mr. Wheeler could tell me anything about this Rev.

* Pronounced Cal-e-*va*-ras.

† From "The Jumping Frog and Other Sketches," by Mark Twain. Copyright, 1903, by Harper & Bros.

Leonidas W. Smiley, I would feel under many obligations to him.

Simon Wheeler backed me into a corner and blockaded me there with his chair, and then sat down and reeled off the monotonous narrative which follows this paragraph. He never smiled, he never frowned, he never changed his voice from the gentle-flowing key to which he tuned his initial sentence, he never betrayed the slightest suspicion of enthusiasm; but all through the interminable narrative there ran a vein of impressive earnestness and sincerity, which showed me plainly that, so far from his imagining that there was anything ridiculous or funny about his story, he regarded it as a really important matter, and admired its two heroes as men of transcendent genius in *finesse*. I let him go on in his own way, and never interrupted him once.

" Rev. Leonidas W. H'm, Reverend Le—well, there was a feller here once by the name of *Jim* Smiley, in the winter of '49—or maybe it was the spring of '50—I don't recollect exactly, somehow, though what makes me think it was one or the other is because I remember the big flume warn't finished when he first come to the camp; but anyway, he was the curiosest man about always betting on anything that turned up you ever see, if he could get anybody to bet on the other side; and if he couldn't he'd change sides. Any way that suited the other man would suit *him*—any way just so's he got a bet, *he* was satisfied. But still he was lucky, uncommon lucky; he 'most always come out winner. He was always ready and laying for a chance; there couldn't be no solit'ry thing mentioned but that feller'd offer to bet on it, and take ary side you please, as I was just telling you. If there was a horse-race, you'd find him flush or you'd find him busted at the end of it; if there was a dog-fight, he'd bet on it; if there was a cat-fight, he'd bet on it; if there was a chicken-fight, he'd bet on it; why, if there was two birds setting on a fence, he would bet you which one would fly first; or if there was a camp-meeting, he would be there reg'lar to bet on Parson Walker, which he judged to be the best exhorter about here, and so he was, too, and a good man. If he even see a straddle-bug start to go anywheres, he would bet you how long it would take him to get to—to wherever he was going to, and if you took him up, he would foller that straddle-bug to Mexico but what he would find out where he was bound for and how long he was on the road. Lots of the boys here has seen that Smiley, and can tell you about him. Why, it never made no difference to *him*—he'd bet on *any* thing—the dangdest feller. Parson Walker's wife laid very sick once, for a good while, and it seemed as if they warn't going to save her; but one morning he come in, and Smiley up and asked him how she was, and he said she was consid'able better—thank the Lord for his inf'nite mercy—and coming on so smart that with the blessing of Prov'-dence she'd get well yet; and Smiley, before he thought, says: ' Well, I'll resk two-and-a-half she don't anyway.'

" Thish-yer Smiley had a mare—the boys called her the fifteen-minute nag, but that was only in fun, you know, because, of course, she was faster than that—and he used to win money on that horse, for all she was so slow and always had the asthma, or the distemper, or the consumption, or something of that kind. They used to give her two or three hundred yards start, and then pass her under way; but always at the fag end of the race she'd get excited and desperate like, and come cavorting and straddling up, and scattering her legs around limber, sometimes in the air, and sometimes out to one side among the fences, and kicking up

m-o-r-e dust and raising m-o-r-e racket with her coughing and sneezing and blowing her nose—and *always*
fetch up at the stand just about a neck ahead, as near
as you could cipher it down.

" And he had a little small bull-pup, that to look
at him you'd think he warn't worth a cent but to set
around and look ornery and lay for a chance to steal
something. But as soon as money was up on him he
was a different dog; his under-jaw'd begin to stick out
like the fo'castle of a steamboat, and his teeth would
uncover and shine like the furnaces. And a dog might
tackle him and bully-rag him, and bite him, and throw
him over his shoulder two or three times, and Andrew
Jackson—which was the name of the pup—Andrew
Jackson would never let on but what *he* was satisfied,
and hadn't expected nothing else—and the bets being
doubled and doubled on the other side all the time,
till the money was all up; and then all of a sudden
he would grab that other dog jest by the j'int of his
hind leg and freeze to it—not chaw, you understand,
but only just grip and hang on till they throwed up
the sponge, if it was a year. Smiley always come out
winner on that pup, till he harnessed a dog once that
didn't have no hind legs, because they'd been sawed
off in a circular saw, and when the thing had gone
along far enough, and the money was all up, and he
come to make a snatch for his pet holt, he see in a
minute how he'd been imposed on, and how the other
dog had him in the door, so to speak, and he 'peared
surprised, and then he looked sorter discouraged-like
and didn't try no more to win the fight, and so he got
shucked out bad. He give Smiley a look, as much as
to say his heart was broke, and it was *his* fault, for
putting up a dog that hadn't no hind legs for him to
take holt of, which was his main dependence in a fight,

and then he limped off a piece and laid down and died. It was a good pup, was that Andrew Jackson, and would have made a name for hisself if he'd lived, for the stuff was in him and he had genius—I know it, because he hadn't no opportunities to speak of, and it don't stand to reason that a dog could make such a fight as he could under them circumstances if he hadn't no talent. It always makes me feel sorry when I think of that last fight of his'n, and the way it turned out.

" Well, thish-yer Smiley had rat-tarriers, and chicken cocks, and tomcats, and all them kind of things, till you couldn't rest, and you couldn't fetch nothing for him to bet on but he'd match you. He ketched a frog one day, and took him home, and said he cal'lated to educate him; and so he never done nothing for three months but set in his back yard and learn that frog to jump. And you bet you he *did* learn him, too. He'd give him a little punch behind, and the next minute you'd see that frog whirling in the air like a doughnut—see him turn one summerset, or maybe a couple, if he got a good start, and come down flat-footed and all right, like a cat. He got him up so in the matter of ketching flies, and kep' him in practice so constant, that he'd nail a fly every time as fur as he could see him. Smiley said all a frog wanted was education, and he could do 'most anything—and I believe him. Why, I've seen him set Dan'l Webster down here on this floor—Dan'l Webster was the name of the frog—and sing out, ' Flies, Dan'l, flies! ' and quicker'n you could wink he'd spring straight up and snake a fly off'n the counter there, and flop down on the floor ag'in as solid as a gob of mud, and fall to scratching the side of his head with his hind foot as indifferent as if he hadn't no idea he'd been doin' any more'n any frog might do. You never see a frog so modest and straightfor'ard as he was, for all he was so gifted. And when it come to fair and square jumping on a dead level, he could get over more ground at one straddle than any animal of his breed you ever see. Jumping on a dead level was his strong suit, you understand; and when it come to that, Smiley would ante up money on him as long as he had a red. Smiley was monstrous proud of his frog, and well he might be, for fellers that had travelled and been everywheres all said he laid over any frog that ever *they* see.

" Well, Smiley kep' the beast in a little lattice box, and he used to fetch him down-town sometimes and lay for a bet. One day a feller—a stranger in the camp, he was—come acrost him with his box, and says:

" ' What might it be that you've got in the box? '

" And Smiley says, sorter indifferent-like: ' It might be a parrot, or it might be a canary, maybe, but it ain't —it's only just a frog.'

" And the feller took it, and looked at it careful, and turned it round this way and that, and says: ' H'm— so 'tis. Well, what's *he* good for? '

" ' Well,' Smiley says, easy and careless, ' he's good enough for *one* thing, I should judge—he can outjump any frog in Calaveras county.'

" The feller took the box again, and took another long, particular look, and give it back to Smiley, and says, very deliberate, ' Well,' he says, ' I don't see no p'ints about that frog that's any better'n any other frog.'

" ' Maybe you don't,' Smiley says. ' Maybe you understand frogs and maybe you don't understand 'em; maybe you've had experience, and maybe you ain't only a amature, as it were. Anyways, I've got *my* opinion, and I'll resk forty dollars that he can outjump any frog in Calaveras county.'

" And the feller studied a minute, and then says,

kinder sad like, ' Well, I'm only a stranger here, and I ain't got no frog; but if I had a frog, I'd bet you.'

" And then Smiley says, ' That's all right—that's all right—if you'll hold my box a minute, I'll go and get you a frog.' And so the feller took the box, and put up his forty dollars along with Smiley's, and set down to wait.

" So he set there a good while thinking and thinking to hisself, and then he got the frog out and prized his mouth open and took a teaspoon and filled him full of quail shot—filled him pretty near up to his chin—and set him on the floor. Smiley he went to the swamp and slopped around in the mud for a long time, and finally he ketched a frog, and fetched him in, and give him to this feller, and says:

" ' Now, if you're ready, set him alongside of Dan'l, with his forepaws just even with Dan'l's, and I'll give the word.' Then he says, ' One—two—three—*git!* ' and him and the feller touched up the frogs from behind, and the new frog hopped off lively, but Dan'l give a heave, and hysted up his shoulders—so—like a Frenchman, but it warn't no use—he couldn't budge; he was planted as solid as a church, and he couldn't no more stir than if he was anchored out. Smiley was a good deal surprised, and he was disgusted too, but he didn't have no idea what the matter was, of course.

" The feller took the money and started away; and when he was going out at the door, he sorter jerked his thumb over his shoulder—so—at Dan'l, and says again, very deliberate, ' Well,' he says, ' *I* don't see no p'ints about that frog that's any better'n any other frog.'

" Smiley he stood scratching his head and looking down at Dan'l a long time, and at last he says, ' I do

wonder what in the nation that frog throw'd off for—
I wonder if there ain't something the matter with
him—he 'pears to look mighty baggy, somehow.' And
he ketched Dan'l by the nap of the neck, and hefted
him, and says, ' Why, blame my cats if he don't weigh
five pound!' and turned him upside down and he
belched out a double handful of shot. And then he
see how it was, and he was the maddest man—he set
the frog down and took out after that feller, but he
never ketched him. And——"

[Here Simon Wheeler heard his name called from
the front yard, and got up to see what was wanted.]
And turning to me as he moved away, he said: " Just
set where you are, stranger, and rest easy—I ain't
going to be gone a second."

But, by your leave, I did not think that a continua-
tion of the history of the enterprising vagabond *Jim*
Smiley would be likely to afford me much information
concerning the Rev. *Leonidas W.* Smiley, and so I
started away.

At the door I met the sociable Wheeler returning,
and he button-holed me and re-commenced:

" Well, thish-yer Smiley had a yeller one-eyed cow
that didn't have no tail, only just a short stump like
a bannanner, and——"

However, lacking both time and inclination, I did
not wait to hear about the afflicted cow, but took my
leave.

the vast audience, with bowed heads and downcast hearts, wended slowly their homeward way, mourning greatly that one so young and fair, or so old and respected, should have merited so dire a fate.

But if the accused person opened the other door, there came forth from it a lady, the most suitable to his years and station that his Majesty could select among his fair subjects; and to this lady he was immediately married, as a reward of his innocence. It mattered not that he might already possess a wife and family, or that his affections might be engaged upon an object of his own selection. The king allowed no such subordinate arrangements to interfere with his great scheme of retribution and reward. The exercises, as in the other instance, took place immediately, and in the arena. Another door opened beneath the king, and a priest, followed by a band of choristers, and dancing maidens blowing joyous airs on golden horns and treading an epithalamic measure, advanced to where the pair stood side by side, and the wedding was promptly and cheerily solemnized. Then the gay brass bells rang forth their merry peals, the people shouted glad hurrahs, and the innocent man, preceded by children strewing flowers on his path, led his bride to his home.

This was the king's semi-barbaric method of administering justice. Its perfect fairness is obvious. The criminal could not know out of which door would come the lady. He opened either he pleased, without having the slightest idea whether, in the next instant, he was to be devoured or married. On some occasions the tiger came out of one door, and on some out of the other. The decisions of this tribunal were not only fair —they were positively determinate. The accused person was instantly punished if he found himself guilty, and if innocent he was rewarded on the spot, whether he liked it or not. There was no escape from the judgments of the king's arena.

The institution was a very popular one. When the people gathered together on one of the great trial days, they never knew whether they were to witness a bloody slaughter or a hilarious wedding. This element of uncertainty lent an interest to the occasion which it could not otherwise have attained. Thus the masses were entertained and pleased, and the thinking part of the community could bring no charge of unfairness against this plan; for did not the accused person have the whole matter in his own hands?

This semi-barbaric king had a daughter as blooming as his most florid fancies, and with a soul as fervent and imperious as his own. As is usual in such cases, she was the apple of his eye, and was loved by him above all humanity. Among his courtiers was a young man of that fineness of blood and lowness of station common to the conventional heroes of romance who love royal maidens. This royal maiden was well satisfied with her lover, for he was handsome and brave to a degree unsurpassed in all this kingdom, and she loved him with an ardor that had enough of barbarism in it to make it exceedingly warm and strong. This love affair moved on happily for many months, until, one day, the king happened to discover its existence. He did not hesitate nor waver in regard to his duty in the premises. The youth was immediately cast into prison, and a day was appointed for his trial in the king's arena. This, of course, was an especially important occasion, and his Majesty, as well as all the people, was greatly interested in the workings and development of this trial. Never before had such a case occurred—never before had a subject dared to love the daughter of a king. In after years such things became commonplace enough, but then they were, in no slight degree, novel and startling.

The tiger cages of the kingdom were searched for the most savage and relentless beasts, from which the fiercest monster might be selected for the arena, and the ranks of maiden youth and beauty throughout the land were carefully surveyed by competent judges, in order that the young man might have a fitting bride in case fate did not determine for him a different destiny. Of course, everybody knew that the deed with which the accused was charged had been done. He had loved the princess, and neither he, she, nor any one else thought of denying the fact. But the king would not think of allowing any fact of this kind to interfere with the workings of the tribunal, in which he took such great delight and satisfaction. No matter how the affair turned out, the youth would be disposed of, and the king would take an æsthetic pleasure in watching the course of events which would determine whether or not the young man had done wrong in allowing himself to love the princess.

The appointed day arrived. From far and near the people gathered, and thronged the great galleries of the arena, while crowds, unable to gain admittance, massed themselves against its outside walls. The king and his court were in their places, opposite the twin doors—those fateful portals, so terrible in their similarity!

All was ready. The signal was given. A door beneath the royal party opened, and the lover of the princess walked into the arena. Tall, beautiful, fair, his appearance was greeted with a low hum of admiration and anxiety. Half the audience had not known so grand a youth had lived among them. No wonder the princess loved him! What a terrible thing for him to be there!

As the youth advanced into the arena, he turned, as the custom was, to bow to the king. But he did not think at all of that royal personage; his eyes were fixed upon the princess, who sat to the right of her father. Had it not been for the moiety of barbarism in her nature, it is probable that lady would not have been there. But her intense and fervid soul would not allow her to be absent on an occasion in which she was so terribly interested. From the moment that the decree had gone forth that her lover should decide his fate in the king's arena, she had thought of nothing, night or day, but this great event and the various subjects connected with it. Possessed of more power, influence, and force of character than any one who had ever before been interested in such a case, she had done what no other person had done—she had possessed herself of the secret of the doors. She knew in which of the two rooms behind those doors stood the cage of the tiger, with its open front, and in which waited the lady. Through these thick doors, heavily curtained with skins on the inside, it was impossible that any noise or suggestion should come from within to the person who should approach to raise the latch of one of them. But gold, and the power of a woman's will, had brought the secret to the princess.

Not only did she know in which room stood the lady, ready to emerge, all blushing and radiant, should her door be opened, but she knew who the lady was. It was one of the fairest and loveliest of the damsels of the court who had been selected as the reward of the accused youth, should he be proved innocent of the crime of aspiring to one so far above him; and the princess hated her. Often had she seen, or imagined that she had seen, this fair creature throwing glances of admiration upon the person of her lover, and sometimes she thought these glances were perceived and even returned. Now and then she had seen them talking together. It was but for a moment or two, but much can be said in a brief space. It may have been on most unimportant topics, but how could she know that? The girl was lovely, but she had dared to raise her eyes to the loved one of the princess, and, with all the intensity of the savage blood transmitted to her through long lines of wholly barbaric ancestors, she hated the woman who blushed and trembled behind that silent door.

When her lover turned and looked at her, and his eye met hers as she sat there paler and whiter than any one in the vast ocean of anxious faces about her, he saw, by that power of quick perception which is given to those whose souls are one, that she knew behind which door crouched the tiger, and behind which stood the lady. He had expected her to know it. He understood her nature, and his soul was assured that she would never rest until she had made plain to herself this thing, hidden to all other lookers-on, even to the king. The only hope for the youth in which there was any element of certainty was based upon the success of the princess in discovering this mystery, and the moment he looked upon her, he saw she had succeeded.

Then it was that his quick and anxious glance asked the question, " Which? " It was as plain to her as if he shouted it from where he stood. There was not an instant to be lost. The question was asked in a flash; it must be answered in another.

Her right arm lay on the cushioned parapet before her. She raised her hand, and made a slight, quick movement toward the right. No one but her lover saw her. Every eye but his was fixed on the man in the arena.

He turned, and with a firm and rapid step he walked across the empty space. Every heart stopped beating, every breath was held, every eye was fixed immovably upon that man. Without the slightest hesitation, he went to the door on the right, and opened it.

Now, the point of the story is this: Did the tiger come out of that door, or did the lady?

The more we reflect upon this question, the harder it is to answer. It involves a study of the human heart which leads us through devious mazes of passion, out of which it is difficult to find our way. Think of it, fair reader, not as if the decision of the question depended upon yourself, but upon that hot-blooded, semi-barbaric princess, her soul at a white heat beneath the combined fires of despair and jealousy. She had lost him, but who should have him?

How often, in her waking hours and in her dreams, had she started in wild horror and covered her face with her hands as she thought of her lover opening the door on the other side of which waited the cruel fangs of the tiger!

But how much oftener had she seen him at the other door! How in her grievous reveries had she gnashed her teeth and torn her hair when she saw his start of rapturous delight as he opened the door of the lady! How her soul had burned in agony when she had seen him rush to meet that woman, with her flushing cheek and sparkling eye of triumph; when she had seen him lead her forth, his whole frame kindled with the joy of recovered life; when she had heard the glad shouts from the multitude, and the wild ringing of the happy bells; when she had seen the priest, with his joyous followers, advance to the couple, and make them man and wife before her very eyes; and when she had seen them walk away together upon their path of flowers, followed by the tremendous shouts of the hilarious multitude, in which her one despairing shriek was lost and drowned!

Would it not be better for him to die at once, and go to wait for her in the blessed regions of semi-barbaric futurity?

And yet, that awful tiger, those shrieks, that blood!

Her decision had been indicated in an instant, but it had been made after days and nights of anguished deliberation. She had known she would be asked, she had decided what she would answer, and, without the slightest hesitation, she had moved her hand to the right.

The question of her decision is one not to be lightly considered, and it is not for me to presume to set up myself as the one person able to answer it. So I leave it with all of you: Which came out of the opened door— the lady or the tiger?

THE OUTCASTS OF POKER FLAT

BY

FRANCIS BRET HARTE

This is often called a story of local color. And it is. It is rich in the characteristics of California in the gold-seeking days. It is also classified as a story of setting. And it is. The setting is a determining factor in the conduct of these outcasts. They are men and women as inevitably drawn to the mining camp as the ill-fated ship in '' The Arabian Nights '' was attracted to the lode-stone mountain, and with as much certainty of shipwreck. These the blizzard of the west gathers into its embrace, and compels them to reveal their better selves. But it is more than a story of local color and of setting. It is also an illustration of the artistic blending of plot, character, and setting, and of the magical power of youth to see life at the time truly enough, but to transform it later into something fine and noble.

THE OUTCASTS OF POKER FLAT *

As Mr. John Oakhurst, gambler, stepped into the main street of Poker Flat on the morning of the twenty-third of November, 1850, he was conscious of a change in its moral atmosphere since the preceding night. Two or three men, conversing earnestly together, ceased as he approached, and exchanged significant glances. There was a Sabbath lull in the air, which, in a settlement unused to Sabbath influences, looked ominous.

Mr. Oakhurst's calm, handsome face betrayed small concern of these indications. Whether he was conscious of any predisposing cause, was another question. "I reckon they're after somebody," he reflected; "likely it's me." He returned to his pocket the handkerchief with which he had been whipping away the red dust of Poker Flat from his neat boots, and quietly discharged his mind of any further conjecture.

In point of fact, Poker Flat was "after somebody." It had lately suffered the loss of several thousand dollars, two valuable horses, and a prominent citizen. It was experiencing a spasm of virtuous reaction, quite as lawless and ungovernable as any of the acts that had provoked it. A secret committee had determined to rid the town of all improper persons. This was done permanently in regard of two men who were then hanging from the boughs of a sycamore in the gulch, and

* From "The Luck of Roaring Camp," by Francis Bret Harte. Copyright, 1906, by Houghton Mifflin Company. Reprinted by special arrangement with Houghton Mifflin Company, the authorized publishers of Bret Harte's works.

temporarily in the banishment of certain other objectionable characters. I regret to say that some of these were ladies. It is but due to the sex, however, to state that their impropriety was professional, and it was only in such easily established standards of evil that Poker Flat ventured to sit in judgment.

Mr. Oakhurst was right in supposing that he was included in this category. A few of the committee had urged hanging him as a possible example, and a sure method of reimbursing themselves from his pockets of the sums he had won from them. " It's agin justice," said Jim Wheeler, " to let this yer young man from Roaring Camp—an entire stranger—carry away our money." But a crude sentiment of equity residing in the breasts of those who had been fortunate enough to win from Mr. Oakhurst overruled this narrower local prejudice.

Mr. Oakhurst received his sentence with philosophic calmness, none the less coolly that he was aware of the hesitation of his judges. He was too much of a gambler not to accept Fate. With him life was at best an uncertain game, and he recognized the usual percentage in favor of the dealer.

A body of armed men accompanied the deported wickedness of Poker Flat to the outskirts of the settlement. Besides Mr. Oakhurst, who was known to be a coolly desperate man, and for whose intimidation the armed escort was intended, the expatriated party consisted of a young woman familiarly known as " The Duchess "; another, who had gained the infelicitous title of " Mother Shipton "; and " Uncle Billy," a suspected sluice-robber and confirmed drunkard. The cavalcade provoked no comments from the spectators, nor was any word uttered by the escort. Only, when the gulch which marked the uttermost limit of Poker Flat was reached, the leader spoke briefly and to the point. The exiles were forbidden to return at the peril of their lives.

As the escort disappeared, their pent-up feelings found vent in a few hysterical tears from "The Duchess," some bad language from Mother Shipton, and a Parthian volley of expletives from Uncle Billy. The philosophic Oakhurst alone remained silent. He listened calmly to Mother Shipton's desire to cut somebody's heart out, to the repeated statements of "The Duchess" that she would die in the road, and to the alarming oaths that seemed to be bumped out of Uncle Billy as he rode forward. With the easy good-humor characteristic of his class, he insisted upon exchanging his own riding-horse, "Five Spot," for the sorry mule which the Duchess rode. But even this act did not draw the party into any closer sympathy. The young woman readjusted her somewhat draggled plumes with a feeble, faded coquetry; Mother Shipton eyed the possessor of "Five Spot" with malevolence, and Uncle Billy included the whole party in one sweeping anathema.

The road to Sandy Bar—a camp that, not having as yet experienced the regenerating influences of Poker Flat, consequently seemed to offer some invitation to the emigrants—lay over a steep mountain range. It was distant a day's severe journey. In that advanced season, the party soon passed out of the moist, temperate regions of the foot-hills into the dry, cold, bracing air of the Sierras. The trail was narrow and difficult. At noon the Duchess, rolling out of her saddle upon the ground, declared her intention of going no farther, and the party halted.

The spot was singularly wild and impressive. A wooded amphitheatre, surrounded on three sides by pre-

cipitous cliffs of naked granite, sloped gently toward
the crest of another precipice that overlooked the valley. It was undoubtedly the most suitable spot for a
camp, had camping been advisable. But Mr. Oakhurst
knew that scarcely half the journey to Sandy Bar was
accomplished, and the party were not equipped or pro-
visioned for delay. This fact he pointed out to his companions curtly, with a philosophic commentary on the
folly of ''throwing up their hand before the game
was played out.'' But they were furnished with liquor,
which in this emergency stood them in place of food,
fuel, rest, and prescience. In spite of his remonstrances,
it was not long before they were more or less under
its influence. Uncle Billy passed rapidly from a belli-
cose state into one of stupor, the Duchess became maud-
lin, and Mother Shipton snored. Mr. Oakhurst alone
remained erect, leaning against a rock, calmly survey-
ing them.

Mr. Oakhurst did not drink. It interfered with a
profession which required coolness, impassiveness, and
presence of mind, and, in his own language, he
''couldn't afford it.'' As he gazed at his recumbent
fellow-exiles, the loneliness begotten of his pariah-trade,
his habits of life, his very vices, for the first time seriously oppressed him. He bestirred himself in dusting
his black clothes, washing his hands and face, and other
acts characteristic of his studiously neat habits, and for
a moment forgot his annoyance. The thought of de-
serting his weaker and more pitiable companions never
perhaps occurred to him. Yet he could not help feeling the want of that excitement which, singularly
enough, was most conducive to that calm equanimity for
which he was notorious. He looked at the gloomy walls
that rose a thousand feet sheer above the circling pines
around him; at the sky, ominously clouded; at the

valley below, already deepening into shadow. And, doing so, suddenly he heard his own name called.

A horseman slowly ascended the trail. In the fresh,
open face of the new-comer Mr. Oakhurst recognized
Tom Simson, otherwise known as "The Innocent"
of Sandy Bar. He had met him some months before
over a "little game," and had, with perfect equanimity,
won the entire fortune—amounting to some forty dollars—of that guileless youth. After the game was finished, Mr. Oakhurst drew the youthful speculator behind the door and thus addressed him: "Tommy,
you're a good little man, but you can't gamble worth
a cent. Don't try it over again." He then handed him
his money back, pushed him gently from the room, and
so made a devoted slave of Tom Simson.

There was a remembrance of this in his boyish and
enthusiastic greeting of Mr. Oakhurst. He had started,
he said, to go to Poker Flat to seek his fortune.
"Alone?" No, not exactly alone; in fact—a giggle—
he had run away with Piney Woods. Didn't Mr. Oakhurst remember Piney? She that used to wait on the
table at the Temperance House? They had been engaged a long time, but old Jake Woods had objected,
and so they had run away, and were going to Poker
Flat to be married, and here they were. And they were
tired out, and how lucky it was they had found a place
to camp and company. All this the Innocent delivered rapidly, while Piney—a stout, comely damsel of
fifteen—emerged from behind the pine-tree, where she
had been blushing unseen, and rode to the side of her
lover.

Mr. Oakhurst seldom troubled himself with sentiment,
still less with propriety; but he had a vague idea that
the situation was not felicitous. He retained, however,
his presence of mind sufficiently to kick Uncle Billy,

who was about to say something, and Uncle Billy was sober enough to recognize in Mr. Oakhurst's kick a superior power that would not bear trifling. He then endeavored to dissuade Tom Simson from delaying further, but in vain. He even pointed out the fact that there was no provision, nor means of making a camp. But, unluckily, " The Innocent " met this objection by assuring the party that he was provided with an extra mule loaded with provisions, and by the discovery of a rude attempt at a log-house near the trail. " Piney can stay with Mrs. Oakhurst," said the Innocent, pointing to the Duchess, " and I can shift for myself."

Nothing but Mr. Oakhurst's admonishing foot saved Uncle Billy from bursting into a roar of laughter. As it was, he felt compelled to retire up the cañon until he could recover his gravity. There he confided the joke to the tall pine-trees, with many slaps of his leg, contortions of his face, and the usual profanity. But when he returned to the party, he found them seated by a fire—for the air had grown strangely chill and the sky overcast—in apparently amicable conversation. Piney was actually talking in an impulsive, girlish fashion to the Duchess, who was listening with an interest and animation she had not shown for many days. The Innocent was holding forth, apparently with equal effect, to Mr. Oakhurst and Mother Shipton, who was actually relaxing into amiability. " Is this yer a d——d picnic ? " said Uncle Billy, with inward scorn, as he surveyed the sylvan group, the glancing fire-light, and the tethered animals in the foreground. Suddenly an idea mingled with the alcoholic fumes that disturbed his brain. It was apparently of a jocular nature, for he felt impelled to slap his leg again and cram his fist into his mouth.

As the shadows crept slowly up the mountain, a slight breeze rocked the tops of the pine-trees, and moaned through their long and gloomy aisles. The ruined cabin, patched and covered with pine boughs, was set apart for the ladies. As the lovers parted, they unaffectedly exchanged a kiss, so honest and sincere that it might have been heard above the swaying pines. The frail Duchess and the malevolent Mother Shipton were probably too stunned to remark upon this last evidence of simplicity, and so turned without a word to the hut. The fire was replenished, the men lay down before the door, and in a few minutes were asleep.

Mr. Oakhurst was a light sleeper. Toward morning he awoke benumbed and cold. As he stirred the dying fire, the wind, which was now blowing strongly, brought to his cheek that which caused the blood to leave it,— snow!

He started to his feet with the intention of awakening the sleepers, for there was no time to lose. But turning to where Uncle Billy had been lying, he found him gone. A suspicion leaped to his brain and a curse to his lips. He ran to the spot where the mules had been tethered; they were no longer there. The tracks were already rapidly disappearing in the snow.

The momentary excitement brought Mr. Oakhurst back to the fire with his usual calm. He did not waken the sleepers. The Innocent slumbered peacefully, with a smile on his good-humored, freckled face; the virgin Piney slept beside her frailer sisters as sweetly as though attended by celestial guardians, and Mr. Oakhurst, drawing his blanket over his shoulders, stroked his mustachios and waited for the dawn. It came slowly in a whirling mist of snowflakes, that dazzled and confused the eye. What could be seen of the landscape appeared magically changed. He looked over the val-

ley, and summed up the present and future in two
words,—" Snowed in! "

A careful inventory of the provisions, which, fortu-
nately for the party, had been stored within the hut,
and so escaped the felonious fingers of Uncle Billy, disclosed the fact that with care and prudence they might
last ten days longer. " That is," said Mr. Oakhurst,
sotto voce to the Innocent, " if you're willing to board
us. If you ain't—and perhaps you'd better not—you
can wait till Uncle Billy gets back with provisions."
For some occult reason, Mr. Oakhurst could not bring
himself to disclose Uncle Billy's rascality, and so offered the hypothesis that he had wandered from the
camp and had accidentally stampeded the animals. He
dropped a warning to the Duchess and Mother Shipton,
who of course knew the facts of their associate's de-
fection. " They'll find out the truth about us *all*, when
they find out anything," he added, significantly, " and
there's no good frightening them now."

Tom Simson not only put all his worldly store at
the disposal of Mr. Oakhurst, but seemed to enjoy the
prospect of their enforced seclusion. " We'll have a
good camp for a week, and then the snow'll melt, and
we'll all go back together." The cheerful gaiety of
the young man and Mr. Oakhurst's calm infected the
others. The Innocent, with the aid of pine boughs, ex-
temporized a thatch for the roofless cabin, and the
Duchess directed Piney in the rearrangement of the
interior with a taste and tact that opened the blue eyes
of that provincial maiden to their fullest extent. " I
reckon now you're used to fine things at Poker Flat,"
said Piney. The Duchess turned away sharply to con-
ceal something that reddened her cheek through its professional tint, and Mother Shipton requested Piney not
to " chatter." But when Mr. Oakhurst returned from

a weary search for the trail, he heard the sound of happy laughter echoed from the rocks. He stopped in some alarm, and his thoughts first naturally reverted to the whiskey, which he had prudently *cachéd*. "And yet it don't somehow sound like whiskey," said the gambler. It was not until he caught sight of the blazing fire through the still blinding storm, and the group around it, that he settled to the conviction that it was "square fun."

Whether Mr. Oakhurst had *cachéd* his cards with the whiskey as something debarred the free access of the community, I cannot say. It was certain that, in Mother Shipton's words, he "didn't say cards once" during that evening. Haply the time was beguiled by an accordion, produced somewhat ostentatiously by Tom Simson, from his pack. Notwithstanding some difficulties attending the manipulation of this instrument, Piney Woods managed to pluck several reluctant melodies from its keys, to an accompaniment by the Innocent on a pair of bone castanets. But the crowning festivity of the evening was reached in a rude camp-meeting hymn, which the lovers, joining hands, sang with great earnestness and vociferation. I fear that a certain defiant tone and Covenanter's swing to its chorus, rather than any devotional quality, caused it speedily to infect the others, who at last joined in the refrain:

"'I'm proud to live in the service of the Lord,
And I'm bound to die in His army.'"

The pines rocked, the storm eddied and whirled above the miserable group, and the flames of their altar leaped heavenward, as if in token of the vow.

At midnight the storm abated, the rolling clouds parted, and the stars glittered keenly above the sleeping camp. Mr. Oakhurst, whose professional habits had enabled him to live on the smallest possible amount of sleep, in dividing the watch with Tom Simson, somehow managed to take upon himself the greater part of that duty. He excused himself to the Innocent, by saying that he had "often been a week without sleep." "Doing what?" asked Tom. "Poker!" replied Oakhurst, sententiously; "when a man gets a streak of luck,—nigger-luck,—he don't get tired. The luck gives in first. Luck," continued the gambler, reflectively, "is a mighty queer thing. All you know about it for certain is that it's bound to change. And it's finding out when it's going to change that makes you. We've had a streak of bad luck since we left Poker Flat—you come along, and slap you get into it, too. If you can hold your cards right along you're all right. For," added the gambler, with cheerful irrelevance,

> "'I'm proud to live in the service of the Lord,
>   And I'm bound to die in His army.'"

The third day came, and the sun, looking through the white-curtained valley, saw the outcasts divide their slowly decreasing store of provisions for the morning meal. It was one of the peculiarities of that mountain climate that its rays diffused a kindly warmth over the wintry landscape, as if in regretful commiseration of the past. But it revealed drift on drift of snow piled high around the hut; a hopeless, uncharted, trackless sea of white lying below the rocky shores to which the castaways still clung. Through the marvellously clear air, the smoke of the pastoral village of Poker Flat rose miles away. Mother Shipton saw it, and from a remote pinnacle of her rocky fastness, hurled in that

direction a final malediction. It was her last vitu-
perative attempt, and perhaps for that reason was in-
vested with a certain degree of sublimity. It did her
good, she privately informed the Duchess. " Just you
go out there and cuss, and see." She then set herself
to the task of amusing " the child," as she and the
Duchess were pleased to call Piney. Piney was no
chicken, but it was a soothing and ingenious theory of
the pair thus to account for the fact that she didn't
swear and wasn't improper.

When night crept up again through the gorges, the
reedy notes of the accordion rose and fell in fitful
spasms and long-drawn gasps by the flickering camp-
fire. But music failed to fill entirely the aching void
left by insufficient food, and a new diversion was proposed by Piney—story-telling. Neither Mr. Oakhurst
nor his female companions caring to relate their personal experiences, this plan would have failed, too, but
for the Innocent. Some months before he had chanced
upon a stray copy of Mr. Pope's ingenious translation
of the Iliad. He now proposed to narrate the principal incidents of that poem—having thoroughly mas-
tered the argument and fairly forgotten the words—in
the current vernacular of Sandy Bar. And so for
the rest of that night the Homeric demigods again
walked the earth. Trojan bully and wily Greek wrestled
in the winds, and the great pines in the cañon seemed
to bow to the wrath of the son of Peleus. Mr. Oakhurst listened with quiet satisfaction. Most especially
was he interested in the fate of " Ash-heels," as the
Innocent persisted in denominating the " swift-footed
Achilles."

So with small food and much of Homer and the accordion, a week passed over the heads of the outcasts.
The sun again forsook them, and again from leaden

skies the snowflakes were sifted over the land. Day by
day closer around them drew the snowy circle, until
at last they looked from their prison over drifted walls
of dazzling white, that towered twenty feet above their
heads. It became more and more difficult to replenish
their fires, even from the fallen trees beside them, now
half hidden in the drifts. And yet no one complained.
The lovers turned from the dreary prospect and looked
into each other's eyes, and were happy. Mr. Oakhurst
settled himself coolly to the losing game before him.
The Duchess, more cheerful than she had been, assumed the care of Piney. Only Mother Shipton—once
the strongest of the party—seemed to sicken and fade.
At midnight on the tenth day she called Oakhurst to
her side. " I'm going," she said, in a voice of querulous
weakness, " but don't say anything about it. Don't
waken the kids. Take the bundle from under my head
and open it." Mr. Oakhurst did so. It contained
Mother Shipton's rations for the last week, untouched.
" Give 'em to the child," she said, pointing to the sleeping Piney. " You've starved yourself," said the gambler. " That's what they call it," said the woman,
querulously, as she lay down again, and, turning her
face to the wall, passed quietly away.

The accordion and the bones were put aside that day,
and Homer was forgotten. When the body of Mother
Shipton had been committed to the snow, Mr. Oakhurst
took the Innocent aside, and showed him a pair of
snowshoes, which he had fashioned from the old pack-
saddle. " There's one chance in a hundred to save
her yet," he said, pointing to Piney; " but it's there,"
he added, pointing toward Poker Flat. " If you can
reach there in two days she's safe." " And you?"
asked Tom Simson. " I'll stay here," was the curt
reply.

The lovers parted with a long embrace. " You are not going, too? " said the Duchess, as she saw Mr. Oakhurst apparently waiting to accompany him. " As far as the cañon," he replied. He turned suddenly, and kissed the Duchess, leaving her pallid face aflame, and her trembling limbs rigid with amazement.

Night came, but not Mr. Oakhurst. It brought the storm again and the whirling snow. Then the Duchess, feeding the fire, found that some one had quietly piled beside the hut enough fuel to last a few days longer. The tears rose to her eyes, but she hid them from Piney.

The women slept but little. In the morning, looking into each other's faces, they read their fate. Neither spoke; but Piney, accepting the position of the stronger, drew near and placed her arm around the Duchess's waist. They kept this attitude for the rest of the day. That night the storm reached its greatest fury, and, rending asunder the protecting pines, invaded the very hut.

Toward morning they found themselves unable to feed the fire, which gradually died away. As the embers slowly blackened, the Duchess crept closer to Piney, and broke the silence of many hours: " Piney, can you pray? " " No, dear," said Piney, simply. The Duchess, without knowing exactly why, felt relieved, and, putting her head upon Piney's shoulder, spoke no more. And so reclining, the younger and purer pillowing the head of her soiled sister upon her virgin breast, they fell asleep.

The wind lulled as if it feared to waken them. Feathery drifts of snow, shaken from the long pine boughs, flew like white-winged birds, and settled about them as they slept. The moon through the rifted clouds looked down upon what had been the camp. But all human stain, all trace of earthly travail, was hidden beneath the spotless mantle mercifully flung from above.

They slept all that day and the next, nor did they waken when voices and footsteps broke the silence of the camp. And when pitying fingers brushed the snow from their wan faces, you could scarcely have told from the equal peace that dwelt upon them, which was she that had sinned. Even the Law of Poker Flat recognized this, and turned away, leaving them still locked in each other's arms.

But at the head of the gulch, on one of the largest pine-trees, they found the deuce of clubs pinned to the bark with a bowie knife. It bore the following, written in pencil, in a firm hand:

†

BENEATH THIS TREE
LIES THE BODY

OF

JOHN OAKHURST,

WHO STRUCK A STREAK OF BAD LUCK
ON THE 23D OF NOVEMBER, 1850,

AND

HANDED IN HIS CHECKS
ON THE 7TH DECEMBER, 1850.

⸸

And, pulseless and cold, with a Derringer by his side and a bullet in his heart, though still calm as in life, beneath the snow lay he who was at once the strongest and yet the weakest of the outcasts of Poker Flat.

THE REVOLT OF "MOTHER"

BY

MARY E. WILKINS FREEMAN

This is a story of character against a New England background. Each character is worked out with the delicacy and minuteness of a cameo. Each is intensely realistic, yet, as in the cameo, palely flushed with romance. "Mother," along with her originality of action and long-concealed ideals, has the saving quality of common-sense, which makes its powerful appeal to the daily realities of life. Thus when "Father," dazed by the unexpected revelation of the character and ideals of the woman he has misunderstood for forty years, stands uncertain whether to assert or to surrender his long-established supremacy, she decides him in her favor by a practical suggestion of acquiescence: "You'd better take your coat off an' get washed—there's the wash-basin —an' then we'll have supper."

THE REVOLT OF "MOTHER" *

" Father! "

" What is it? "

" What are them men diggin' over there in the field for? "

There was a sudden dropping and enlarging of the lower part of the old man's face, as if some heavy weight had settled therein; he shut his mouth tight, and went on harnessing the great bay mare. He hustled the collar on to her neck with a jerk.

" Father! "

The old man slapped the saddle upon the mare's back.

" Look here, father, I want to know what them men are diggin' over in the field for, an' I'm goin' to know."

" I wish you'd go into the house, mother, an' 'tend to your own affairs," the old man said then. He ran his words together, and his speech was almost as inarticulate as a growl.

But the woman understood; it was her most native tongue. " I ain't goin' into the house till you tell me what them men are doin' over there in the field," said she.

Then she stood waiting. She was a small woman, short and straight-waisted like a child in her brown cotton gown. Her forehead was mild and benevolent between the smooth curves of gray hair; there were

* From "A New England Nun and Other Stories," by Mary E. Wilkins Freeman. Copyright, 1891, by Harper & Bros. Reprinted by special permission.

meek downward lines about her nose and mouth; but her eyes, fixed upon the old man, looked as if the meekness had been the result of her own will, never of the will of another.

They were in the barn, standing before the wide-open doors. The spring air, full of the smell of growing grass and unseen blossoms, came in their faces. The deep yard in front was littered with farm wagons and piles of wood; on the edges, close to the fence and the house, the grass was a vivid green, and there were some dandelions.

The old man glanced doggedly at his wife as he tightened the last buckles on the harness. She looked as immovable to him as one of the rocks in his pastureland, bound to the earth with generations of blackberry vines. He slapped the reins over the horse, and started forth from the barn.

" *Father!* " said she.

The old man pulled up. " What is it? "

" I want to know what them men are diggin' over there in that field for."

" They're diggin' a cellar, I s'pose, if you've got to know."

" A cellar for what? "

" A barn."

" A barn? You ain't goin' to build a barn over there where we was goin' to have a house, father? "

The old man said not another word. He hurried the horse into the farm wagon, and clattered out of the yard, jouncing as sturdily on his seat as a boy.

The woman stood a moment looking after him, then she went out of the barn across a corner of the yard to the house. The house, standing at right angles with the great barn and a long reach of sheds and outbuildings, was infinitesimal compared with them. It was scarcely as commodious for people as the little boxes under the barn eaves were for doves.

A pretty's girl's face, pink and delicate as a flower, was looking out of one of the house windows. She was watching three men who were digging over in the field which bounded the yard neɑr the road line. She turned quietly when the woman entered.

" What are they digging for, mother? " said she. " Did he tell you? "

" They're diggin' for—a cellar for a new barn."

" Oh, mother, he ain't going to build another barn? "

" That's what he says."

A boy stood before the kitchen glass combing his hair. He combed slowly and painstakingly, arranging his brown hair in a smooth hillock over his forehead. He did not seem to pay any attention to the conversation.

" Sammy, did you know father was going to build a new barn? " asked the girl.

The boy combed assiduously.

" Sammy ! "

He turned, and showed a face like his father's under his smooth crest of hair. " Yes, I s'pose I did," he said, reluctantly.

" How long have you known it? " asked his mother.

" 'Bout three months, I guess."

" Why didn't you tell of it? "

" Didn't think 'twould do no good."

" I don't see what father wants another barn for," said the girl, in her sweet, slow voice. She turned again to the window, and stared out at the digging men in the field. Her tender, sweet face was full of a gentle distress. Her forehead was as bald and innocent as a baby's, with the light hair strained back from it in a row of curl-papers. She was quite large, but her soft curves did not look as if they covered muscles.

Her mother looked sternly at the boy. " Is he goin'
to buy more cows? " said she.

The boy did not reply; he was tying his shoes.

" Sammy, I want you to tell me if he's goin' to buy
more cows."

" I s'pose he is."

" How many? "

" Four, I guess."

His mother said nothing more. She went into the
pantry, and there was a clatter of dishes. The boy
got his cap from a nail behind the door, took an old
arithmetic from the shelf, and started for school. He
was lightly built, but clumsy. He went out of the
yard with a curious spring in the hips, that made his
loose home-made jacket tilt up in the rear.

The girl went to the sink, and began to wash the
dishes that were piled up there. Her mother came
promptly out of the pantry, and shoved her aside.
" You wipe 'em," said she; " I'll wash. There's a good
many this mornin'."

The mother plunged her hands vigorously into the
water, the girl wiped the plates slowly and dreamily.
" Mother," said she, " don't you think it's too bad
father's going to build that new barn, much as we need
a decent house to live in? "

Her mother scrubbed a dish fiercely. " You ain't
found out yet we're women-folks, Nanny Penn," said
she. " You ain't seen enough of men-folks yet to. One
of these days you'll find it out, an' then you'll know
that we know only what men-folks think we do,
so far as any use of it goes, an' how we'd ought
to reckon men-folks in with Providence, an' not complain of what they do any more than we do of the
weather."

" I don't care; I don't believe George is anything like

that, anyhow," said Nanny. Her delicate face flushed pink, her lips pouted softly, as if she were going to cry.

" You wait an' see. I guess George Eastman ain't no better than other men. You hadn't ought to judge father, though. He can't help it, 'cause he don't look at things jest the way we do. An' we've been pretty comfortable here, after all. The roof don't leak—ain't never but once—that's one thing. Father's kept it shingled right up."

" I do wish we had a parlor."

" I guess it won't hurt George Eastman any to come to see you in a nice clean kitchen. I guess a good many girls don't have as good a place as this. Nobody's ever heard me complain."

" I ain't complained either, mother."

" Well, I don't think you'd better, a good father an' a good home as you've got. S'pose your father made you go out an' work for your livin'? Lots of girls have to that ain't no stronger an' better able to than you be."

Sarah Penn washed the frying-pan with a conclusive air. She scrubbed the outside of it as faithfully as the inside. She was a masterly keeper of her box of a house. Her one living-room never seemed to have in it any of the dust which the friction of life with inanimate matter produces. She swept, and there seemed to be no dirt to go before the broom; she cleaned, and one could see no difference. She was like an artist so perfect that he has apparently no art. To-day she got out a mixing bowl and a board, and rolled some pies, and there was no more flour upon her than upon her daughter who was doing finer work. Nanny was to be married in the fall, and she was sewing on some white cambric and embroidery. She sewed industriously while her mother cooked, her soft milk-white hands and wrists showed whiter than her delicate work.

"We must have the stove moved out in the shed before long," said Mrs. Penn. "Talk about not havin' things, it's been a real blessin' to be able to put a stove up in that shed in hot weather. Father did one good thing when he fixed that stove-pipe out there."

Sarah Penn's face as she rolled her pies had that expression of meek vigor which might have characterized one of the New Testament saints. She was making mince-pies. Her husband, Adoniram Penn, liked them better than any other kind. She baked twice a week. Adoniram often liked a piece of pie between meals. She hurried this morning. It had been later than usual when she began, and she wanted to have a pie baked for dinner. However deep a resentment she might be forced to hold against her husband, she would never fail in sedulous attention to his wants.

Nobility of character manifests itself at loop-holes when it is not provided with large doors. Sarah Penn's showed itself to-day in flaky dishes of pastry. So she made the pies faithfully, while across the table she could see, when she glanced up from her work, the sight that rankled in her patient and steadfast soul—the digging of the cellar of the new barn in the place where Adoniram forty years ago had promised her their new house should stand.

The pies were done for dinner. Adoniram and Sammy were home a few minutes after twelve o'clock. The dinner was eaten with serious haste. There was never much conversation at the table in the Penn family. Adoniram asked a blessing, and they ate promptly, then rose up and went about their work.

Sammy went back to school, taking soft sly lopes out

of the yard like a rabbit. He wanted a game of marbles before school, and feared his father would give him some chores to do. Adoniram hastened to the door and called after him, but he was out of sight.

"I don't see what you let him go for, mother," said he. "I wanted him to help me unload that wood."

Adoniram went to work out in the yard unloading wood from the wagon. Sarah put away the dinner dishes, while Nanny took down her curl-papers and changed her dress. She was going down to the store to buy some more embroidery and thread.

When Nanny was gone, Mrs. Penn went to the door. "Father!" she called.

"Well, what is it!"

"I want to see you jest a minute, father."

"I can't leave this wood nohow. I've got to git it unloaded an' go for a load of gravel afore two o'clock. Sammy had ought to helped me. You hadn't ought to let him go to school so early."

"I want to see you jest a minute."

"I tell ye I can't, nohow, mother."

"Father, you come here." Sarah Penn stood in the door like a queen; she held her head as if it bore a crown; there was that patience which makes authority royal in her voice. Adoniram went.

Mrs. Penn led the way into the kitchen, and pointed to a chair. "Sit down, father," said she; "I've got somethin' I want to say to you."

He sat down heavily; his face was quite stolid, but he looked at her with restive eyes. "Well, what is it, mother?"

"I want to know what you're buildin' that new barn for, father?"

"I ain't got nothin' to say about it."

"It can't be you think you need another barn?"

"I tell ye I ain't got nothin' to say about it, mother; an' I ain't goin' to say nothin'."

"Be you goin' to buy more cows?"

Adoniram did not reply; he shut his mouth tight.

"I know you be, as well as I want to. Now, father, look here"—Sarah Penn had not sat down; she stood before her husband in the humble fashion of a Scripture woman—"I'm goin' to talk real plain to you; I never have sence I married you, but I'm goin' to now. I ain't never complained, an' I ain't goin' to complain now, but I'm goin' to talk plain. You see this room here, father; you look at it well. You see there ain't no carpet on the floor, an' you see the paper is all dirty, an' droppin' off the walls. We ain't had no new paper on it for ten year, an' then I put it on myself, an' it didn't cost but ninepence a roll. You see this room, father; it's all the one I've had to work in an' eat in an' sit in sence we was married. There ain't another woman in the whole town whose husband ain't got half the means you have but what's got better. It's all the room Nanny's got to have her company in; an' there ain't one of her mates but what's got better, an' their fathers not so able as hers is. It's all the room she'll have to be married in. What would you have thought, father, if we had had our weddin' in a room no better than this? I was married in my mother's parlor, with a carpet on the floor, an' stuffed furniture, an' a mahogany card-table. An' this is all the room my daughter will have to be married in. Look here, father!"

Sarah Penn went across the room as though it were a tragic stage. She flung open a door and disclosed a tiny bedroom, only large enough for a bed and bureau, with a path between. "There, father," said she— "there's all the room I've had to sleep in forty year.

All my children were born there—the two that died, an' the two that's livin'. I was sick with a fever there."

She stepped to another door and opened it. It led into the small, ill-lighted pantry. "Here," said she, "is all the buttery I've got—every place I've got for my dishes, to set away my victuals in, an' to keep my milk-pans in. Father, I've been takin' care of the milk of six cows in this place, an' now you're goin' to build a new barn, an' keep more cows, an' give me more to do in it."

She threw open another door. A narrow crooked flight of stairs wound upward from it. "There, father," said she, "I want you to look at the stairs that go up to them two unfinished chambers that are all the places our son an' daughter have had to sleep in all their lives. There ain't a prettier girl in town nor a more ladylike one than Nanny, an' that's the place she has to sleep in. It ain't so good as your horse's stall; it ain't so warm an' tight."

Sarah Penn went back and stood before her husband. "Now, father," said she, "I want to know if you think you're doin' right an' accordin' to what you profess. Here, when we was married, forty year ago, you promised me faithful that we should have a new house built in that lot over in the field before the year was out. You said you had money enough, an' you wouldn't ask me to live in no such place as this. It is forty year now, an' you've been makin' more money, an' I've been savin' of it for you ever sence, an' you ain't built no house yet. You've built sheds an' cow-houses an' one new barn, an' now you're goin' to build another. Father, I want to know if you think it's right. You're lodgin' your dumb beasts better than you are your own flesh an' blood. I want to know if you think it's right."

" I ain't got nothin' to say."

" You can't say nothin' without ownin' it ain't right, father. An' there's another thing—I ain't complained; I've got along forty year, an' I s'pose I should forty more, if it wa'n't for that—if we don't have another house. Nanny she can't live with us after she's married. She'll have to go somewheres else to live away from us, an' it don't seem as if I could have it so, noways, father. She wa'n't ever strong. She's got considerable color, but there wa'n't never any backbone to her. I've always took the heft of everything off her, an' she ain't fit to keep house an' do everything herself. She'll be all worn out inside of a year. Think of her doin' all the washin' an' ironin' an' bakin' with them soft white hands an' arms, an' sweepin'! I can't have it so, noways, father."

Mrs. Penn's face was burning; her mild eyes gleamed. She had pleaded her little cause like a Webster; she had ranged from severity to pathos; but her opponent employed that obstinate silence which makes eloquence futile with mocking echoes. Adoniram arose clumsily.

" Father, ain't you got nothin' to say?" said Mrs. Penn.

" I've got to go off after that load of gravel. I can't stan' here talkin' all day."

" Father, won't you think it over, an' have a house built there instead of a barn?"

" I ain't got nothin' to say."

Adoniram shuffled out. Mrs. Penn went into her bedroom. When she came out, her eyes were red. She had a roll of unbleached cotton cloth. She spread it out on the kitchen table, and began cutting out some shirts for her husband. The men over in the field had a team to help them this afternoon; she could hear their halloos. She had a scanty pattern for the shirts; she had to plan and piece the sleeves.

Nanny came home with her embroidery, and sat down with her needlework. She had taken down her curl-papers, and there was a soft roll of fair hair like an aureole over her forehead; her face was as delicately fine and clear as porcelain. Suddenly she looked up, and the tender red flamed all over her face and neck. " Mother," said she.

" What say? "

" I've been thinking—I don't see how we're goin' to have any—wedding in this room. I'd be ashamed to have his folks come if we didn't have anybody else."

" Mebbe we can have some new paper before then; I can put it on. I guess you won't have no call to be ashamed of your belongin's."

" We might have the wedding in the new barn," said Nanny, with gentle pettishness. " Why, mother, what makes you look so? "

Mrs. Penn had started, and was staring at her with a curious expression. She turned again to her work, and spread out a pattern carefully on the cloth. " Nothin'," said she.

Presently Adoniram clattered out of the yard in his two-wheeled dump cart, standing as proudly upright as a Roman charioteer. Mrs. Penn opened the door and stood there a minute looking out; the halloos of the men sounded louder.

It seemed to her all through the spring months that she heard nothing but the halloos and the noises of saws and hammers. The new barn grew fast. It was a fine edifice for this little village. Men came on pleas-ant Sundays, in their meeting suits and clean shirt bosoms, and stood around it admiringly. Mrs. Penn did not speak of it, and Adoniram did not mention it to her, although sometimes, upon a return from inspecting it, he bore himself with injured dignity.

"It's a strange thing how your mother feels about the new barn," he said, confidentially, to Sammy one day.

Sammy only grunted after an odd fashion for a boy; he had learned it from his father.

The barn was all completed ready for use by the third week in July. Adoniram had planned to move his stock in on Wednesday; on Tuesday he received a letter which changed his plans. He came in with it early in the morning. "Sammy's been to the post-office," said he, "an' I've got a letter from Hiram." Hiram was Mrs. Penn's brother, who lived in Vermont.

"Well," said Mrs. Penn, "what does he say about the folks?"

"I guess they're all right. He says he thinks if I come up country right off there's a chance to buy jest the kind of a horse I want." He stared reflectively out of the window at the new barn.

Mrs. Penn was making pies. She went on clapping the rolling-pin into the crust, although she was very pale, and her heart beat loudly.

"I dun' know but what I'd better go," said Adoniram. "I hate to go off jest now, right in the midst of hayin', but the ten-acre lot's cut, an' I guess Rufus an' the others can git along without me three or four days. I can't get a horse round here to suit me, nohow, an' I've got to have another for all that wood-haulin' in the fall. I told Hiram to watch out, an' if he got wind of a good horse to let me know. I guess I'd better go."

"I'll get out your clean shirt an' collar," said Mrs. Penn, calmly.

She laid out Adoniram's Sunday suit and his clean clothes on the bed in the little bedroom. She got his shaving-water and razor ready. At last she buttoned on his collar and fastened his black cravat.

Adoniram never wore his collar and cravat except on extra occasions. He held his head high, with a rasped dignity. When he was all ready, with his coat and hat brushed, and a lunch of pie and cheese in a paper bag, he hesitated on the threshold of the door. He looked at his wife, and his manner was defiantly apologetic. "*If* them cows come to-day, Sammy can drive 'em into the new barn," said he; "an' when they bring the hay up, they can pitch it in there."

"Well," replied Mrs. Penn.

Adoniram set his shaven face ahead and started. When he had cleared the door-step, he turned and looked back with a kind of nervous solemnity. "I shall be back by Saturday if nothin' happens," said he.

"Do be careful, father," returned his wife.

She stood in the door with Nanny at her elbow and watched him out of sight. Her eyes had a strange, doubtful expression in them; her peaceful forehead was contracted. She went in, and about her baking again. Nanny sat sewing. Her wedding-day was drawing nearer, and she was getting pale and thin with her steady sewing. Her mother kept glancing at her.

"Have you got that pain in your side this mornin'?" she asked.

"A little."

Mrs. Penn's face, as she worked, changed, her perplexed forehead smoothed, her eyes were steady, her lips firmly set. She formed a maxim for herself, although incoherently with her unlettered thoughts. "Unsolicited opportunities are the guide-posts of the Lord to the new roads of life," she repeated in effect, and she made up her mind to her course of action.

"S'posin' I *had* wrote to Hiram," she muttered once,

when she was in the pantry—" s'posin' I had wrote, an' asked him if he knew of any horse? But I didn't, an' father's goin' wa'n't none of my doin'. It looks like a providence." Her voice rang out quite loud at the last.

" What you talkin' about, mother? " called Nanny.

" Nothin'."

Mrs. Penn hurried her baking; at eleven o'clock it was all done. The load of hay from the west field came slowly down the cart track, and drew up at the new barn. Mrs. Penn ran out. " Stop! " she screamed— " stop! "

The men stopped and looked; Sammy upreared from the top of the load, and stared at his mother.

" Stop! " she cried out again. " Don't you put the hay in that barn; put it in the old one."

" Why, he said to put it in here," returned one of the haymakers, wonderingly. He was a young man, a neighbor's son, whom Adoniram hired by the year to help on the farm.

" Don't you put the hay in the new barn; there's room enough in the old one, ain't there? " said Mrs. Penn.

" Room enough," returned the hired man, in his thick, rustic tones. " Didn't need the new barn, no-how, far as room's concerned. Well, I s'pose he changed his mind." He took hold of the horses' bridles.

Mrs. Penn went back to the house. Soon the kitchen windows were darkened, and a fragrance like warm honey came into the room.

Nanny laid down her work. " I thought father wanted them to put the hay into the new barn? " she said, wonderingly.

" It's all right," replied her mother.

Sammy slid down from the load of hay, and came in to see if dinner was ready.

"I ain't goin' to get a regular dinner to-day, as long as father's gone," said his mother. "I've let the fire go out. You can have some bread an' milk an' pie. I thought we could get along." She set out some bowls of milk, some bread, and a pie on the kitchen table. "You'd better eat your dinner now," said she. "You might jest as well get through with it. I want you to help me afterward."

Nanny and Sammy stared at each other. There was something strange in their mother's manner. Mrs. Penn did not eat anything herself. She went into the pantry, and they heard her moving dishes while they ate. Presently she came out with a pile of plates. She got the clothes-basket out of the shed, and packed them in it. Nanny and Sammy watched. She brought out cups and saucers, and put them in with the plates.

"What you goin' to do, mother?" inquired Nanny, in a timid voice. A sense of something unusual made her tremble, as if it were a ghost. Sammy rolled his eyes over his pie.

"You'll see what I'm goin' to do," replied Mrs. Penn. "If you're through, Nanny, I want you to go upstairs an' pack up your things; an' I want you, Sammy, to help me take down the bed in the bedroom."

"Oh, mother, what for?" gasped Nanny.

"You'll see."

During the next few hours a feat was performed by this simple, pious New England mother which was equal in its way to Wolfe's storming of the Heights of Abraham. It took no more genius and audacity of bravery for Wolfe to cheer his wondering soldiers up those steep precipices, under the sleeping eyes of the enemy, than for Sarah Penn, at the head of her children, to move all their little household goods into the new barn while her husband was away.

Nanny and Sammy followed their mother's instructions without a murmur; indeed, they were overawed. There is a certain uncanny and superhuman quality about all such purely original undertakings as their mother's was to them. Nanny went back and forth with her light loads, and Sammy tugged with sober energy.

At five o'clock in the afternoon the little house in which the Penns had lived for forty years had emptied itself into the new barn.

Every builder builds somewhat for unknown purposes, and is in a measure a prophet. The architect of Adoniram Penn's barn, while he designed it for the comfort of four-footed animals, had planned better than he knew for the comfort of humans. Sarah Penn saw at a glance its possibilities. Those great box-stalls, with quilts hung before them, would make better bedrooms than the one she had occupied for forty years, and there was a tight carriage-room. The harness-room, with its chimney and shelves, would make a kitchen of her dreams. The great middle space would make a parlor, by-and-by, fit for a palace. Upstairs there was as much room as down. With partitions and windows, what a house would there be! Sarah looked at the row of stanchions before the allotted space for cows, and reflected that she would have her front entry there.

At six o'clock the stove was up in the harness-room, the kettle was boiling, and the table set for tea. It looked almost as home-like as the abandoned house across the yard had ever done. The young hired man milked, and Sarah directed him calmly to bring the milk to the new barn. He came gaping, dropping little blots of foam from the brimming pails on the grass. Before the next morning he had spread the story of Adoniram Penn's wife moving into the new barn all over the little village. Men assembled in the store and talked it over, women with shawls over their heads scuttled into each other's houses before their work was done. Any deviation from the ordinary course of life in this quiet town was enough to stop all progress in it. Everybody paused to look at the staid, independent figure on the side track. There was a difference of opinion with regard to her. Some held her to be insane; some, of a lawless and rebellious spirit.

Friday the minister went to see her. It was in the forenoon, and she was at the barn door shelling peas for dinner. She looked up and returned his salutation with dignity, then she went on with her work. She did not invite him in. The saintly expression of her face remained fixed, but there was an angry flush over it.

The minister stood awkwardly before her, and talked. She handled the peas as if they were bullets. At last she looked up, and her eyes showed the spirit that her meek front had covered for a lifetime.

"There ain't no use talkin', Mr. Hersey," said she. "I've thought it all over an' over, an' I believe I'm doin' what's right. I've made it the subject of prayer, an' it's betwixt me an' the Lord an' Adoniram. There ain't no call for nobody else to worry about it."

"Well, of course, if you have brought it to the Lord in prayer, and feel satisfied that you are doing right, Mrs. Penn," said the minister, helplessly. His thin gray-bearded face was pathetic. He was a sickly man; his youthful confidence had cooled; he had to scourge himself up to some of his pastoral duties as relentlessly as a Catholic ascetic, and then he was prostrated by the smart.

"I think it's right jest as much as I think it was right for our forefathers to come over from the old country 'cause they didn't have what belonged to 'em," said Mrs. Penn. She arose. The barn threshold might have been Plymouth Rock from her bearing. " I don't doubt you mean well, Mr. Hersey," said she, " but there are things people hadn't ought to interfere with. I've been a member of the church for over forty year. I've got my own mind an' my own feet, an' I'm goin' to think my own thoughts an' go my own ways, an' nobody but the Lord is goin' to dictate to me unless I've a mind to have him. Won't you come in an' set down? How is Mis' Hersey? "

" She is well, I thank you," replied the minister. He added some more perplexed apologetic remarks; then he retreated.

He could expound the intricacies of every character study in the Scriptures, he was competent to grasp the Pilgrim Fathers and all historical innovators, but Sarah Penn was beyond him. He could deal with primal cases, but parallel ones worsted him. But, after all, although it was aside from his province, he wondered more how Adoniram Penn would deal with his wife than how the Lord would. Everybody shared the wonder. When Adoniram's four new cows arrived, Sarah ordered three to be put in the old barn, the other in the house shed where the cooking-stove had stood. That added to the excitement. It was whispered that all four cows were domiciled in the house.

Towards sunset on Saturday, when Adoniram was expected home, there was a knot of men in the road near the new barn. The hired man had milked, but he still hung around the premises. Sarah Penn had supper all ready. There were brown-bread and baked beans and a custard pie; it was the supper that Adoniram loved on a Saturday night. She had on a clean calico, and she bore herself imperturbably. Nanny and Sammy

kept close at her heels. Their eyes were large, and
Nanny was full of nervous tremors. Still there was to
them more pleasant excitement than anything else. An
inborn confidence in their mother over their father as-
serted itself.

Sammy looked out of the harness-room window.
"There he is," he announced, in an awed whisper. He
and Nanny peeped around the casing. Mrs. Penn kept
on about her work. The children watched Adoniram
leave the new horse standing in the drive while he
went to the house door. It was fastened. Then he
went around to the shed. That door was seldom locked,
even when the family was away. The thought how
her father would be confronted by the cow flashed upon
Nanny. There was a hysterical sob in her throat.
Adoniram emerged from the shed and stood looking
about in a dazed fashion. His lips moved; he was saying something, but they could not hear what it was.
The hired man was peeping around a corner of the
old barn, but nobody saw him.

Adoniram took the new horse by the bridle and led
him across the yard to the new barn. Nanny and
Sammy slunk close to their mother. The barn doors
rolled back, and there stood Adoniram, with the long
mild face of the great Canadian farm horse looking
over his shoulder.

Nanny kept behind her mother, but Sammy stepped
suddenly forward, and stood in front of her.

Adoniram stared at the group. "What on airth you
all down here for?" said he. "What's the matter over
to the house?"

"We've come here to live, father," said Sammy.
His shrill voice quavered out bravely.

"What"—Adoniram sniffed—"what is it smells like
cookin'?" said he. He stepped forward and looked

in the open door of the harness-room. Then he turned
to his wife. His old bristling face was pale and frightened. " What on airth does this mean, mother? " he
gasped.

" You come in here, father," said Sarah. She led the
way into the harness-room and shut the door. " Now,
father," said she, " you needn't be scared. I ain't
crazy. There ain't nothin' to be upset over. But we've
come here to live, an' we're goin' to live here. We've
got jest as good a right here as new horses an' cows.
The house wa'n't fit for us to live in any longer, an'
I made up my mind I wa'n't goin' to stay there. I've
done my duty by you forty year, an' I'm goin' to do
it now; but I'm goin' to live here. You've got to put
in some windows and partitions; an' you'll have to buy
some furniture."

" Why, mother! " the old man gasped.

" You'd better take your coat off an' get washed—
there's the wash-basin—an' then we'll have supper."

" Why, mother! "

Sammy went past the window, leading the new horse
to the old barn. The old man saw him, and shook his
head speechlessly. He tried to take off his coat, but his
arms seemed to lack the power. His wife helped him.
She poured some water into the tin basin, and put in a
piece of soap. She got the comb and brush, and
smoothed his thin gray hair after he had washed.
Then she put the beans, hot bread, and tea on the table.
Sammy came in, and the family drew up. Adoniram
sat looking dazedly at his plate, and they waited.

" Ain't you goin' to ask a blessin', father? " said
Sarah.

And the old man bent his head and mumbled.

All through the meal he stopped eating at intervals,

and stared furtively at his wife; but he ate well. The home food tasted good to him, and his old frame was too sturdily healthy to be affected by his mind. But after supper he went out, and sat down on the step of the smaller door at the right of the barn, through which he had meant his Jerseys to pass in stately file, but which Sarah designed for her front house door, and he leaned his head on his hands.

After the supper dishes were cleared away and the milk-pans washed, Sarah went out to him. The twilight was deepening. There was a clear green glow in the sky. Before them stretched the smooth level of field; in the distance was a cluster of hay-stacks like the huts of a village; the air was very cool and calm and sweet. The landscape might have been an ideal one of peace.

Sarah bent over and touched her husband on one of his thin, sinewy shoulders. "Father!"

The old man's shoulders heaved: he was weeping.

"Why, don't do so, father," said Sarah.

"I'll—put up the—partitions, an'—everything you—want, mother."

Sarah put her apron up to her face; she was overcome by her own triumph.

Adoniram was like a fortress whose walls had no active resistance, and went down the instant the right besieging tools were used. "Why, mother," he said, hoarsely, "I hadn't no idee you was so set on't as all this comes to."

MARSE CHAN

A TALE OF OLD VIRGINIA

THOMAS NELSON PAGE

Here plot, character, and setting are happily blended. The story is sufficient to move smoothly and interestingly; the characters, both black and white, reveal the Southerner at his best; and the setting not only furnishes an appropriate background for plot and characters, but is significant of the leisure, the isolation, and the pride of the people.

MARSE CHAN *

One afternoon, in the autumn of 1872, I was riding
leisurely down the sandy road that winds along the
top of the water-shed between two of the smaller rivers
of eastern Virginia. The road I was travelling, following " the ridge " for miles, had just struck me as most
significant of the character of the race whose only
avenue of communication with the outside world it had
formerly been. Their once splendid mansions, now fast
falling to decay, appeared to view from time to time, set
back far from the road, in proud seclusion, among groves
of oak and hickory, now scarlet and gold with the early
frost. Distance was nothing to this people; time was
of no consequence to them. They desired but a level
path in life, and that they had, though the way was
longer, and the outer world strode by them as they
dreamed.

I was aroused from my reflections by hearing some
one ahead of me calling, " Heah!—heah—whoo-oop,
heah! "

Turning the curve in the road, I saw just before
me a negro standing, with a hoe and a watering-pot
in his hand. He had evidently just gotten over the
" worm-fence " into the road, out of the path which
led zigzag across the " old field " and was lost to sight
in the dense growth of sassafras. When I rode up, he
was looking anxiously back down this path for his dog.
So engrossed was he that he did not even hear my horse,

* From " In Ole Virginia," by Thomas Nelson Page. Copyright,
1887, by Charles Scribner's Sons.

and I reined in to wait until he should turn around and satisfy my curiosity as to the handsome old place half a mile off from the road.

The numerous out-buildings and the large barns and stables told that it had once been the seat of wealth, and the wild waste of sassafras that covered the broad fields gave it an air of desolation that greatly excited my interest. Entirely oblivious of my proximity, the negro went on calling "Whoo-oop, heah!" until along the path, walking very slowly and with great dignity, appeared a noble-looking old orange and white setter, gray with age, and corpulent with excessive feeding. As soon as he came in sight, his master began:

"Yes, dat you! You gittin' deaf as well as bline, I s'pose! Kyarnt heah me callin', I reckon? Whyn't yo' come on, dawg?"

The setter sauntered slowly up to the fence and stopped, without even deigning a look at the speaker, who immediately proceeded to take the rails down, talking meanwhile:

"Now, I got to pull down de gap, I s'pose! Yo' so sp'ilt yo' kyahn hardly walk. Jes' ez able to git over it as I is! Jes' like white folks—think 'cuz you's white and I'se black, I got to wait on yo' all de time. Ne'm mine, I ain' gwi' do it!"

The fence having been pulled down sufficiently low to suit his dogship, he marched sedately through, and, with a hardly perceptible lateral movement of his tail, walked on down the road. Putting up the rails carefully, the negro turned and saw me.

"Sarvent, marster," he said, taking his hat off. Then, as if apologetically for having permitted a stranger to witness what was merely a family affair, he added: "He know I don' mean nothin' by what I sez. He's Marse Chan's dawg, an' he's so ole he kyahn git

long no pearter. He know I'se jes' prodjickin' wid
'im.''

"Who is Marse Chan?" I asked; "and whose place
is that over there, and the one a mile or two back—
the place with the big gate and the carved stone
pillars?''

"Marse Chan," said the darky, "he's Marse Channin'—my young marster; an' dem places—dis one's
Weall's, an' de one back dyar wid de rock gate-pos's
is ole Cun'l Chahmb'lin's. Dey don' nobody live dyar
now, 'cep' niggers. Arfter de war some one or nurr
bought our place, but his name done kind o' slipped
me. I nuver hearn on 'im befo'; I think dey's half-
strainers. I don' ax none on 'em no odds. I lives down
de road heah, a little piece, an' I jes' steps down of a
evenin' and looks arfter de graves.''

"Well, where is Marse Chan?" I asked.

"Hi! don' you know? Marse Chan, he went in de
army. I was wid 'im. Yo' know he warn' gwine an'
lef' Sam.''

"Will you tell me all about it?" I said, dismounting.

Instantly, and as if by instinct, the darky stepped
forward and took my bridle. I demurred a little; but
with a bow that would have honored old Sir Roger, he
shortened the reins, and taking my horse from me, led
him along.

"Now tell me about Marse Chan," I said.

"Lawd, marster, hit's so long ago, I'd a'most forgit
all about it, ef I hedn' been wid him ever sence he wuz
born. Ez 'tis, I remembers it jes' like 'twuz yistiddy.
Yo' know Marse Chan an' me—we wuz boys togerr. I
wuz older'n he wuz, jes' de same ez he wuz whiter'n me.
I wuz born plantin' corn time, de spring arfter big Jim
an' de six steers got washed away at de upper ford
right down dyar b'low de quarters ez he wuz a-bringin'

de Chris'mas things home; an' Marse Chan, he warn'
born tell mos' to de harves' arfter my sister Nancy married Cun'l Chahmb'lin's Torm, 'bout eight years arfter-
woods.

"Well, when Marse Chan wuz born, dey wuz de
grettes' doin's at home you ever did see. De folks all
hed holiday, jes' like in de Chris'mas. Ole marster
(we didn' call 'im *ole* marster tell arfter Marster Chan
wuz born—befo' dat he wuz jes' de marster, so)—well,
cle marster, his face fyar shine wid pleasure, an' all
de folks wuz mighty glad, too, 'cause dey all loved ole
marster, and aldo' dey did step aroun' right peart when
ole marster was lookin' at 'em, dyar warn' nyar han'
on de place but what, ef he wanted anythin', would
walk up to de back poach, an' say he warn' to see de
marster. An' ev'ybody wuz talkin' 'bout de young
marster, an' de maids an' de wimmens 'bout de kitchen
wuz sayin' how 'twuz de purties' chile dey ever see;
an' at dinner-time de mens (all on 'em hed holiday)
come roun' de poach an' ax how de missis an' de young
marster wuz, an' ole marster come out on de poach an'
smile wus'n a 'possum, an' sez, 'Thankee! Bofe doin'
fust rate, boys'; an' den he stepped back in de house,
sort o' laughin' to hisse'f, an' in a minute he come out
ag'in wid de baby in he arms, all wrapped up in flan-
nens an' things, an' sez, 'Heah he is, boys.' All de
folks den, dey went up on de poach to look at 'im, drap-
pin' dey hats on de steps, an' scrapin' dey feets ez dey
went up. An' pres'n'y old marster, lookin' down at we
all chil'en all packed togerr down dyah like a parecel
'y' sheep-burrs, cotch sight *o' me* (he knowed my name,
'cause I use' to hole he hoss fur 'im sometimes; but he
didn't know all de chile'n by name, dey wuz so many
on 'em), an' he sez, 'Come up heah!' So up I goes
tippin', skeered like, an' old marster sez, 'Ain' you

Mymie's son?' 'Yass, seh,' sez I. 'Well,' sez he, 'I'm gwine to give you to yo' young Marse Channin' to be his body-servant,' an' he put de baby right in my arms (it's de truth I'm tellin' yo'!), an' yo' jes' ought to a-heard de folks sayin', 'Lawd! marster, dat boy'll drap dat chile!' 'Naw, he won't,' sez marster; 'I kin trust 'im.' And den he sez: 'Now, Sam, from dis time you belong to yo' young Marse Channin'; I wan' you to tek keer on 'im ez long ez he lives. You are to be his boy from dis time. An' now,' he sez, 'carry 'im in de house.' An' he walks arfter me an' opens de do's fur me, an' I kyars 'im in my arms, an' lays 'im down on de bed. An' from dat time I was tooken in de house to be Marse Channin's body-servant.

"Well, you nuver see a chile grow so. Pres'n'y he growed up right big, an' ole marster sez he must have some edication. So he sont 'im to school to ole Miss Lawry down dyar, dis side o' Cun'l Chahmb'lin's, an' I use' to go 'long wid 'im an' tote he books an' we all's snacks; an' when he larnt to read an' spell right good, an' got 'bout so-o big, old Miss Lawry she died, an' old marster said he mus' have a man to teach 'im an' trounce 'im. So we all went to Mr. Hall, whar kep' de school-house beyant de creek, an' dyar we went ev'y day, 'cep Sat'd'ys of co'se, an' sich days ez Marse Chan din' warn' go, an' ole missis begged 'im off.

"Hit wuz down dyar Marse Chan fust took notice o' Miss Anne. Mr. Hall, he taught gals ez well ez boys, an' Cun'l Chahmb'lin he sont his daughter (dat's Miss Anne I'm talkin' about). She wuz a leetle bit o' gal when she fust come. Yo' see, her ma wuz dead, an' old Miss Lucy Chahmb'lin, she lived wid her brurr an' kep' house for 'im; an' he wuz so busy wid politics, he didn' have much time to spyar, so he sont Miss Anne to Mr. Hall's by a 'ooman wid a note. When she come

dat day in de school-house, an' all de chil'en looked at
her so hard, she tu'n right red, an' tried to pull her
long curls over her eyes, an' den put bofe de backs of
her little han's in her two eyes, an' begin to cry to herse'f. Marse Chan he was settin' on de een' o' de bench
nigh de do', an' he jes' reached out an' put he arm
'roun' her an' drawed her up to 'im. An' he kep' whisperin' to her, an' callin' her name, an' coddlin' her; an'
pres'n'y she took her han's down an' begin to laugh.

"Well, dey 'peared to tek' a gre't fancy to each
urr from dat time. Miss Anne she warn' nuthin' but a
baby hardly, an' Marse Chan he wuz a good big boy
'bout mos' thirteen years ole, I reckon. Hows'ever, dey
sut'n'y wuz sot on each urr an' (yo' heah me!) ole
marster an' Cun'l Chahmb'lin dey 'peared to like it
'bout well ez de chil'en. Yo' see, Cun'l Chahmb'lin's
place j'ined ourn, an' it looked jes' ez natural fur
dem two chil'en to marry an' mek it one plantation, ez
it did fur de creek to run down de bottom from our
place into Cun'l Chahmb'lin's. I don' rightly think de
chil'en thought 'bout gittin' *married,* not den, no mo'n
I thought 'bout marryin' Judy when she wuz a little
gal at Cun'l Chahmb'lin's, runnin' 'bout de house,
huntin' fur Miss Lucy's spectacles; but dey wuz good
frien's from de start. Marse Chan he use' to kyar Miss
Anne's books fur her ev'y day, an' ef de road wuz
muddy or she wuz tired, he use' to tote her; an' 'twarn'
hardly a day passed dat he didn' kyar her some'n' to
school—apples or hick'y nuts, or some'n. He wouldn't
let none o' de chil'en tease her, nurr. Heh! One day,
one o' de boys poked he finger at Miss Anne, and arfter
school Marse Chan he axed 'im 'roun' 'hine de school-
house out o' sight, an' ef he didn't whop 'im!

"Marse Chan, he wuz de peartes' scholar ole Mr.
Hall hed, an' Mr. Hall he wuz mighty proud o' 'im. I

don' think he use' to beat 'im ez much ez he did de urrs, aldo' he wuz de head in all debilment dat went on, jes' ez he wuz in sayin' he lessons.

"Heh! one day in summer, jes' fo' de school broke up, dyah come up a storm right sudden, an' riz de creek (dat one yo' cross' back yonder), an' Marse Chan he toted Miss Anne home on he back. He ve'y off'n did dat when de parf wuz muddy. But dis day when dey come to de creek, it had done washed all de logs 'way. 'Twuz still mighty high, so Marse Chan he put Miss Anne down, an' he took a pole an' waded right in. Hit took 'im long up to de shoulders. Den he waded back, an' took Miss Anne up on his head an' kyared her right over. At fust she wuz skeered; but he tol' her he could swim an' wouldn' let her git hu't, an' den she let 'im kyar her 'cross, she hol'in' his han's. I warn' 'long dat day, but he sut'n'y did dat thing.

"Ole marster he wuz so pleased 'bout it, he giv' Marse Chan a pony; an' Marse Chan rode 'im to school de day arfter he come, so proud, an' sayin' how he wuz gwine to let Anne ride behine 'im; an' when he come home dat evenin' he wuz walkin'. 'Hi! where's yo' pony?' said ole marster. 'I give 'im to Anne,' says Marse Chan. 'She liked 'im, an'—I kin walk.' 'Yes,' sez ole marster, laughin', 'I s'pose you's already done giv' her yo'se'f, an' nex' thing I know you'll be givin' her this plantation and all my niggers.'

"Well, about a fortnight or sich a matter arfter dat, Cun'l Chahmb'lin sont over an' invited all o' we all over to dinner, an' Marse Chan wuz 'spressly named in de note whar Ned brought; an' arfter dinner he made ole Phil, whar wuz his ker'ige-driver, bring 'roun' Marse Chan's pony wid a little side-saddle on 'im, an' a beautiful little hoss wid a bran'-new saddle an' bridle on 'im; an' he gits up an' meks Marse Chan a gre't speech,

an' presents 'im de little hoss; an' den he calls Miss
Anne, an' she comes out on de poach in a little ridin'
frock, an' dey puts her on her pony, an' Marse Chan
mounts his hoss, an' dey goes to ride, while de grown
folks is a-laughin' an' chattin' an' smokin' dey cigars.

"Dem wuz good ole times, marster—de bes' Sam
ever see! Dey wuz, in fac'! Niggers didn' hed nothin'
't all to do—jes' hed to 'ten' to de feedin' an' cleanin'
de hosses, an' doin' what de marster tell 'em to do;
an' when dey wuz sick, dey had things sont 'em out de
house, an' de same doctor come to see 'em whar 'ten' to
de white folks when dey wuz po'ly. Dyar warn' no
trouble nor nothin'.

"Well, things tuk a change arfter dat. Marse Chan
he went to de bo'din' school, whar he use' to write to me
constant. Ole missis use' to read me de letters, an'
den I'd git Miss Anne to read 'em ag'in to me when I'd
see her. He use' to write to her too, an' she use' to write
to him too. Den Miss Anne she wuz sont off to school
too. An' in de summer time dey'd bofe come home, an'
yo' hardly knowed whether Marse Chan lived at home
or over at Cun'l Chahmb'lin's. He wuz over dyah constant. 'Twuz always ridin' or fishin' down dyah in de
river; or sometimes he' go over dyah, an' 'im an' she'd
go out an' set in de yard onder de trees; she settin' up
mekin' out she wuz knittin' some sort o' bright-
cullored some'n', wid de grarss growin' all up 'g'inst
her, an' her hat th'owed back on her neck, an' he
readin' to her out books; an' sometimes dey'd bofe read
out de same book, fust one an' den todder. I use' to
see 'em! Dat wuz when dey wuz growin' up like.

"Den ole marster he run for Congress, an' ole Cun'l
Chahmb'lin he wuz put up to run 'g'inst ole marster
by de Dimicrats; but ole marster he beat 'im. Yo' know
he wuz gwine do dat! Co'se he wuz! Dat made ole

Cun'l Chahmb'lin mighty mad, and dey stopt visitin' each urr reg'lar, like dey had been doin' all 'long. Den Cun'l Chahmb'lin he sort o' got in debt, an' sell some o' he niggers, an' dat's de way de fuss begun. Dat's whar de lawsuit cum from. Ole marster he didn' like nobody to sell niggers, an' knowin' dat Cun'l Chahmb'lin wuz sellin' o' his, he writ an' offered to buy his M'ria an' all her chil'en, 'cause she hed married our Zeek'yel. An' don' yo' think, Cun'l Chahmb'lin axed ole marster mo' 'n th'ee niggers wuz wuth fur M'ria! Befo' old marster bought her, dough, de sheriff cum an' levelled on M'ria an' a whole parecel o' urr niggers. Ole marster he went to de sale, an' bid for 'em; but Cun'l Chahmb'lin he got some one to bid 'g'inst ole marster. Dey wuz knocked out to ole marster dough, an' den dey hed a big lawsuit, an' ole marster wuz agwine to co't, off an' on, fur some years, till at lars' de co't decided dat M'ria belonged to ole marster. Ole Cun'l Chahmb'lin den wuz so mad he sued ole marster for a little strip o' lan' down dyah on de line fence, whar he said belonged to 'im. Ev'ybody knowed hit belonged to ole marster. Ef yo' go down dyah now, I kin show it to yo', inside de line fence, whar it hed done bin ever sence long befo' Cun'l Chahmb'lin wuz born. But Cun'l Chahmb'lin wuz a mons'us perseverin' man, an' ole marster he wouldn' let nobody run over 'im. No, dat he wouldn'! So dey wuz agwine down to co't about dat, fur I don' know how long, till ole marster beat 'im.

"All dis time, yo' know, Marse Chan wuz agoin' back'ads an' for'ads to college, an' wuz growed up a ve'y fine young man. He wuz a ve'y likely gent'man! Miss Anne she hed done mos' growed up too—wuz puttin' her hyar up like old missis use' to put hers up, an' 'twuz jes' ez bright ez de sorrel's mane when de sun

cotch on it, an' her eyes wuz gre't big dark eyes, like
her pa's, on'y bigger an' not so fierce, an' 'twarn' none
o' de young ladies ez purty ez she wuz. She an' Marse
Chan still set a heap o' sto' by one 'nurr, but I don'
think dey wuz easy wid each urr ez when he used to
tote her home from school on his back. Marse Chan he
use' to love de ve'y groun' she walked on, dough, in my
'pinion. Heh! His face 'twould light up whenever
she come into chu'ch, or anywhere, jes' like de sun hed
come th'oo a chink on it suddenly.

" Den' ole marster lost he eyes. D' yo' ever heah
'bout dat? Heish! Didn' yo'? Well, one night de
big barn cotch fire. De stables, yo' know, wuz under
de big barn, an' all de hosses wuz in dyah. Hit 'peared
to me like 'twarn' no time befo' all de folks an' de
neighbors dey come, an' dey wuz a-totin' water, an'
a-tryin' to save de po' critters, and dey got a heap on
'em out; but de ker'ige-hosses dey wouldn' come out,
an' dey wuz a-runnin' back'ads an' for'ads inside de
stalls, a-nikerin' an' a-screamin', like dey knowed dey
time hed come. Yo' could heah 'em so pitiful, an'
pres'n'y old marster said to Ham Fisher (he wuz de
ker'ige-driver), ' Go in dyah an' try to save 'em; don'
let 'em bu'n to death.' An' Ham he went right in. An'
jest arfter he got in, de shed whar it hed fus' cotch
fell in, an' de sparks shot 'way up in de air; an' Ham
didn' come back, an' de fire begun to lick out under de
eaves over whar de ker'ige-hosses' stalls wuz, an' all
of a sudden ole marster tu'ned an' kissed ole missis, who
wuz standin' nigh him, wid her face jes' ez white ez a
sperit's, an', befo' anybody knowed what he wuz gwine
do, jumped right in de do', an' de smoke come po'in'
out behine 'im. Well, seh, I nuver 'spects to heah tell
Judgment sich a soun' ez de folks set up! Ole missis
she jes' drapt down on her knees in de mud an' prayed

out loud. Hit 'peared like her pra'r wuz heard; for in
a minit, right out de same do', kyarin' Ham Fisher in
his arms, come ole marster, wid his clo's all blazin'.
Dey flung water on 'im, an' put 'im out; an', ef you
b'lieve me, yo' wouldn't a-knowed 'twuz ole marster.
Yo' see, he had find Ham Fisher done fall down in de
smoke right by the ker'ige-hoss' stalls, whar he sont
him, an' he hed to tote 'im back in his arms th'oo de fire
what hed done cotch de front part o' de stable, and
to keep de flame from gittin' down Ham Fisher's th'oat
he hed tuk off his own hat and mashed it all over Ham
Fisher's face, an' he hed kep' Ham Fisher from bein'
so much bu'nt; but *he* wuz bu'nt dreadful! His beard
an' hyar wuz all nyawed off, an' his face an' han's an'
neck wuz scorified terrible. Well, he jes' laid Ham
Fisher down, an' then he kind o' staggered for'ad, an'
ole missis ketch' 'im in her arms. Ham Fisher, he
warn' bu'nt so bad, an' he got out in a month to two;
an' arfter a long time, ole marster he got well, too; but
he wuz always stone blind arfter that. He nuver could
see none from dat night.

   " Marse Chan he comed home from college toreckly,
an' he sut'n'y did nuss ole marster faithful—jes' like a
'ooman. Den he took charge of de plantation arfter
dat; an' I use' to wait on 'im jes' like when we wuz
boys togedder; an' sometimes we'd slip off an' have a
fox-hunt, an' he'd be jes' like he wuz in ole times, befo'
ole marster got bline, an' Miss Anne Chahmb'lin stopt
comin' over to our house, an' settin' onder de trees,
readin' out de same book.

   " He sut'n'y wuz good to me. Nothin' nuver made
no diffunce 'bout dat. He nuver hit me a lick in his
life—an' nuver let nobody else do it, nurr.

   " I 'members one day, when he wuz a leetle bit o'
boy, ole marster hed done tole we all chil'en not to slide

on de straw-stacks; an' one day me an' Marse Chan
thought ole marster hed done gone 'way from home. We
watched him git on he hoss an' ride up de road out o'
sight, an' we wuz out in de field a-slidin' an' a-slidin',
when up comes ole marster. We started to run; but he
hed done see us, an' he called us to come back; an'
sich a whuppin' ez he did gi' us!

"Fust he took Marse Chan, an' den he teched me
up. He nuver hu't me, but in co'se I wuz a-hollerin'
ez hard ez I could stave it, 'cause I knowed dat wuz
gwine mek him stop. Marse Chan he hed'n open he
mouf long ez ole marster wuz tunin' 'im; but soon ez
he commence warmin' me an' I begin to holler, Marse
Chan he bu'st out cryin', an' stept right in befo' ole
marster an' ketchin' de whup, sed:

"'Stop, seh! Yo' sha'n't whup 'im; he b'longs to
me, an' ef you hit 'im another lick I'll set 'im free!'

"I wish yo' hed see old marster. Marse Chan he
warn' mo'n eight years ole, an' dyah dey wuz—old
marster stan'in' wid he whup raised up, an' Marse Chan
red an' cryin', hol'in' on to it, an' sayin' I b'longst
to 'im.

"Ole marster, he raise' de whup, an' den he drapt
it, an' broke out in a smile over he face, an' he chuck'
Marse Chan onder de chin, an' tu'n right 'roun' an'
went away, laughin' to hisse'f, an' I heah 'im tellin'
ole missis dat evenin', an' laughin' 'bout it.

"'Twan' so mighty long arfter dat when dey fust
got to talkin' 'bout de war. Dey wuz a-dictatin'
back'ads an' for'ads 'bout it fur two or th'ee years 'fo'
it come sho' nuff, you know. Ole marster, he was a
Whig, an' of co'se Marse Chan he tuk after he pa.
Cun'l Chahmb'lin, he wuz a Dimicrat. He wuz in favor
of de war, an' ole marster and Marse Chan dey wuz
agin' it. Dey wuz a-talkin' 'bout it all de time, an'

purty soon Cun'l Chahmb'lin he went about ev'ywhar speakin' an' noratin' 'bout Firginia ought to secede; an' Marse Chan he wuz picked up to talk agin' 'im. Dat wuz de way dey come to fight de duil. I sut'n'y wuz skeered fur Marse Chan dat mawnin', an' he was jes' ez cool! Yo' see, it happen so: Marse Chan he wuz a-speakin' down at de Deep Creek Tavern, an' he kind o' got de bes' of ole Cun'l Chahmb'lin. All de white folks laughed an' hoorawed, an' ole Cun'l Chahmb'lin— my Lawd! I t'ought he'd 'a' bu'st, he was so mad. Well, when it come to his time to speak, he jes' light into Marse Chan. He call 'im a traitor, an' a ab'li-tionis', an' I don' know what all. Marse Chan, he jes' kep' cool till de ole Cun'l light into he pa. Ez soon ez he name ole marster, I seen Marse Chan sort o' lif' up he head. D' yo' ever see a hoss rar he head up right sudden at night when he see somethin' comin' to'ds 'im from de side an' he don' know what 'tis? Ole Cun'l Chahmb'lin he went right on. He said ole marster hed taught Marse Chan; dat ole marster wuz a wuss ab'li-tionis' dan he son. I looked at Marse Chan, an' sez to myse'f: 'Fo' Gord! old Cun'l Chahmb'lin better min', an' I hedn' got de wuds out, when ole Cun'l Chahmb'lin 'cuse' old marster o' cheatin' 'im out o' he niggers, an' stealing piece o' he lan'—dat's de lan' I tole you 'bout. Well, seh, nex' thing I knowed, I heahed Marse Chan—hit all happen right 'long togerr, like lightnin' and thunder when they hit right at you— I heah 'im say:

" ' Cun'l Chahmb'lin, what you say is false, an' yo' know it to be so. You have wilfully slandered one of de pures' an' nobles' men Gord ever made, an' nothin' but yo' gray hyars protects you.'

" Well, ole Cun'l Chahmb'lin, he ra'd an' he pitch'd. He said he wan' too ole, an' he'd show 'im so.

" ' Ve'y well,' says Marse Chan.

" De meetin' broke up den. I wuz hol'in' de hosses out dyar in de road by dee een' o' de poach, an' I see Marse Chan talkin' an' talkin' to Mr. Gordon an' anudder gent'man, and den he come out an' got on de sorrel an' galloped off. Soon ez he got out o' sight he pulled up, an' we walked along tell we come to de road whar leads off to'ds Mr. Barbour's. He wuz de big lawyer o' de country. Dar he tu'ned off. All dis time he hedn' sed a wud, 'cep' to kind o' mumble to hisse'f now and den. When we got to Mr. Barbour's, he got down an' went in. Dat wuz in de late winter; de folks wuz jes' beginnin' to plough fur corn. He stayed dyar 'bout two hours, an' when he come out Mr. Barbour come out to de gate wid 'im an' shake han's arfter he got up in de saddle. Den we all rode off. 'Twuz late den—good dark; an' we rid ez hard ez we could, tell we come to de ole school-house at ole Cun'l Chahmb'lin's gate. When we got dar, Marse Chan got down an' walked right slow 'roun' de house. After lookin' 'roun' a little while an' tryin' de do' to see ef it wuz shet, he walked down de road tell he got to de creek. He stop' dyar a little while an' picked up two or three little rocks an' frowed 'em in, an' pres'n'y he got up an' we come on home. Ez he got down, he tu'ned to me an', rubbin' de sorrel's nose, said: ' Have 'em well fed, Sam; I'll want 'em early in de mawnin'.'

" Dat night at supper he laugh an' talk, an' he set at de table a long time. Arfter ole marster went to bed, he went in de charmber an' set on de bed by 'im talkin' to 'im an' tellin' 'im 'bout de meetin' an' ev'y-thing; but he nuver mention ole Cun'l Chahmb'lin's name. When he got up to come out to de office in de yard, whar he slept, he stooped down an' kissed 'im jes' like he wuz a baby layin' dyar in de bed, an' he'd hardly let ole missis go at all. I knowed some'n wuz up, an' nex' mawnin' I called 'im early befo' light, like he tole me, an' he dressed an' come out pres'n'y jes' like he wuz goin' to church. I had de hosses ready, an' we went out de back way to'ds de river. Ez we rode along, he said:

"'Sam, you an' I wuz boys togedder, wa'n't we?'

"'Yes,' sez I, 'Marse Chan, dat we wuz.'

"'You have been ve'y faithful to me,' sez he, 'an' I have seen to it that you are well provided fur. You want to marry Judy, I know, an' you'll be able to buy her ef you want to.'

"Den he tole me he wuz goin' to fight a duil, an' in case he should git shot, he had set me free an' giv' me nuff to tek keer o' me an' my wife ez long ez we lived. He said he'd like me to stay an' tek keer o' ole marster an' ole missis ez long ez dey lived, an' he said it wouldn' be very long, he reckoned. Dat wuz de on'y time he voice broke—when he said dat; an' I couldn' speak a wud, my th'oat choked me so.

"When we come to de river, we tu'ned right up de bank, an' arfter ridin' 'bout a mile or sich a matter, we stopped whar dey wuz a little clearin' wid elder bushes on one side an' two big gum-trees on de urr, an' de sky wuz all red, an' de water down to'ds whar the sun wuz comin' wuz jes' like de sky.

"Pres'n'y Mr. Gordon he come, wid a 'hogany box 'bout so big 'fore 'im, an' he got down, an' Marse Chan tole me to tek all de hosses an' go 'roun' behine de bushes whar I tell you 'bout—off to one side; an' 'fore I got 'roun' dar, ole Cun'l Chahmb'lin an' Mr. Hennin an' Dr. Call come ridin' from t'urr way, to'ds ole Cun'l Chahmb'lin's. When dey hed tied dey hosses, de urr gent'mens went up to whar Mr. Gordon wuz, an' arfter some chattin' Mr. Hennin step' off 'bout fur ez 'cross dis road, or mebbe it mout be a little furder;

an' den I seed 'em th'oo de bushes loadin' de pistils, an' talk a little while; an' den Marse Chan an' ole Cun'l Chahmb'lin walked up wid de pistils in dey han's, an' Marse Chan he stood wid his face right to'ds de sun. I seen it shine on him jes' ez it come up over de low groun's, an' he look like he did sometimes when he come out of church. I wuz so skeered I couldn' say nothin'. Ole Cun'l Chahmb'lin could shoot fust rate, an' Marse Chan he never missed.

"Den I heared Mr. Gordon say, 'Gent'mens, is yo' ready?' and bofe of 'em sez, 'Ready,' jes' so.

"An' he sez, 'Fire, one, two'—an' ez he said 'one,' old Cun'l Chahmb'lin raised he pistil an' shot right at Marse Chan. De ball went th'oo his hat. I seen he hat sort o' settle on he head ez de bullit hit it, an' *he* jes' tilted his pistil up in de a'r an' shot—*bang;* an' ez de pistil went *bang,* he sez to Cun'l Chahmb'lin, 'I mek you a present to yo' fam'ly, seh!'

"Well, dey had some talkin' arfter dat. I didn't git rightly what it wuz; but it 'peared like Cun'l Chahmb'lin he warn't satisfied, an' wanted to have anurr shot. De seconds dey wuz talkin', an' pres'n'y dey put de pistils up, an' Marse Chan an' Mr. Gordon shook han's wid Mr. Hennin an' Dr. Call, an' come an' got on dey hosses. An' Cun'l Chahmb'lin he got on his hoss an' rode away wid de urr gent'mens, lookin' like he did de day befo' when all de people laughed at 'im.

"I b'lieve ole Cun'l Chahmb'lin wan' to shoot Marse Chan, anyway!

"We come on home to breakfast, I totin' de box wid de pistils befo' me on de roan. Would you b'lieve me, seh, Marse Chan he nuver said a wud 'bout it to ole marster or nobody. Ole missis didn' fin' out 'bout it for mo'n a month, an' den, Lawd! how she did cry and kiss Marse Chan; an' ole marster, aldo' he never say much, he wuz jes' ez please' ez ole missis. He call me in de room an' made me tole 'im all 'bout it, an' when I got th'oo he gi' me five dollars an' a pyar of breeches.

"But ole Cun'l Chahmb'lin he nuver did furgive Marse Chan, an' Miss Anne she got mad too. Wimmens is mons'us onreasonable nohow. Dey's jes' like a catfish: you can n' tek hole on 'em like udder folks, an' when you gits 'im yo' can n' always hole 'em.

"What meks me think so? Heaps o' things—dis: Marse Chan he done gi' Miss Anne her pa jes' ez good ez I gi' Marse Chan's dawg sweet 'taters, an' she git mad wid 'im ez if he hed kill 'im 'stid o' sen'in' 'im back to her dat mawnin' whole an' soun'. B'lieve me! she wouldn' even speak to him arfter dat!

"Don' I 'member dat mawnin'!

"We wuz gwine fox-huntin', 'bout six weeks or sich a matter arfter de duil, an' we met Miss Anne ridin' 'long wid anurr lady an' two gent'mens whar wuz stayin' at her house. Dyar wuz always some one or nurr dyar co'ting her. Well, dat mawnin' we meet 'em right in de road. 'Twuz de fust time Marse Chan had see her sence de duil, an' he raises he hat ez he pahss, an' she looks right at 'im wid her head up in de yair like she nuver see 'im befo' in her born days; an' when she comes by me, she sez, 'Good-mawnin', Sam!' Gord! I nuver see nuthin' like de look dat come on Marse Chan's face when she pahss 'im like dat. He gi' de sorrel a pull dat fotch 'im back settin' down in de san' on he hanches. He ve'y lips wuz white. I tried to keep up wid 'im, but 'twarn' no use. He sont me back home pres'n'y, an' he rid on. I sez to myself, 'Cun'l Chahmb'lin, don' yo' meet Marse Chan dis mawnin'. He ain' bin lookin' 'roun' de ole school-house, whar he an' Miss Anne use' to go to school to ole Mr. Hall together, fur nuffin'. He won' stan' no prod-jickin' to-day.'

" He nuver come home dat night tell 'way late, an' ef he'd been fox-huntin' it mus' ha' been de ole red whar lives down in de greenscum mashes he'd been chasin'. De way de sorrel wuz gormed up wid sweat an' mire sut'n'y did hu't me. He walked up to de stable wid he head down all de way, an' I'se seen 'im go eighty miles of a winter day, an' prance into de stable at night ez fresh ez if he hed jes' cantered over to ole Cun'l Chahmb'lin's to supper. I nuver seen a hoss beat so sence I knowed de fetlock from de fo'lock, an' bad ez he wuz he wan' ez bad ez Marse Chan.

" Whew! he didn' git over dat thing, seh—he nuver did git over it.

" De war come on jes' den, an' Marse Chan wuz elected cap'n; but he wouldn' tek it. He said Firginia hadn' seceded, an' he wuz gwine stan' by her. Den dey 'lected Mr. Gordon cap'n.

" I sut'n'y did wan' Marse Chan to tek de place, cuz I knowed he wuz gwine tek me wid 'im. He wan' gwine widout Sam. An' beside, he look so po' an' thin, I thought he wuz gwine die.

" Of co'se, ole missis she heared 'bout it, an' she met Miss Anne in de road, an' cut her jes' like Miss Anne cut Marse Chan.

" Ole missis, she wuz proud ez anybody! So we wuz mo' strangers dan ef we hadn' live' in a hundred miles of each urr. An' Marse Chan he wuz gittin' thinner an' thinner, an' Firginia she come out, an' den Marse Chan he went to Richmond an' listed, an' come back an' sey he wuz a private, an' he didn' know whe'r he could tek me or not. He writ to Mr. Gordon, hows'-ever, an' 'twuz 'cided dat when he went I wuz to go

'long an' wait on him an' de cap'n too. I didn' min'
dat, yo' know, long ez I could go wid Marse Chan, an'
I like' Mr. Gordon, anyways.

"Well, one night Marse Chan come back from de
offis wid a telegram dat say, ' Come at once,' so he wuz
to start nex' mawnin'. He uniform wuz all ready,
gray wid yaller trimmin's, an' mine wuz ready too, an'
he had ole marster's sword, whar de State gi' 'im in de
Mexikin war; an' he trunks wuz all packed wid ev'ry-
thing in 'em, an' my chist was packed too, an' Jim
Rasher he druv 'em over to de depo' in de waggin, an'
we wuz to start nex' mawnin' 'bout light. Dis wuz
'bout de las' o' spring, you know. Dat night ole missis
made Marse Chan dress up in he uniform, an' he sut'n'y
did look splendid, wid he long mustache an' he wavin'
hyar an' he tall figger.

"Arfter supper he come down an' sez: ' Sam, I wan'
you to tek dis note an' kyar it over to Cun'l Chahm-
b'lin's, an' gi' it to Miss Anne wid yo' own han's, an'
bring me wud what she sez. Don' let any one know
'bout it, or know why you've gone.' ' Yes, seh,' sez I.

"Yo' see, I knowed Miss Anne's maid over at ole
Cun'l Chahmb'lin's—dat wuz Judy whar is my wife
now—an' I knowed I could wuk it. So I tuk de roan
an' rid over, an' tied 'im down de hill in de cedars,
an' I wen' 'roun' to de back yard. 'Twuz a right blowy
sort o' night; de moon wuz jes' risin', but de clouds wuz
so big it didn' shine 'cep' th'oo a crack now an' den.
I soon foun' my gal, an' arfter tellin' her two or three
lies 'bout herse'f, I got her to go in an' ax Miss Anne
to come to de do'. When she come, I gi' her de note,
an' arfter a little while she bro't me anurr, an' I tole
her good-bye, an' she gi' me a dollar, an' I come home
an' gi' de letter to Marse Chan. He read it, an' tole
me to have de hosses ready at twenty minits to twelve

at de corner of de garden. An' jes' befo' dat he come out ez ef he wuz gwine to bed, but instid he come, an' we all struck out to'ds Cun'l Chahmb'lin's. When we got mos' to de gate, de hosses got sort o' skeered, an' I see dey wuz some'n or somebody standin' jes' inside; an' Marse Chan he jumpt off de sorrel an' flung me de bridle an' he walked up.

" She spoke fust ('twuz Miss Anne had done come out dyar to meet Marse Chan), an' she sez, jes' ez cold ez a chill, ' Well, seh, I granted your favor. I wished to relieve myse'f of de obligations you placed me under a few months ago, when you made me a present of my father, whom you fust insulted an' then prevented from gittin' satisfaction.'

" Marse Chan he didn' speak fur a minit, an' den he said: ' Who is with you?' Dat wuz ev'y wud.

" ' No one,' sez she; ' I came alone.'

" ' My God!' sez he, ' you didn' come all through those woods by yourse'f at this time o' night?'

" ' Yes, I'm not afraid,' sez she. (An' heah dis nigger! I don' b'lieve she wuz.)

" De moon come out, an' I cotch sight o' her stan'in' dyar in her white dress, wid de cloak she had wrapped herse'f up in drapped off on de groun', an' she didn' look like she wuz 'feared o' nuthin'. She wuz mons'us purty ez she stood dyar wid de green bushes behine her, an' she hed jes' a few flowers in her breas'—right hyah —and some leaves in her sorrel hyar; an' de moon come out an' shined down on her hyar an' her frock an' 'peared like de light wuz jes' stan'in' off it ez she stood dyar lookin' at Marse Chan wid her head tho'd back, jes' like dat mawnin' when she pahss Marse Chan in de road widout speakin' to 'im, an' sez to me, ' Good-mawnin', Sam.'

" Marse Chan, he den tole her he hed come to say

good-bye to her, ez he wuz gwine 'way to de war nex'
mawnin'. I wuz watchin' on her, an' I tho't, when
Marse Chan tole her dat, she sort o' started an' looked
up at 'im like she wuz mighty sorry, an' 'peared like
she didn' stan' quite so straight arfter dat. Den Marse
Chan he went on talkin' right fars' to her; an' he tole
her how he had loved her ever sence she wuz a little
bit o' baby mos', an' how he nuver 'membered de time
when he hedn't 'spected to marry her. He tole her
it wuz his love for her dat hed made 'im stan' fust at
school an' collige, an' hed kep' 'im good an' pure; an'
now he wuz gwine 'way, wouldn't she let it be like 'twuz
in ole times, an' ef he come back from de war wouldn'
she try to think on him ez she use' to do when she wuz
a little guirl?

"Marse Chan he had done been talkin' so serious,
he hed done tuk Miss Anne's han', an' wuz lookin' down
in her face like he wuz list'nin' wid his eyes.

"Arfter a minit Miss Anne she said somethin', an'
Marse Chan he cotch her urr han' an' sez:

"'But if you love me, Anne?'

"When he said dat, she tu'ned her head 'way from
'im, an' wait' a minit, an' den she said—right clear:

"'But I don' love yo'.' (Jes' dem th'ee wuds!)
De wuds fall right slow—like dirt falls out a spade on
a coffin when yo's buryin' anybody, an' seys, ' Uth to
uth.' Marse Chan he jes' let her hand drap, an' he
stiddy hisse'f 'g'inst de gate-pos', an' he didn' speak
torekly. When he did speak, all he sez wuz:

"'I mus' see you home safe.'

"I 'clar, marster, I didn' know 'twuz Marse Chan's
voice tell I look at 'im right good. Well, she wouldn'
let 'im go wid her. She jes' wrap' her cloak 'roun' her
shoulders, an' wen' 'long back by herse'f, widout doin'
more'n jes' look up once at Marse Chan leanin' dyah

'g'inst de gate-pos' in he sodger clo's, wid he eyes on de groun'. She said ' Good-bye ' sort o' sorf, an' Marse Chan, widout lookin' up, shake han's wid her, an' she wuz done gone down de road. Soon ez she got 'mos' 'roun' de curve, Marse Chan he followed her, keepin' under de trees so ez not to be seen, an' I led de hosses on down de road behine 'im. He kep' 'long behine her tell she wuz safe in de house, an' den he come an' got on he hoss, an' we all come home.

" Nex' mawnin' we all come off to j'ine de army. An' dey wuz a-drillin' an' a-drillin' all 'bout for a while, an' dey went 'long wid all de res' o' de army, an' I went wid Marse Chan an' clean he boots, an' look arfter de tent, an' tek keer o' him an' de hosses. An' Marse Chan, he wan' a bit like he use' to be. He wuz so solumn an' moanful all de time, at leas' 'cep' when dyah wuz gwine to be a fight. Den he'd peartin' up, an' he alwuz rode at de head o' de company, 'cause he wuz tall; an' hit wan' on'y in battles whar all his company wuz dat *he* went, but he use' to volunteer whenever de cun'l wanted anybody to fine out anythin', an' 'twuz so dangersome he didn' like to mek one man go no sooner'n anurr, yo' know, an' ax'd who'd volunteer. *He* 'peared to like to go prowlin' aroun' 'mong dem Yankees, an' he use' to tek me wid 'im whenever he could. Yes, seh, he sut'n'y wuz a good sodger! He didn' mine bullets no more'n he did so many draps o' rain. But I use' to be pow'ful skeered sometimes. It jes' use' to 'pear like fun to 'im. In camp he use' to be so sorrerful he'd hardly open he mouf. You'd 'a' tho't he wuz seekin', he used to look so moanful; but jes' le' 'im git into danger, an' he use' to be like ole times—jolly an' laughin' like when he wuz a boy.

" When Cap'n Gordon got he leg shot off, dey mek Marse Chan cap'n on de spot, 'cause one o' de lieutenants got kilt de same day, an' turr one (named Mr. Ronny) wan' no 'count, an' de company said Marse Chan wuz de man.

"An' Marse Chan he wuz jes' de same. He didn' never mention Miss Anne's name, but I knowed he wuz thinkin' on her constant. One night he wuz settin' by de fire in camp, an' Mr. Ronny—he wuz de secon' lieutenant—got to talkin' 'bout ladies, an' he say all sorts o' things 'bout 'em, an' I see Marse Chan kinder lookin' mad; an' de lieutenant mention Miss Anne's name. He had been courtin' Miss Anne 'bout de time Marse Chan fit de duil wid her pa, an' Miss Anne hed kicked 'im, dough he wuz mighty rich, 'cause he warn' nuthin' but a half-strainer, an' 'cause she like Marse Chan, I believe, dough she didn' speak to 'im; an' Mr. Ronny he got drunk, an' 'cause Cun'l Chahmb'lin tole 'im not to come dyah no more, he got mighty mad. An' dat evenin' I'se tellin' yo' 'bout, he wuz talkin', an' he mention' Miss Anne's name. I see Marse Chan tu'n he eye 'roun' on 'im an' keep it on he face, and pres'n'y Mr. Ronny said he wuz gwine hev some fun dyah yit. He didn' mention her name dat time; but he said dey wuz all on 'em a parecel of stuck-up 'risticrats, an' her pa wan' no gent'man anyway, an'—— I don' know what he wuz gwine say (he nuver said it), fur ez he got dat far Marse Chan riz up an' hit 'im a crack, an' he fall like he hed been hit wid a fence-rail. He challenged Marse Chan to fight a duil, an' Marse Chan he excepted de challenge, an' dey wuz gwine fight; but some on 'em tole 'im Marse Chan wan' gwine mek a present o' him to his fam'ly, an' he got somebody to bre'k up de duil; 'twan' nuthin' dough, but he wuz 'fred to fight Marse Chan. An' purty soon he lef' de comp'ny.

"Well, I got one o' de gent'mens to write Judy a

letter for me, an' I tole her all 'bout de fight, an' how Marse Chan knock Mr. Ronny over fur speakin' discontemptuous o' Cun'l Chahmb'lin, an' I tole her how Marse Chan wuz a-dyin' fur love o' Miss Anne. An' Judy she gits Miss Anne to read de letter fur her. Den Miss Anne she tells her pa, an'—you mind, Judy tells me all dis arfterwards, an' she say when Cun'l Chahmb'lin hear 'bout it, he wuz settin' on de poach, an' he set still a good while, an' den he sey to hisse'f:

" ' Well, he carn' he'p bein' a Whig.'

" An' den he gits up an' walks up to Miss Anne an' looks at her right hard; an' Miss Anne she hed done tu'n away her haid an' wuz makin' out she wuz fixin' a rose-bush 'g'inst de poach; an' when her pa kep' lookin' at her, her face got jes' de color o' de roses on de bush, and pres'n'y her pa sez:

" ' Anne ! '

" An' she tu'ned roun', an' he sez:

" ' Do yo' want 'im ? '

" An' she sez, ' Yes,' an' put her head on he shoulder an' begin to cry; an' he sez:

" ' Well, I won' stan' between yo' no longer. Write to 'im an' say so.'

" We didn' know nuthin' 'bout dis den. We wuz a-fightin' an' a-fightin' all dat time; an' come one day a letter to Marse Chan, an' I see 'im start to read it in his tent, an' he face hit look so cu'ious, an' he han's trembled so I couldn' mek out what wuz de matter wid 'im. An' he fol' de letter up an' wen' out an' wen' way down 'hine de camp, an' stayed dyah 'bout nigh an hour. Well, seh, I wuz on de lookout for 'im when he come back, an', fo' Gord, ef he face didn' shine like a angel's! I say to myse'f, ' Um'm! ef de glory o' Gord ain' done shine on 'im ! ' An' what yo' 'spose 'twuz?

" He tuk me wid 'im dat evenin', an' he tell me he

hed done git a letter from Miss Anne, an' Marse Chan
he eyes look like gre't big stars, an' he face wuz jes'
like 'twuz dat mawnin' when de sun riz up over de
low groun', an' I see 'im stan'in' dyah wid de pistil in
he han', lookin' at it, an' not knowin' but what it mout
be de lars' time, an' he done mek up he mine not to
shoot ole Cun'l Chahmb'lin fur Miss Anne's sake, what
writ 'im de letter.

"He fol' de letter wha' was in his han' up, an' put
it in he inside pocket—right dyar on de lef' side; an'
den he tole me he tho't mebbe we wuz gwine hev some
warm wuk in de nex' two or th'ee days, an' arfter dat
ef Gord speared 'im he'd git a leave o' absence fur a
few days, an' we'd go home.

"Well, dat night de orders come, an' we all hed to
git over to'ds Romney; an' we rid all night till 'bout
light; an' we halted right on a little creek, an' we
stayed dyah till mos' breakfas' time, an' I see Marse
Chan set down on de groun' 'hine a bush an' read dat
letter over an' over. I watch 'im, an' de battle wuz
a-goin' on, but we had orders to stay 'hine de hill, an'
ev'y now an' den de bullets would cut de limbs o' de
trees right over us, an' one o' dem big shells what goes
' Awhar—awhar—awhar! ' would fall right 'mong us;
but Marse Chan he didn' mine it no mo'n nuthin'! Den
it 'peared to git closer an' thicker, and Marse Chan
he calls me, an' I crep' up, an' he sez:

"' Sam, we'se goin' to win in dis battle, an' den
we'll go home an' git married; an' I'se goin' home wid a
star on my collar.' An' den he sez, ' Ef I'm wounded,
kyar me home, yo' hear?' An' I sez, ' Yes, Marse
Chan.'

"Well, jes' den dey blowed boots an' saddles, an' we
mounted; an' de orders come to ride 'roun' de slope,
an' Marse Chan's comp'ny wuz de secon', an' when we

got 'roun' dyah, we wuz right in it. Hit wuz de wust place ever dis nigger got in. An' dey said, ' Charge 'em! ' an' my king! ef ever you see bullets fly, dey did dat day. Hit wuz jes' like hail; an' we wen' down de slope (I 'long wid de res') an' up de hill right to'ds de cannons, an' de fire wuz so strong dyar (dey hed a whole rigiment o' infintrys layin' down dyar onder de cannons) our lines sort o' broke an' stop; de cun'l was kilt, an' I b'lieve dey wuz jes' 'bout to bre'k all to pieces, when Marse Chan rid up an' cotch hol' de fleg an' hollers, ' Foller me! ' an' rid strainin' up de hill 'mong de cannons. I seen 'im when he went, de sorrel four good length ahead o' ev'y urr hoss, jes' like he use' to be in a fox-hunt, an' de whole rigiment right arfter 'im. Yo' ain' nuver hear thunder! Fust thing I knowed, de roan roll' head over heels an' flung me up 'g'inst de bank, like yo' chuck a nubbin over 'g'inst de foot o' de corn pile. An' dat's what kep' me from bein' kilt, I 'spects. Judy she say she think 'twuz Providence, but I think 'twuz de bank. O' co'se, Providence put de bank dyah, but how come Providence nuver saved Marse Chan? When I look' 'roun', de roan wuz layin' dyah by me, stone dead, wid a cannon-ball gone 'mos' th'oo him, an' our men hed done swep' dem on t'urr side from de top o' de hill. 'Twan' mo'n a minit, de sorrel come gallupin' back wid his mane flyin', an' de rein hangin' down on one side to his knee. ' Dyar! ' says I, ' fo' Gord! I 'specks dey done kill Marse Chan, an' I promised to tek care on him.'

" I jumped up an' run over de bank, an' dyar, wid a whole lot o' dead men, an' some not dead yit, onder one o' de guns wid de fleg still in he han', an' a bullet right th'oo he body, lay Marse Chan. I tu'n 'im over an' call 'im, ' Marse Chan! ' but 'twan' no use, he wuz done gone home, sho' 'nuff. I pick' 'im up in my arms

wid de fleg still in he han's, an' toted 'im back jes' like
I did dat day when he wuz a baby, an' ole marster gin
'im to me in my arms, an' sez he could trus' me, an'
tell me to tek keer on 'im long ez he lived. I kyar'd
'im 'way off de battlefiel' out de way o' de balls, an' I
laid 'im down onder a big tree till I could git somebody
to ketch de sorrel for me. He wuz cotched arfter a
while, an' I hed some money, so I got some pine plank
an' made a coffin dat evenin', an' wrapt Marse Chan's
body up in de fleg, an' put 'im in de coffin; but I didn'
nail de top on strong, 'cause I knowed ole missis wan'
see 'im; an' I got a' ambulance an' set out for home dat
night. We reached dyar de nex' evein', arfter travel-
lin' all dat night an' all nex' day.

"Hit 'peared like somethin' hed tole ole missis we
wuz comin' so; for when we got home she wuz waitin'
for us—done drest up in her best Sunday-clo'es, an'
stan'n' at de head o' de big steps, an' ole marster settin'
in his big cheer—ez we druv up de hill to'ds de house,
I drivin' de ambulance an' de sorrel leadin' 'long behine
wid de stirrups crost over de saddle.

"She come down to de gate to meet us. We took de
coffin out de ambulance an' kyar'd it right into de big
parlor wid de pictures in it, whar dey use' to dance in
ole times when Marse Chan wuz a schoolboy, an' Miss
Anne Chahmb'lin use' to come over, an' go wid ole
missis into her charmber an' tek her things off. In dyar
we laid de coffin on two o' de cheers, an' ole missis
nuver said a wud; she jes' looked so ole an' white.

"When I had tell 'em all 'bout it, I tu'ned right
'roun' an' rid over to Cun'l Chahmb'lin's, 'cause I
knowed dat wuz what Marse Chan he'd 'a' wanted me
to do. I didn' tell nobody whar I wuz gwine, 'cause yo'
know none on 'em hadn' nuver speak to Miss Anne, not
sence de duil, an' dey didn' know 'bout de letter.

" When I rid up in de yard, dyar wuz Miss Anne a-stan'in' on de poach watchin' me ez I rid up. I tied my hoss to de fence, an' walked up de parf. She knowed by de way I walked dyar wuz somethin' de mot-ter, an' she wuz mighty pale. I drapt my cap down on de een' o' de steps an' went up. She nuver opened her mouf; jes' stan' right still an' keep her eyes on my face. Fust, I couldn' speak; den I cotch my voice, an' I say, ' Marse Chan, he done got he furlough.'

" Her face was mighty ashy, an' she sort o' shook, but she didn' fall. She tu'ned 'roun' an' said, ' Git me de ker'ige ! ' Dat wuz all.

" When de ker'ige come 'roun', she hed put on her bonnet, an' wuz ready. Ez she got in, she sey to me, ' Hev yo' brought him home ? ' an' we drove 'long, I ridin' behine.

" When we got home, she got out, an' walked up de big walk—up to de poach by herse'f. Ole missis hed done fin' de letter in Marse Chan's pocket, wid de love in it, while I wuz 'way, an' she wuz a-waitin' on de poach. Dey sey dat wuz de fust time ole missis cry when she find de letter, an' dat she sut'n'y did cry over it, pintedly.

" Well, seh, Miss Anne she walks right up de steps, mos' up to ole missis stan'in' dyar on de poach, an' jes' falls right down mos' to her, on her knees fust, an' den flat on her face right on de flo', ketchin' at ole missis' dress wid her two han's—so.

" Ole missis stood for 'bout a minit lookin' down at her, an' den she drapt down on de flo' by her, an' took her in bofe her arms.

" I couldn' see, I wuz cryin' so myse'f, an' ev'ybody wuz cryin'. But dey went in arfter a while in de par-lor, an' shet de do'; an' I heahd 'em say, Miss Anne she

tuk de coffin in her arms an' kissed it, an' kissed Marse
Chan, an' call 'im by his name, an' her darlin', an' ole
missis lef' her cryin' in dyar tell some on 'em went in,
an' found her done faint on de flo'.

" Judy (she's my wife) she tell me she heah Miss
Anne when she axed ole missis mout she wear mo'nin'
fur 'im. I don' know how dat is; but when we buried
'im nex' day, she wuz de one whar walked arfter de
coffin, holdin' ole marster, an' ole missis she walked
next to 'em.

" Well, we buried Marse Chan dyar in de ole grabeyard, wid de fleg wrapped roun' 'im, an' he face lookin'
like it did dat mawnin' down in de low groun's, wid de
new sun shinin' on it so peaceful.

" Miss Anne she nuver went home to stay arfter dat;
she stay wid ole marster an' ole missis ez long ez dey
lived. Dat warn' so mighty long, 'cause ole marster he
died dat fall, when dey wuz fallerin' fur wheat—I had
jes' married Judy den—an' ole missis she warn' long
behine him. We buried her by him next summer. Miss
Anne she went in de hospitals toreckly arfter ole missis
died; an' jes' fo' Richmond fell she come home sick
wid de fever. Yo' nuver would 'a' knowed her fur de
same ole Miss Anne. She wuz light ez a piece o' peth,
an' so white, 'cep' her eyes an' her sorrel hyar, an' she
kep' on gittin' whiter an' weaker. Judy she sut'n'y did
nuss her faithful. But she nuver got no betterment!
De fever an' Marse Chan's bein' kilt hed done strain
her, an' she died jes' fo' de folks wuz sot free.

" So we buried Miss Anne right by Marse Chan, in
a place whar ole missis hed tole us to leave, an' dey's
bofe on 'em sleep side by side over in de ole grabeyard
at home.

" An' will yo' please tell me, marster? Dey tells me
dat de Bible sey dyar won' be marryin' nor givin' in

marriage in heaven, but I don' b'lieve it signifies dat—does you?''

I gave him the comfort of my earnest belief in some other interpretation, together with several spare '' eighteen-pences,'' as he called them, for which he seemed humbly grateful. And as I rode away I heard him calling across the fence to his wife, who was standing in the door of a small whitewashed cabin, near which we had been standing for some time:

'' Judy, have Marse Chan's dawg got home?''

"POSSON JONE'"

BY

GEORGE W. CABLE

Bliss Perry mentions this story as one that presents "people and events and circumstances, blended into an artistic whole that defies analysis." It illustrates dramatic incident, local color, and complex character analysis.

"POSSON JONE'" *

To Jules St.-Ange—elegant little heathen—there yet remained at manhood a remembrance of having been to school, and of having been taught by a stony-headed Capuchin that the world is round—for example, like a cheese. This round world is a cheese to be eaten through, and Jules had nibbled quite into his cheese-world already at twenty-two.

He realized this as he idled about one Sunday morning where the intersection of Royal and Conti streets some seventy years ago formed a central corner of New Orleans. Yes, yes, the trouble was he had been wasteful and honest. He discussed the matter with that faithful friend and confidant, Baptiste, his yellow body-servant. They concluded that, papa's patience and *tante's* pin-money having been gnawed away quite to the rind, there were left open only these few easily enumerated resorts: to go to work—they shuddered; to join Major Innerarity's filibustering expedition; or else—why not?—to try some games of confidence. At twenty-two one must begin to be something. Nothing else tempted; could that avail? One could but try. It is noble to try; and, besides, they were hungry. If one could "make the friendship" of some person from the country, for instance, with money, not expert at cards or dice, but, as one would say, willing to learn, one might find cause to say some "Hail Marys."

The sun broke through a clearing sky, and Baptiste

* From "Old Creole Days," by George W. Cable. Copyright, 1890, by Charles Scribner's Sons.

pronounced it good for luck. There had been a hurricane in the night. The weed-grown tile-roofs were still dripping, and from lofty brick and low adobe walls a rising steam responded to the summer sunlight. Up-street, and across the Rue du Canal, one could get glimpses of the gardens in Faubourg Ste.-Marie standing in silent wretchedness, so many tearful Lucretias, tattered victims of the storm. Short remnants of the wind now and then came down the narrow street in erratic puffs heavily laden with odors of broken boughs and torn flowers, skimmed the little pools of rain-water in the deep ruts of the unpaved street, and suddenly went away to nothing, like a juggler's butterflies or a young man's money.

It was very picturesque, the Rue Royale. The rich and poor met together. The locksmith's swinging key creaked next door to the bank; across the way, crouching, mendicant-like, in the shadow of a great importing-house, was the mud laboratory of the mender of broken combs. Light balconies overhung the rows of showy shops and stores open for trade this Sunday morning, and pretty Latin faces of the higher class glanced over their savagely pronged railings upon the passers below. At some windows hung lace curtains, flannel duds at some, and at others only the scraping and sighing one-hinged shutter groaning toward Paris after its neglectful master.

M. St.-Ange stood looking up and down the street for nearly an hour. But few ladies, only the inveterate mass-goers, were out. About the entrance of the frequent *cafés* the masculine gentility stood leaning on canes, with which now one and now another beckoned to Jules, some even adding pantomimic hints of the social cup.

M. St.-Ange remarked to his servant without turn-

ing his head that somehow he felt sure he should soon
return those *bons* that the mulatto had lent him.

" What will you do with them? "

" Me! " said Baptiste, quickly; " I will go and see
the bull-fight in the Place Congo."

" There is to be a bull-fight? But where is M.
Cayetano? "

" Ah, got all his affairs wet in the tornado. Instead
of his circus, they are to have a bull-fight—not an ordinary bull-fight with sick horses, but a buffalo-and-tiger
fight. I would not miss it——"

Two or three persons ran to the opposite corner, and
commenced striking at something with their canes.
Others followed. Can M. St.-Ange and servant, who
hasten forward—can the Creoles, Cubans, Spaniards,
San Domingo refugees, and other loungers—can they
hope it is a fight? They hurry forward. Is a man
in a fit? The crowd pours in from the side-streets.
Have they killed a so-long snake? Bareheaded shopmen
leave their wives, who stand upon chairs. The crowd
huddles and packs. Those on the outside make little
leaps into the air, trying to be tall.

" What is the matter? "

" Have they caught a real live rat? "

" Who is hurt? " asks some one in English.

" *Personne,*" replies a shopkeeper; " a man's hat
blow' in the gutter; but he has it now. Jules pick' it.
See, that is the man, head and shoulders on top the
res'."

" He in the homespun? " asks a second shopkeeper. " Humph! an *Américain*—a West-Floridian;
bah! "

" But wait; 'st! he is speaking; listen! "

" To who is he speak——? "

" Sh-sh-sh! to Jules."

" Jules who? "

" Silence, you! To Jules St.-Ange, what howe me a bill since long time. Sh-sh-sh! "

Then the voice was heard.

Its owner was a man of giant stature, with a slight stoop in his shoulders, as if he was making a constant, good-natured attempt to accommodate himself to ordinary doors and ceilings. His bones were those of an ox. His face was marked more by weather than age, and his narrow brow was bald and smooth. He had instantaneously formed an opinion of Jules St.-Ange, and the multitude of words, most of them lingual curiosities, with which he was rasping the wide-open ears of his listeners, signified, in short, that, as sure as his name was Parson Jones, the little Creole was a " plum gentleman."

M. St.-Ange bowed and smiled, and was about to call attention, by both gesture and speech, to a singular object on top of the still uncovered head, when the nervous motion of the *Américain* anticipated him, as, throwing up an immense hand, he drew down a large roll of bank-notes. The crowd laughed, the West-Floridian joining, and began to disperse.

" Why, that money belongs to Smyrny Church," said the giant.

" You are very dengerous to make your money expose like that, Misty Posson Jone'," said St.-Ange, counting it with his eyes.

The countryman gave a start and smile of surprise.

" How d'dyou know my name was Jones? " he asked; but, without pausing for the Creole's answer, furnished in his reckless way some further specimens of West-Floridian English; and the conciseness with which he presented full intelligence of his home, family, calling, lodging-house, and present and future plans, might have

passed for consummate art, had it not been the most
run-wild nature. "And I've done been to Mobile, you
know, on busi*ness* for Bethesdy Church. It's the on'yest
time I ever been from home; now you wouldn't of believed that, would you? But I admire to have saw you,
that's so. You've got to come and eat with me. Me
and my boy ain't been fed yit. What might one call yo'
name? Jools? Come on, Jools. Come on, Colossus.
That's my niggah—his name's Colossus of Rhodes. Is
that yo' yallah boy, Jools? Fetch him along, Colossus.
It seems like a special provi*dence.*—Jools, do you believe
in a special provi*dence?*"

Jules said he did.

The new-made friends moved briskly off, followed
by Baptiste and a short, square, old negro, very black
and grotesque, who had introduced himself to the
mulatto, with many glittering and cavernous smiles, as
"d'body-sarvant of d'Rev'n' Mr. Jones."

Both pairs enlivened their walk with conversation.
Parson Jones descanted upon the doctrine he had mentioned, as illustrated in the perplexities of cotton-
growing, and concluded that there would always be "a
special provi*dence* again' cotton untell folks quits
a-pressin' of it and haulin' of it on Sundays!"

"*Je dis,*" said St.-Ange, in response, "I thing you
is juz right. I believe, me, strong-strong in the improvi-
dence, yes. You know my papa he hown a sugah-
plantation, you know. 'Jules, me son,' he say one time
to me, 'I goin' to make one baril sugah to fedge the
moze high price in New Orleans.' Well, he take his bez
baril sugah—I nevah see a so careful man like me papa
always to make a so beautiful sugah *et sirop.* 'Jules,
go at Father Pierre an' ged this lill pitcher fill with holy-
water, an' tell him sen' his tin bucket, and I will make
it fill with *quitte.*' I ged the holy-water; my papa

sprinkle it over the baril, an' make one cross on the 'ead of the baril.''

'' Why, Jools,'' said Parson Jones, '' that didn't do no good.''

'' Din do no good! Id broughd the so great value! You can strike me dead if thad baril sugah din fedge the more high cost than any other in the city. *Parce-que*, the man what buy that baril sugah he make a mistake of one hundred pound ''—falling back—'' *Mais* certainlee! ''

'' And you think that was growin' out of the holy-water? '' asked the parson.

'' *Mais*, what could make it else? Id could not be the *quitte*, because my papa keep the bucket, an' forget to sen' the *quitte* to Father Pierre.''

Parson Jones was disappointed.

'' Well, now, Jools, you know, I don't think that was right. I reckon you must be a plum Catholic.''

M. St.-Ange shrugged. He would not deny his faith.

'' I am a *Catholique, mais* ''—brightening as he hoped to recommend himself anew—'' not a good one.''

'' Well, you know,'' said Jones—'' where's Colossus? Oh! all right. Colossus strayed off a minute in Mobile, and I plum lost him for two days. Here's the place; come in. Colossus and this boy can go to the kitchen.— Now, Colossus, what *air* you a-beckonin' at me faw? ''

He let his servant draw him aside and address him in a whisper.

'' Oh, go 'way! '' said the parson with a jerk. '' Who's goin' to throw me? What? Speak louder. Why, Colossus, you shayn't talk so, saw. 'Pon my soul, you're the mightiest fool I ever taken up with. Jest you go down that alley-way with this yalla boy, and don't show yo' face untell yo' called! ''

The negro begged; the master wrathily insisted.

" Colossus, will you do ez I tell you, or shell I hev
to strike you, saw ? "

" O Mahs Jimmy, I—I's gwine; but "—he ventured
nearer—" don't on no account drink nothin', Mahs
Jimmy."

Such was the negro's earnestness that he put one
foot in the gutter, and fell heavily against his master.
The parson threw him off angrily.

" Thar, now! Why, Colossus, you most of been dosted
with sumthin'; yo' plum crazy.—Humph, come on,
Jools, let's eat! Humph! to tell me that when I never
taken a drop, exceptin' for chills, in my life—which he
knows so as well as me! "

The two masters began to ascend a stair.

" *Mais,* he is a sassy; I would sell him, me," said the
young Creole.

" No, I wouldn't do that," replied the parson;
" though there is people in Bethesdy who says he is
a rascal. He's a powerful smart fool. Why, that boy's
got money, Jools; more money than religion, I reckon.
I'm shore he fallen into mighty bad company "—they
passed beyond earshot.

Baptiste and Colossus, instead of going to the tavern
kitchen, passed to the next door and entered the dark
rear corner of a low grocery, where, the law notwithstanding, liquor was covertly sold to slaves. There,
in the quiet company of Baptiste and the grocer, the
colloquial powers of Colossus, which were simply prodigious, began very soon to show themselves.

" For whilst," said he, " Mahs Jimmy has eddication,
you know—whilst he has eddication, I has 'scretion. He
has eddication and I has 'scretion, an' so we gits
along."

He drew a black bottle down the counter, and, laying
half his length upon the damp board, continued:

" As a p'inciple I discredits de imbimin' of awjus
liquors. De imbimin' of awjus liquors, de wiolution of
de Sabbaf, de playin' of de fiddle, and de usin' of by-
words, dey is de fo' sins of de conscience; an' if
any man sin de fo' sins of de conscience, de deb-
ble done sharp his fork fo' dat man.—Ain't that so,
boss ? "

The grocer was sure it was so.

" Neberdeless, mind you "—here the orator brimmed
his glass from the bottle and swallowed the contents
with a dry eye—" mind you, a roytious man, sech as
ministers of de gospel and dere body-sarvants, can take
a *leetle* for de weak stomach."

But the fascinations of Colossus's eloquence must not
mislead us; this is the story of a true Christian; to wit,
Parson Jones.

The parson and his new friend ate. But the coffee
M. St.-Ange declared he could not touch; it was too
wretchedly bad. At the French Market, near by, there
was some noble coffee. This, however, would have to
be bought, and Parson Jones had scruples.

" You see, Jools, every man has his conscience to
guide him, which it does so in——"

" Oh, yes! " cried St.-Ange, " conscien'; thad is the
bez, Posson Jone'. Certainlee! I am a *Catholique,* you
is a *schismatique;* you thing it is wrong to dring some
coffee—well, then, it *is* wrong; you thing it is wrong to
make the sugah to ged the so large price—well, then, it *is*
wrong; I thing it is right—well, then, it *is* right; it is
all 'abit; *c'est tout.* What a man thing is right, *is right;*
'tis all 'abit. A man muz nod go again' his conscien'.
My faith! do you thing I would go again' my conscien'?
Mais allons, led us go and ged some coffee."

" Jools."

" W'at ? "

" Jools, it ain't the drinkin' of coffee, but the buyin'
of it on a Sabbath. You must really excuse me, Jools,
it's again' conscience, you know."

" Ah! " said St.-Ange, " *c'est* very true. For you it
would be a sin, *mais* for me it is only 'abit. Rilligion is
a very strange; I know a man one time, he thing it was
wrong to go to cock-fight Sunday evening. I thing it is
all 'abit. *Mais,* come, Posson Jone'; I have got one
friend, Miguel; led us go at his house and ged some
coffee. Come; Miguel have no familie; only him and
Joe—always like to see friend; *allons,* led us come
yonder."

" Why, Jools, my dear friend, you know," said the
shamefaced parson, " I never visit on Sundays."

" Never w'at? " asked the astounded Creole.

" No," said Jones, smiling awkwardly.

" Never visite? "

" Exceptin' sometimes amongst church-members,"
said Parson Jones.

" *Mais,*" said the seductive St.-Ange, " Miguel and
Joe is church-member'—certainlee! They love to talk
about rilligion. Come at Miguel and talk about some
rilligion. I am nearly expire for me coffee."

Parson Jones took his hat from beneath his chair
and rose up.

" Jools," said the weak giant, " I ought to be in
church right now."

" *Mais,* the church is right yonder at Miguel', yes. •
Ah! " continued St.-Ange, as they descended the stairs,
" I thing every man muz have the rilligion he like'
the bez—me, I like the *Catholique* rilligion the bez—for
me it *is* the bez. Every man will sure go to heaven if
he like his rilligion the bez."

" Jools," said the West-Floridian, laying his great
hand tenderly upon the Creole's shoulder, as they

stepped out upon the *banquette*, " do you think you have any shore hopes of heaven? "

" Yass! " replied St.-Ange; " I am sure-sure. I thing everybody will go to heaven. I thing you will go, *et* I thing Miguel will go, *et* Joe—everybody, I thing—*mais,* hof course, not if they not have been christen'. Even I thing some niggers will go."

" Jools," said the parson, stopping in his walk—" Jools, I *don't* want to lose my niggah."

" You will not loose him. With Baptiste he *cannot* ged loose."

But Colossus's master was not reassured.

" Now," said he, still tarrying, " this is jest the way; had I of gone to church——"

" Posson Jone'," said Jules.

" What? "

" I tell you. We goin' to church! "

" Will you? " asked Jones, joyously.

" *Allons,* come along," said Jules, taking his elbow.

They walked down the Rue Chartres, passed several corners, and by and by turned into a cross street. The parson stopped an instant as they were turning and looked back up the street.

" W'at you lookin'? " asked his companion.

" I thought I saw Colossus," answered the parson, with an anxious face; " I reckon 'twa'n't him, though." And they went on.

The street they now entered was a very quiet one. The eye of any chance passer would have been at once drawn to a broad, heavy, white brick edifice on the lower side of the way, with a flag-pole standing out like a bowsprit from one of its great windows, and a pair of lamps hanging before a large closed entrance. It was a theatre, honey-combed with gambling-dens. At this morning hour all was still, and the only sign of life was a knot of little barefoot girls gathered within its narrow shade, and each carrying an infant relative. Into this place the parson and M. St.-Ange entered, the little nurses jumping up from the sills to let them pass in.

A half-hour may have passed. At the end of that time the whole juvenile company were laying alternate eyes and ears to the chinks, to gather what they could of an interesting quarrel going on within.

" I did not, saw! I given you no cause of offence, saw! It's not so, saw! Mister Jools simply mistaken the house, thinkin' it was a Sabbath-school! No such thing, saw; I *ain't* bound to bet! Yes, I kin git out. Yes, without bettin'! I hev a right to my *o*pinion; I reckon I'm *a white man*, saw! No, saw! I on'y said I didn't think you could get the game on them cards. 'Sno such thing, saw! I do *not* know how to play! I wouldn't hev a rascal's money ef I should win it! Shoot, ef you dare! You can kill me, but you cayn't scare me! No, I shayn't bet! I'll die first! Yes, saw; Mr. Jools can bet for me if he admires to; I ain't his mostah."

Here the speaker seemed to direct his words to St.-Ange.

" Saw, I don't understand you, saw. I never said I'd loan you money to bet for me. I didn't suspicion this from you, saw. No, I won't take any more lemonade; it's the most notorious stuff I ever drank, saw! "

M. St.-Ange's replies were in *falsetto* and not without effect; for presently the parson's indignation and anger began to melt. " Don't ask me, Jools, I can't help you. It's no use; it's a matter of conscience with me, Jools."

" *Mais oui!* 'tis a matt' of conscien' wid me, the same."

" But, Jools, the money's none o' mine, nohow; it belongs to Smyrny, you know."

" If I could make jus' *one* bet," said the persuasive St.-Ange, " I would leave this place, fas'-fas', yes. If I had thing—*mais* I did not soupspicion this from you, Posson Jone'——"

" Don't, Jools, don't! "

" No! Posson Jone'."

" You're bound to win? " said the parson, wavering.

" *Mais certainement!* But it is not to win that I want; 'tis me conscien'—me honor! "

" Well, Jools, I hope I'm not a-doin' no wrong. I'll loan you some of this money if you say you'll come right out 'thout takin' your winnin's."

All was still. The peeping children could see the parson as he lifted his hand to his breast-pocket. There it paused a moment in bewilderment, then plunged to the bottom. It came back empty, and fell lifelessly at his side. His head dropped upon his breast, his eyes were for a moment closed, his broad palms were lifted and pressed against his forehead, a tremor seized him, and he fell all in a lump to the floor. The children ran off with their infant-loads, leaving Jules St.-Ange swearing by all his deceased relatives, first to Miguel and Joe, and then to the lifted parson, that he did not know what had become of the money " except if " the black man had got it.

In the rear of ancient New Orleans, beyond the sites of the old rampart, a trio of Spanish forts, where the town has since sprung up and grown old, green with all the luxuriance of the wild Creole summer, lay the Congo Plains. Here stretched the canvas of the historic Cayetano, who Sunday after Sunday sowed the sawdust for his circus-ring.

But to-day the great showman had fallen short of his printed promise. The hurricane had come by night, and with one fell swash had made an irretrievable sop of everything. The circus trailed away its bedraggled magnificence, and the ring was cleared for the bull.

Then the sun seemed to come out and work for the people. "See," said the Spaniards, looking up at the glorious sky with its great, white fleets drawn off upon the horizon—"see—heaven smiles upon the bull-fight!"

In the high upper seats of the rude amphitheatre sat the gaily-decked wives and daughters of the Gascons, from the *métaries* along the Ridge, and the chattering Spanish women of the Market, their shining hair unbonneted to the sun. Next below were their husbands and lovers in Sunday blouses, milkmen, butchers, bakers, black-bearded fishermen, Sicilian fruiterers, swarthy Portuguese sailors, in little woollen caps, and strangers of the graver sort; mariners of England, Germany, and Holland. The lowest seats were full of trappers, smugglers, Canadian *voyageurs*, drinking and singing; *Américains,* too—more's the shame—from the upper rivers—who will not keep their seats—who ply the bottle, and who will get home by and by and tell how wicked Sodom is; broad-brimmed, silver-braided Mexicans, too, with their copper cheeks and bat's eyes, and their tinkling spurred heels. Yonder, in that quieter section, are the quadroon women in their black lace shawls—and there is Baptiste; and below them are the turbaned black women, and there is—but he vanishes—Colossus.

The afternoon is advancing, yet the sport, though loudly demanded, does not begin. The *Américains* grow derisive and find pastime in gibes and raillery. They mock the various Latins with their national inflections, and answer their scowls with laughter. Some of the more aggressive shout pretty French greetings to the women of Gascony, and one bargeman, amid peals of applause, stands on a seat and hurls a kiss to the quadrooms. The mariners of England, Germany, and Holland, as spectators, like the fun, while the Spaniards look black and cast defiant imprecations upon their persecutors. Some Gascons, with timely caution, pick their women out and depart, running a terrible fire of gallantries.

In hope of truce, a new call is raised for the bull: " The bull, the bull!—hush! "

In a tier near the ground a man is standing and calling—standing head and shoulders above the rest—calling in the *Américaine* tongue. Another man, big and red, named Joe, and a handsome little Creole in elegant dress and full of laughter, wish to stop him, but the flat-boatmen, ha-ha-ing and cheering, will not suffer it. Ah, through some shameful knavery of the men, into whose hands he has fallen, he is drunk! Even the women can see that; and now he throws his arms wildly and raises his voice until the whole great circle hears it. He is preaching!

Ah! kind Lord, for a special providence now! The men of his own nation—men from the land of the open English Bible and temperance cup and song are cheering him on to mad disgrace. And now another call for the appointed sport is drowned by the flat-boatmen singing the ancient tune of Mear. You can hear the words—

" Old Grimes is dead, that good old soul "

—from ribald lips and throats turned brazen with laughter, from singers who toss their hats aloft and roll

in their seats; the chorus swells to the accompaniment
of a thousand brogans—

> "He used to wear an old gray coat
> All buttoned down before."

A ribboned man in the arena is trying to be heard,
and the Latins raise one mighty cry for silence. The
big red man gets a hand over the parson's mouth, and
the ribboned man seizes his moment.

" They have been endeavoring for hours," he says,
" to draw the terrible animals from their dens, but
such is their strength and fierceness, that——"

His voice is drowned. Enough has been heard to
warrant the inference that the beasts cannot be whipped
out of the storm-drenched cages to which menagerie-
life and long starvation have attached them, and from
the roar of indignation the man of ribbons flies. The
noise increases. Men are standing up by hundreds,
and women are imploring to be let out of the turmoil.
All at once, like the bursting of a dam, the whole mass
pours down into the ring. They sweep across the
arena and over the showman's barriers. Miguel gets
a frightful trampling. Who cares for gates or doors?
They tear the beasts' houses bar from bar, and, laying
hold of the gaunt buffalo, drag him forth by feet, ears,
and tail; and in the midst of the *mêlée*, still head and
shoulders above all, wilder, with the cup of the wicked,
than any beast, is the man of God from the Florida
parishes!

In his arms he bore—and all the people shouted at
once when they saw it—the tiger. He had lifted it high
up with its back to his breast, his arms clasped under
its shoulders; the wretched brute had curled up cater-
pillar-wise, with its long tail against its belly, and

through its filed teeth grinned a fixed and impotent wrath. And Parson Jones was shouting:

"The tiger and the buffler *shell* lay down together! You dah to say they shayn't and I'll comb you with this varmint from head to foot! The tiger and the buffler *shell* lay down together. They *shell!* Now, you, Joe! Behold! I am here to see it done. The lion and the buffler *shell* lay down together!"

Mouthing these words again and again, the parson forced his way through the surge in the wake of the buffalo. This creature the Latins had secured by a lariat over his head, and were dragging across the old rampart and into a street of the city.

The northern races were trying to prevent, and there was pommelling and knocking down, cursing and knife-drawing, until Jules St.-Ange was quite carried away with the fun, laughed, clapped his hands, and swore with delight, and ever kept close to the gallant parson.

Joe, contrariwise, counted all this child's-play an interruption. He had come to find Colossus and the money. In an unlucky moment he made bold to lay hold of the parson, but a piece of the broken barriers in the hands of a flat-boatman felled him to the sod, the terrible crowd swept over him, the lariat was cut, and the giant parson hurled the tiger upon the buffalo's back. In another instant both brutes were dead at the hands of the mob; Jones was lifted from his feet, and prating of Scripture and the millennium, of Paul at Ephesus and Daniel in the "buffler's" den, was borne aloft upon the shoulders of the huzzaing *Américains*. Half an hour later he was sleeping heavily on the floor of a cell in the *calaboza*.

When Parson Jones awoke, a bell was somewhere tolling for midnight. Somebody was at the door of his cell with a key. The lock grated, the door swung, the turnkey looked in and stepped back, and a ray of moonlight fell upon M. Jules St.-Ange. The prisoner sat upon the empty shackles and ring-bolt in the centre of the floor.

"Misty Posson Jone'," said the visitor, softly.

"O Jools!"

"*Mais*, w'at de matter, Posson Jone'?"

"My sins, Jools, my sins!"

"Ah! Posson Jone', is that something to cry, because a man get sometime a litt' bit intoxicate? *Mais*, if a man keep *all the time* intoxicate, I think that is again' the conscien'."

"Jools, Jools, your eyes is darkened—oh! Jools, where's my pore old niggah?"

"Posson Jone', never min'; he is wid Baptiste."

"Where?"

"I don' know w'ere—*mais* he is wid Baptiste. Baptiste is a beautiful to take care of somebody."

"Is he as good as you, Jools?" asked Parson Jones, sincerely.

Jules was slightly staggered.

"You know, Posson Jone', you know, a nigger cannot be good as a w'ite man—*mais* Baptiste is a good nigger."

The parson moaned and dropped his chin into his hands.

"I was to of left for home to-morrow, sun-up, on the Isabella schooner. Pore Smyrny!" He deeply sighed.

"Posson Jone'," said Jules, leaning against the wall and smiling, "I swear you is the moz funny man I ever see. If I was you I would say, me, ' Ah! 'ow I am lucky! the money I los', it was not mine, anyhow!' My faith! shall a man make hisse'f to be the more sorry because the money he los' is not his? Me, I would say, 'it is a specious providence.'

"Ah! Misty Posson Jone'," he continued, "you make a so droll sermon ad the bull-ring. Ha! ha! I swear I think you can make money to preach thad sermon many time ad the theatre St. Philippe. Hah! you is the moz brave dat I never see, *mais* ad the same time the moz rilligious man. Where I'm goin' to fin' one priest to make like dat? *Mais*, why you can't cheer up an' be 'appy? Me, if I should be miserabl' like that I would kill meself."

The countryman only shook his head.

"*Bien*, Posson Jone', I have the so good news for you."

The prisoner looked up with eager inquiry.

"Las' evening when they lock' you, I come right off at M. De Blanc's house to get you let out of de calaboose; M. De Blanc he is the judge. So soon I was entering—'Ah! Jules, me boy, juz the man to make complete the game!' Posson Jone', it was a specious providence! I win in t'ree hours more dan six hundred dollah! Look." He produced a mass of bank-notes, *bons*, and due-bills.

"And you got the pass?" asked the parson, regarding the money with a sadness incomprehensible to Jules.

"It is here; it take the effect so soon the daylight."

"Jools, my friend, your kindness is in vain."

The Creole's face became a perfect blank.

"Because," said the parson, "for two reasons: firstly, I have broken the laws, and ought to stand the penalty; and secondly—you must really excuse me, Jools, you know, but the pass has been got onfairly, I'm afeerd. You told the judge I was innocent; and in neither case it don't become a Christian (which I hope

I can still say I am one) to ' do evil that good may come.' I muss stay."

M. St.-Ange stood up aghast, and for a moment speechless, at this exhibition of moral heroism; but an artifice was presently hit upon. " *Mais*, Posson Jone'! " —in his old *falsetto*—" de order—you cannot read it, it is in French—compel you to go hout, sir! "

" Is that so? " cried the parson, bounding up with radiant face—" is that so, Jools? "

The young man nodded, smiling; but, though he smiled, the fountain of his tenderness was opened. He made the sign of the cross as the parson knelt in prayer, and even whispered " Hail Mary," etc., quite through, twice over.

Morning broke in summer glory upon a cluster of villas behind the city, nestled under live-oaks and magnolias on the banks of a deep bayou, and known as Suburb St. Jean.

With the first beam came the West-Floridian and the Creole out upon the bank below the village. Upon the parson's arm hung a pair of antique saddle-bags. Baptiste limped wearily behind; both his eyes were encircled with broad, blue rings, and one cheek-bone bore the official impress of every knuckle of Colossus's left hand. The " beautiful to take care of somebody " had lost his charge. At mention of the negro he became wild, and, half in English, half in the " gumbo " dialect, said murderous things. Intimidated by Jules to calmness, he became able to speak confidently on one point; he could, would, and did swear that Colossus had gone home to the Florida parishes; he was almost certain; in fact, he thought so.

There was a clicking of pulleys as the three appeared upon the bayou's margin, and Baptiste pointed out, in the deep shadow of a great oak, the Isabella, moored among the bulrushes, and just spreading her sails for departure. Moving down to where she lay, the parson and his friend paused on the bank, loath to say fare-well.

" O Jools! " said the parson, " supposin' Colossus ain't gone home! O Jools, if you'll look him out for me, I'll never forget you—I'll never forget you, nohow, Jools. No, Jools, I never will believe he taken that money. Yes, I know all niggahs will steal "—he set foot upon the gang-plank—" but Colossus wouldn't steal from me. Good-bye."

" Misty Posson Jone'," said St.-Ange, putting his hand on the parson's arm with genuine affection, " hol' on. You see dis money—w'at I win las' night? Well, I win' it by a specious providence, ain't it? "

" There's no tellin'," said the humbled Jones. " Providence

> " ' Moves in a mysterious way
> His wonders to perform.' "

" Ah! " cried the Creole, " *c'est* very true. I ged this money in the mysterieuze way. *Mais*, if I keep dis money, you know where it goin' be to-night? "

" I really can't say," replied the parson.

" Goin' to de dev'," said the sweetly-smiling young man.

The schooner-captain, leaning against the shrouds, and even Baptiste, laughed outright.

" O Jools, you mustn't! "

" Well, den, w'at I shall do wid *it?* "

" Any thing! " answered the parson; " better do-nate it away to some poor man——"

" Ah! Misty Posson Jone', dat is w'at I want. You los' five hondred dollar'—'twas me fault."

" No, it wa'n't, Jools."

" *Mais*, it was! "

" No! "

" It *was* me fault! I *swear* it was me fault! *Mais*, here is five hondred dollar'; I wish you shall take it. Here! I don't got no use for money.—Oh, my faith! Posson Jone', you must not begin to cry some more."

Parson Jones was choked with tears. When he found voice he said:

" O Jools, Jools, Jools! my pore, noble, dear, mis-guidened friend! ef you hed of hed a Christian raisin'! May the Lord show you your errors better'n I kin, and bless you for your good intentions—oh, no! I cayn't touch that money with a ten-foot pole; it wa'n't rightly got; you must really excuse me, my dear friend, but I cayn't touch it."

St.-Ange was petrified.

" Good-bye, dear Jools," continued the parson. " I'm in the Lord's haynds, and he's very merciful, which I hope and trust you'll find it out. Good-bye! "—the schooner swang slowly off before the breeze—" good-bye! "

St.-Ange roused himself.

" Posson Jone'! make me hany'ow *dis* promise: you never, never, *never* will come back to New Orleans."

" Ah, Jools, the Lord willin', I'll never leave home again! "

" All right! " cried the Creole; " I thing he's willin'. Adieu, Posson Jone'. My faith'! you are the so fight-ing an' moz rilligious man as I never saw! Adieu! Adieu! "

Baptiste uttered a cry and presently ran by his mas-ter toward the schooner, his hands full of clods.

St.-Ange looked just in time to see the sable form of

Colossus of Rhodes emerge from the vessel's hold, and the pastor of Smyrna and Bethesda seize him in his embrace.

" O Colossus! you outlandish old nigger! Thank the Lord! Thank the Lord! "

The little Creole almost wept. He ran down the tow-path, laughing and swearing, and making confused allusion to the entire *personnel* and furniture of the lower regions.

By odd fortune, at the moment that St.-Ange further demonstrated his delight by tripping his mulatto into a bog, the schooner came brushing along the reedy bank with a graceful curve, the sails flapped, and the crew fell to poling her slowly along.

Parson Jones was on the deck, kneeling once more in prayer. His hat had fallen before him; behind him knelt his slave. In thundering tones he was confessing himself " a plum fool," from whom " the conceit had been jolted out," and who had been made to see that even his " nigger had the longest head of the two."

Colossus clasped his hands and groaned.

The parson prayed for a contrite heart.

" Oh, yes! " cried Colossus.

The master acknowledged countless mercies.

" Dat's so! " cried the slave.

The master prayed that they might still be " piled on."

" Glory! " cried the black man, clapping his hands; " pile on! "

" An' now," continued the parson, " bring this pore, backslidin' jackace of a parson and this pore ole fool nigger back to thar home in peace! "

" Pray fo' de money! " called Colossus.

But the parson prayed for Jules.

" Pray fo' de *money!* " repeated the negro.

" And oh, give thy servant back that there lost money ! "

Colossus rose stealthily, and tiptoed by his still shouting master. St.-Ange, the captain, the crew, gazed in silent wonder at the strategist. Pausing but an instant over the master's hat to grin an acknowledgment of his beholders' speechless interest, he softly placed in it the faithfully mourned and honestly prayed-for Smyrna fund; then, saluted by the gesticulative, silent applause of St.-Ange and the schooner-men, he resumed his first attitude behind his roaring master.

" Amen ! " cried Colossus, meaning to bring him to a close.

" Onworthy though I be——" cried Jones.

" *Amen!* " reiterated the negro.

" A-a-amen ! " said Parson Jones.

He rose to his feet, and, stooping to take up his hat, beheld the well-known roll. As one stunned, he gazed for a moment upon his slave, who still knelt with clasped hands and rolling eyeballs; but when he became aware of the laughter and cheers that greeted him from both deck and shore, he lifted eyes and hands to heaven, and cried like the veriest babe. And when he looked at the roll again, and hugged and kissed it, St.-Ange tried to raise a second shout, but choked, and the crew fell to their poles.

And now up runs Baptiste, covered with slime, and prepares to cast his projectiles. The first one fell wide of the mark; the schooner swung round into a long reach of water, where the breeze was in her favor; another shout of laughter drowned the maledictions of the muddy man; the sails filled; Colossus of Rhodes, smiling and bowing as hero of the moment, ducked as the main boom swept round, and the schooner, leaning slightly to the pleasant influence, rustled a moment over the

bulrushes, and then sped far away down the rippling
bayou.

M. Jules St.-Ange stood long, gazing at the receding
vessel as it now disappeared, now reappeared beyond
the tops of the high undergrowth; but, when an arm
of the forest hid it finally from sight, he turned town-
ward, followed by that fagged-out spaniel, his servant,
saying, as he turned, "Baptiste."

"*Miché?*"

"You know w'at I goin' do wid dis money?"

"*Non, m'sieur.*"

"Well, you can strike me dead if I don't goin' to
pay hall my debts! *Allons!*"

He began a merry little song to the effect that his
sweetheart was a wine-bottle, and master and man, leaving care behind, returned to the picturesque Rue Royale.
The ways of Providence are indeed strange. In all
Parson Jones's after-life, amid the many painful remi-
niscences of his visit to the City of the Plain, the sweet
knowledge was withheld from him that by the light of
the Christian virtue that shone from him even in his
great fall, Jules St.-Ange arose, and went to his father
an honest man.

OUR AROMATIC UNCLE

BY

Henry Cuyler Bunner

The title of Mr. Bunner's story is attractive and stimulating to the imagination. The plot is slight, yet clever in its use of the surprise element. Its leading character is a splendid illustration of a hero-worshipper who is himself the real hero. The atmosphere is especially good. It is warmed by family affection and fragrant with romance. This romance, as Mr. Grabo points out in "The Art of the Short Story," is suggested rather than recorded. The running away of the Judge's son and of his little admirer, the butcher-boy, really lies outside the story proper. "With these youthful adventures the story has not directly to do, but the hints of the antecedent action envelop the story with a romantic atmosphere. The reader speculates upon the story suggested, and thereby is the written story enriched and made a part of a larger whole."

OUR AROMATIC UNCLE *

It is always with a feeling of personal tenderness and regret that I recall his story, although it began long before I was born, and must have ended shortly after that important date, and although I myself never laid eyes on the personage of whom my wife and I always speak as " The Aromatic Uncle."

The story begins so long ago, indeed, that I can tell it only as a tradition of my wife's family. It goes back to the days when Boston was so frankly provincial a town that one of its leading citizens, a man of eminent position and ancient family, remarked to a young kinsman whom he was entertaining at his hospitable board, by way of pleasing and profitable discourse: " Nephew, it may interest you to know that it is Mr. Everett who has the *other* hindquarter of this lamb." This simple tale I will vouch for, for I got it from the lips of the nephew, who has been my uncle for so many years that I know him to be a trustworthy authority.

In those days which seem so far away—and yet the space between them and us is spanned by a lifetime of threescore years and ten—life was simpler in all its details; yet such towns as Boston, already old, had well-established local customs which varied not at all from year to year; many of which lingered in later phases of urban growth. In Boston, or at least in that part of Boston where my wife's family dwelt, it was the invariable custom for the head of the family to go to market

* From " Love in Old Cloathes and Other Stories," by F. C. Bunner. Copyright, 1896, by Charles Scribner's Sons.

in the early morning with his wife's list of the day's needs. When the list was filled, the articles were placed in a basket; and the baskets thus filled were systematically deposited by the market-boys at the back-door of the house to which they were consigned. Then the housekeeper came to the back-door at her convenience, and took the basket in. Exposed as this position must have been, such a thing as a theft of the day's edibles was unknown, and the first authentic account of any illegitimate handling of the baskets brings me to the introduction of my wife's uncle.

It was on a summer morning, as far as I can find out, that a little butcher-boy—a very little butcher-boy to be driving so big a cart—stopped in the rear of two houses that stood close together in a suburban street. One of these houses belonged to my wife's father, who was, from all I can gather, a very pompous, severe, and generally objectionable old gentleman; a Judge, and a very considerable dignitary, who apparently devoted all his leisure to making life miserable for his family. The other was owned by a comparatively poor and unimportant man, who did a shipping business in a small way. He had bought it during a period of temporary affluence, and it hung on his hands like a white elephant. He could not sell it, and it was turning his hair gray to pay the taxes on it. On this particular morning he had got up at four o'clock to go down to the wharves to see if a certain ship in which he was interested had arrived. It was due and overdue, and its arrival would settle the question of his domestic comfort for the whole year; for if it failed to appear, or came home with an empty bottom, his fate would be hard indeed; but if it brought him money or marketable goods from its long Oriental trip, he might take heart of grace and look forward to better times.

When the butcher's boy stopped at the house of my wife's father, he set down at the back-door a basket containing fish, a big joint of roast beef, and a generous load of fruit and vegetables, including some fine, fat oranges. At the other door he left a rather unpromising-looking lump of steak and a half-peck of potatoes, not of the first quality. When he had deposited these two burdens he ran back and started his cart up the road.

But he looked back as he did so, and he saw a sight familiar to him, and saw the commission of a deed entirely unfamiliar. A handsome young boy of about his own age stepped out of the back-door of my wife's father's house and looked carelessly around him. He was one of the boys who compel the admiration of all other boys—strong, sturdy, and a trifle arrogant.

He had long ago compelled the admiration of the little butcher-boy. They had been playmates together at the public school, and although the Judge's son looked down from an infinite height upon his poor little comrade, the butcher-boy worshipped him with the deepest and most fervent adoration. He had for him the admiring reverence which the boy who can't lick anybody has for the boy who can lick everybody. He was a superior being, a pattern, a model; an ideal never to be achieved, but perhaps in a crude, humble way to be imitated. And there is no hero-worship in the world like a boy's worship of a boy-hero.

The sight of this fortunate and adorable youth was familiar enough to the butcher-boy, but the thing he did startled and shocked that poor little workingman almost as much as if his idol had committed a capital crime right before his very eyes. For the Judge's son suddenly let a look into his face that meant mischief, glanced around him to see whether anybody was observing him or not, and, failing to notice the butcher-boy, quickly and dexterously changed the two baskets. Then he went back into the house and shut the door on himself.

The butcher-boy reined up his horse and jumped from his cart. His first impulse, of course, was to undo the shocking iniquity which the object of his admiration had committed. But before he had walked back a dozen yards, it struck him that he was taking a great liberty in spoiling the other boy's joke. It was wrong, of course, he knew it; but was it for him to rebuke the wrong-doing of such an exalted personage? If the Judge's son came out again, he would see that his joke had miscarried, and then he would be displeased. And to the butcher-boy it did not seem right in the nature of things that anything should displease the Judge's son. Three times he went hesitatingly backward and forward, trying to make up his mind, and then he made it up. The king could do no wrong. Of course he himself was doing wrong in not putting the baskets back where they belonged; but then he reflected, he took that sin on his own humble conscience, and in some measure took it off the conscience of the Judge's son—if, indeed, it troubled that lightsome conscience at all. And, of course, too, he knew that, being an apprentice, he would be whipped for it when the substitution was discovered. But he didn't mind being whipped for the boy he worshipped. So he drove out along the road; and the wife of the poor shipping-merchant, coming to the back-door, and finding the basket full of good things, and noticing especially the beautiful China oranges, naturally concluded that her husband's ship had come in, and that he had provided his family with a rare treat. And the Judge, when he came home to dinner, and Mrs. Judge introduced him to the rump-steak and potatoes—but I do not wish to make this story any more pathetic than is necessary.

.   .   .   .

A few months after this episode, perhaps indirectly in consequence of it—I have never been able to find out exactly—the Judge's son, my wife's uncle, ran away to sea, and for many years his recklessness, his strength, and his good looks were only traditions in the family, but traditions which he himself kept alive by remembrances than which none could have been more effective.

At first he wrote but seldom, later on more regularly, but his letters—I have seen many of them—were the most uncommunicative documents that I ever saw in my life. His wanderings took him to many strange places on the other side of the globe, but he never wrote of what he saw or did. His family gleaned from them that his health was good, that the weather was such-and-such, and that he wished to have his love, duty, and respects conveyed to his various relatives. In fact, the first positive bit of personal intelligence that they received from him was five years after his departure, when he wrote them from a Chinese port on letter-paper whose heading showed that he was a member of a commercial firm. The letter itself made no mention of the fact. As the years passed on, however, the letters came more regularly and they told less about the weather, and were slightly—very slightly—more expressive of a kind regard for his relatives. But at the best they were cramped by the formality of his day and generation, and we of to-day would have called them cold and perfunctory.

But the practical assurances that he gave of his undiminished—nay, his steadily increasing—affection for the people at home, were of a most satisfying character, for they were convincing proof not only of his love but of his material prosperity. Almost from his first time of writing he began to send gifts to all the members of the family. At first these were mere trifles, little curios of travel such as he was able to purchase out of a seaman's scanty wages; but as the years went on they grew richer and richer, till the munificence of the runaway son became the pride of the whole family.

The old house that had been in the suburbs of Boston was fairly in the heart of the city when I first made its acquaintance, and one of the famous houses of the town. And it was no wonder it was famous, for such a collection of Oriental furniture, bric-à-brac, and objects of art never was seen outside of a museum. There were ebony cabinets, book-cases, tables, and couches wonderfully carved and inlaid with mother-of-pearl. There were beautiful things in bronze and jade and ivory. There were all sorts of strange rugs and curtains and portières. As to the china-ware and the vases, no house was ever so stocked; and as for such trifles as shawls and fans and silk handkerchiefs, why such things were sent not singly but by dozens.

No one could forget his first entrance into that house. The great drawing-room was darkened by heavy curtains, and at first you had only a dim vision of the strange and graceful shapes of its curious furnishing. But you could not but be instantly conscious of the delicate perfume that pervaded the apartment, and, for the matter of that, the whole house. It was a combination of all the delightful Eastern smells—not sandalwood only, nor teak, nor couscous, but all these odors and a hundred others blent in one. Yet it was not heavy nor overpowering, but delightfully faint and sweet, diffused through those ample rooms. There was good reason, indeed, for the children of the generation to which my wife belonged to speak of the generous relative whom they had never seen as " Our Aromatic Uncle."

There were other uncles, and I have no doubt they gave
presents freely, for it was a wealthy and free-handed
family; but there was no other uncle who sent such a
delicate and delightful reminder with every gift, to
breathe a soft memory of him by day and by night.

. . . .

I did my courting in the sweet atmosphere of that
house, and, although I had no earthly desire to live in
Boston, I could not help missing that strangely blended
odor when my wife and I moved into an old house
in an old part of New York, whose former owners had
no connections in the Eastern trade. It was a charming and home-like old house; but at first, although my
wife had brought some belongings from her father's
house, we missed the pleasant flavor of our aromatic
uncle, for he was now my uncle, as well as my wife's.
I say at first, for we did not miss it long. Uncle David
—that was his name—not only continued to send his
fragrant gifts to my wife at Christmas and upon her
birthday, but he actually adopted me, too, and sent me
Chinese cabinets and Chinese gods in various minerals
and metals, and many articles designed for a smoker's
use, which no smoker would ever want to touch with a
ten-foot pole. But I cared very little about the utility
of these presents, for it was not many years before,
among them all, they set up that exquisite perfume in
the house, which we had learned to associate with our
aromatic uncle.

" Foo-choo-li, China, January—, 18—.

" Dear Nephew and Niece: The Present is to inform you that
I have this day shipped to your address, per Steamer Ocean
Queen, one marble and ebony Table, six assorted gods, and a
blue Dinner set; also that I purpose leaving this Country for a
visit to the Land of my Nativity on the 6th of March next, and
will, if same is satisfactory to you, take up my Abode temporarily in your household. Should same not be satisfactory,

please cable at my charge. Messrs. Smithson & Smithson, my
Customs Brokers, will attend to all charges on the goods, and
will deliver them at your readiness. The health of this place
is better than customary by reason of the cool weather, which
Health I am as usual enjoying. Trusting that you both are at
present in possession of the same Blessing, and will so continue,
I remain, dear nephew and niece,

" Your affectionate
" UNCLE."

. . . .

This was, I believe, by four dozen words—those which
he used to inform us of his intention of visiting America
—the longest letter that Uncle David had ever written
to any member of his family. It also conveyed more
information about himself than he had ever given since
the day he ran away to sea. Of course we cabled the
old gentleman that we should be delighted to see him.

And, late that spring, at some date at which he could
not possibly have been expected to arrive, he turned up
at our house.

Of course we had talked a great deal about him, and
wondered what manner of a man we should find him.
Between us, my wife and I had got an idea of his personal appearance which I despair of conveying in words.
Vaguely, I should say that we had pictured him as
something mid-way between an abnormally tall Chinese
mandarin and a benevolent Quaker. What we found
when we got home and were told that our uncle from
India was awaiting us, was a shrunken and bent old
gentleman, dressed very cleanly and neatly in black
broadcloth, with a limp, many-pleated shirt-front of old-
fashioned style, and a plain black cravat. If he had
worn an old-time stock we could have forgiven him
the rest of the disappointment he cost us; but we had
to admit to ourselves that he had the most absolutely
commonplace appearance of all our acquaintance. In
fact, we soon discovered that, except for a taciturnity

the like of which we had never encountered, our aromatic
uncle had positively not one picturesque characteristic
about him. Even his aroma was a disappointment. He
had it, but it was patchouly or some other cheap perfume of the sort, wherewith he scented his handkerchief,
which was not even a bandanna, but a plain decent
white one of the unnecessarily large sort which clergy-
men and old gentlemen affect.

But, even if we could not get one single romantic asso-
ciation to cluster about him, we very soon got to like
the old gentleman. It is true that at our first meeting,
after saying " How d'ye do " to me and receiving in impassive placidity the kiss which my wife gave him, he
relapsed into dead silence, and continued to smoke a clay
pipe with a long stem and a short bowl. This instrument he filled and re-filled every few minutes, and it
seemed to be his only employment. We plied him with
questions, of course, but to these he responded with a
wonderful brevity. In the course of an hour's conversation we got from him that he had had a pleasant voyage,
that it was not a long voyage, that it was not a short
voyage, that it was about the usual voyage, that he had
not been seasick, that he was glad to be back, and that
he was not surprised to find the country very much
changed. This last piece of information was repeated
in the form of a simple " No," given in reply to the
direct question; and although it was given politely, and
evidently without the least unamiable intent, it made us
both feel very cheap. After all, it *was* absurd to ask a
man if he were surprised to find the country changed
after fifty or sixty years of absence. Unless he was an
idiot, and unable to read at that, he must have expected
something of the sort.

But we grew to like him. He was thoroughly kind and
inoffensive in every way. He was entirely willing to be

talked to, but he did not care to talk. If it was absolutely necessary, he *could* talk, and when he did talk he
always made me think of the " French-English Diction-
ary for the Pocket," compiled by the ingenious Mr.
John Bellows; for nobody except that extraordinary
Englishman could condense a greater amount of information into a smaller number of words. During the
time of his stay with us I think I learned more about
China than any other man in the United States knew,
and I do not believe that the aggregate of his utter-
ances in the course of that six months could have
amounted to one hour's continuous talk. Don't ask
me for the information. I had no sort of use for it, and
I forgot it as soon as I could. I like Chinese bric-à-
brac, but my interest in China ends there.

Yet it was not long before Uncle David slid into his
own place in the family circle. We soon found that
he did not expect us to entertain him. He wanted only
to sit quiet and smoke his pipe, to take his two daily
walks by himself, and to read the daily paper one afternoon and Macaulay's " History of England " the next.
He was never tired of sitting and gazing amiably but
silently at my wife; and, to head the list of his good
points, he would hold the baby by the hour, and for
some mysterious reason that baby, who required the exhibition of seventeen toys in a minute to be reasonably
quiet in the arms of anybody else, would sit placidly in
Uncle David's lap, teething away steadily on the old
gentleman's watch-chain, as quiet and as solemn and as
aged in appearance as any one of the assorted gods of
porcelain and jade and ivory which our aromatic uncle
had sent us.

.   .   .   .

The old house in Boston was a thing of the past. My
wife's parents had been dead for some years, and no one

remained of her immediate family except a certain Aunt Lucretia, who had lived with them until shortly before our marriage, when the breaking up of the family sent her West to find a home with a distant relative in California. We asked Uncle Davy if he had stopped to see Aunt Lucretia as he came through California. He said he had not. We asked him if he wanted to have Aunt Lucretia invited on to pass a visit during his stay with us. He answered that he did not. This did not surprise us at all. You might think that a brother might long to see a sister from whom he had been separated nearly all of a long lifetime, but then you might never have met Aunt Lucretia. My wife made the offer only from a sense of duty; and only after a contest with me which lasted three days and nights. Nothing but loss of sleep during an exceptionally busy time at my office induced me to consent to her project of inviting Aunt Lucretia. When Uncle David put his veto upon the proposition I felt that he might have taken back all his rare and costly gifts, and I could still have loved him.

But Aunt Lucretia came, all the same. My wife is afflicted with a New England conscience, originally of a most uncomfortable character. It has been much modified and ameliorated, until it is now considerably less like a case of moral hives; but some wretched lingering remnant of the original article induced her to write to Aunt Lucretia that Uncle David was staying with us, and of course Aunt Lucretia came without invitation and without warning, dropping in on us with ruthless unexpectedness.

. . . .

You may not think, from what I have said, that Aunt Lucretia's visit was a pleasant event. But it was, in some respects; for it was not only the shortest visit she ever paid us, but it was the last with which she ever honored us.

She arrived one morning shortly after breakfast, just as we were preparing to go out for a drive. She would not have been Aunt Lucretia if she had not upset somebody's calculations at every turn of her existence. We welcomed her with as much hypocrisy as we could summon to our aid on short notice, and she was not more than usually offensive, although she certainly did herself full justice in telling us what she thought of us for not inviting her as soon as we even heard of Uncle David's intention to return to his native land. She said she ought to have been the first to embrace her beloved brother—to whom I don't believe she had given one thought in more years than I have yet seen.

Uncle David was dressing for his drive. His long residence in tropical countries had rendered him sensitive to the cold, and although it was a fine, clear September day, with the thermometer at about sixty, he was industriously building himself up with a series of overcoats. On a really snappy day I have known him to get into six of these garments; and when he entered the room on this occasion I think he had on five, at least.

My wife had heard his familiar foot on the stairs, and Aunt Lucretia had risen up and braced herself for an outburst of emotional affection. I could see that it was going to be such a greeting as is given only once in two or three centuries, and then on the stage. I felt sure it would end in a swoon, and I was looking around for a sofa-pillow for the old lady to fall upon, for from what I knew of Aunt Lucretia I did not believe she had ever swooned enough to be able to go through the performance without danger to her aged person.

But I need not have troubled myself. Uncle David toddled into the room, gazed at Aunt Lucretia without a sign of recognition in his features, and toddled out into the hall, where he got his hat and gloves, and went out to the front lawn, where he always paced up and down for a few minutes before taking a drive, in order to stimulate his circulation. This was a surprise, but Aunt Lucretia's behavior was a greater surprise. The moment she set eyes on Uncle David the theatrical fervor went out of her entire system, literally in one instant; and an absolutely natural, unaffected astonishment displayed itself in her expressive and strongly marked features. For almost a minute, until the sound of Uncle David's footsteps had died away, she stood absolutely rigid; while my wife and I gazed at her spellbound.

Then Aunt Lucretia pointed one long bony finger at me, and hissed out with a true feminine disregard of grammar:

" That ain't *him!* "

.   .   .   .

" David," said Aunt Lucretia, impressively, " had only one arm. He lost the other in Madagascar."

I was too dumfounded to take in the situation. I remember thinking, in a vague sort of way, that Madagascar was a curious sort of place to go for the purpose of losing an arm; but I did not apprehend the full significance of this disclosure until I heard my wife's distressed protestations that Aunt Lucretia must be mistaken; there must be some horrible mistake somewhere.

But Aunt Lucretia was not mistaken, and there was no mistake anywhere. The arm had been lost, and lost in Madagascar, and she could give the date of the occurrence, and the circumstances attendant. Moreover, she produced her evidence on the spot. It was an old daguerreotype, taken in Calcutta a year or two after the Madagascar episode. She had it in her hand-bag, and she opened it with fingers trembling with rage and excitement. It showed two men standing side by side near one of those three-foot Ionic pillars that were an indispensable adjunct of photography in its early stages. One of the men was large, broad-shouldered, and handsome—unmistakably a handsome edition of Aunt Lucretia. His empty left sleeve was pinned across his breast. The other man was, making allowance for the difference in years, no less unmistakably the Uncle David who was at that moment walking to and fro under our windows. For one instant my wife's face lighted up.

"Why, Aunt Lucretia," she cried, "there he is! That's Uncle David, dear Uncle David."

"There he is *not*," replied Aunt Lucretia. "That's his business partner—some common person that he picked up on the ship he first sailed in—and, upon my word, I do believe it's that wretched creature outside. And I'll Uncle David *him*."

She marched out like a grenadier going to battle, and we followed her meekly. There was, unfortunately, no room for doubt in the case. It only needed a glance to see that the man with one arm was a member of my wife's family, and that the man by his side, *our* Uncle David, bore no resemblance to him in stature or features.

Out on the lawn Aunt Lucretia sailed into the dear old gentleman in the five overcoats with a volley of vituperation. He did not interrupt her, but stood patiently to the end, listening, with his hands behind his back; and when, with her last gasp of available breath, Aunt Lucretia demanded:

"Who—who—who *are* you, you wretch?" he responded, calmly and respectfully:

"I'm Tommy Biggs, Miss Lucretia."

But just here my wife threw herself on his neck and hugged him, and cried:

"You're my own dear Uncle David, *anyway!*"

It was a fortunate, a gloriously fortunate, inspiration. Aunt Lucretia drew herself up in speechless scorn, stretched forth her bony finger, tried to say something and failed, and then she and her hand-bag went out of my gates, never to come in again.

.   .   .   .

When she had gone, our aromatic uncle—for we shall always continue to think of him in that light, or rather in that odor—looked thoughtfully after her till she disappeared, and then made one of the few remarks I ever knew him to volunteer.

" Ain't changed a mite in forty-seven years."

Up to this time I had been in a dazed condition of mind. As I have said, my wife's family was extinct save for herself and Aunt Lucretia, and she remembered so little of her parents, and she looked herself so little like Aunt Lucretia, that it was small wonder that neither of us remarked Uncle David's unlikeness to the family type. We knew that he did not resemble the ideal we had formed of him; and that had been the only consideration we had given to his looks. Now, it took only a moment of reflection to recall the fact that all the members of the family had been tall and shapely, and that even between the ugly ones, like Aunt Lucretia, and the pretty ones, like my wife, there was a certain resemblance. Perhaps it was only the nose— the nose is the brand in most families, I believe—but whatever it was, I had only to see my wife and Aunt Lucretia together to realize that the man who had passed himself off as our Uncle David had not one feature in common with either of them—nor with the one-armed man in the daguerreotype. I was thinking of this, and looking at my wife's troubled face, when our aromatic uncle touched me on the arm.

" I'll explain," he said, " to you. *You* tell *her*."

We dismissed the carriage, went into the house, and sat down. The old gentleman was perfectly cool and collected, but he lit his clay pipe, and reflected for a good five minutes before he opened his mouth. Then he began:

"Finest man in the world, sir. Finest *boy* in the world. Never anything like him. But, peculiarities. Had 'em. Peculiarities. Wouldn't write home. Wouldn't"—here he hesitated—"send things home. I had to do it. Did it for him. Didn't want his folks to know. Other peculiarities. Never had any money. Other peculiarities. Drank. Other peculiarities. Ladies. Finest man in the world, all the same. Nobody like him. Kept him right with his folks for thirty-one years. Then died. Fever. Canton. Never been myself since. Kept right on writing, all the same. Also"—here he hesitated again—"sending things. Why? Don't know. Been a fool all my life. Never could do anything but make money. No family, no friends. Only *him*. Ran away to sea to look after him. Did look after him. Thought maybe your wife would be some like him. Barring peculiarities, she is. Getting old. Came here for company. Meant no harm. Didn't calculate on Miss Lucretia."

Here he paused and smoked reflectively for a minute or two.

"Hot in the collar—Miss Lucretia. Haughty. Like him, some. Just like she was forty-seven years ago. Slapped my face one day when I was delivering meat, because my jumper wasn't clean. Ain't changed a mite."

This was the first condensed statement of the case of our aromatic uncle. It was only in reply to patient, and, I hope, loving, gentle, and considerate, questioning that the whole story came out—at once pitiful and noble

—of the poor little butcher-boy who ran away to sea to be body-guard, servant, and friend to the splendid, showy, selfish youth whom he worshipped; whose heartlessness he cloaked for many a long year, who lived upon his bounty, and who died in his arms, nursed with a tenderness surpassing that of a brother. And as far as I could find out, ingratitude and contempt had been his only reward.

.   .   .   .

I need not tell you that when I repeated all this to my wife she ran to the old gentleman's room and told him all the things that I should not have known how to say—that we cared for him; that we wanted him to stay with us; that he was far, far more our uncle than the brilliant, unprincipled scapegrace who had died years before, dead for almost a lifetime to the family who idolized him; and that we wanted him to stay with us as long as kind heaven would let him. But it was of no use. A change had come over our aromatic uncle which we could both of us see, but could not understand. The duplicity of which he had been guilty weighed on his spirit. The next day he went out for his usual walk, and he never came back. We used every means of search and inquiry, but we never heard from him until we got this letter from Foo-choo-li:

.   .   .   .

"DEAR NEPHEW AND NIECE: The present is to inform you that I am enjoying the Health that might be expected at my Age, and in my condition of Body, which is to say bad. I ship you by to-day's steamer, Pacific Monarch, four dozen jars of ginger, and two dozen ditto preserved oranges, to which I would have added some other Comfits, which I purposed offering for your acceptance, if it were not that my Physician has forbidden me to leave my Bed. In case of Fatal Results from this trying Condition, my Will, duly attested, and made in your favor, will be placed in your hands by Messrs. Smithson & Smithson, my Customs

Brokers, who will also pay all charges on goods sent. The
Health of this place being unfavorably affected by the Weather,
you are unlikely to hear more from,

"Dear Nephew and Niece,

"Your affectionate

"UNCLE."

And we never did hear more—except for his will—
from Our Aromatic Uncle; but our whole house still
smells of his love.

QUALITY

BY

JOHN GALSWORTHY

Here the emphasis is upon character. The plot is negligible—hardly exists. The setting is carefully worked out because it is essential to the characterization. By means of the shoemaker the author reveals at least a part of his philosophy of life—that there is a subtle relation between a man and his work. Each reacts on the other. If a man recognizes the Soul of Things and strives to give it proper expression, he becomes an Artist and influences for good all who come into contact with him.

QUALITY *

I knew him from the days of my extreme youth, because he made my father's boots; inhabiting with his elder brother two little shops let into one, in a small by-street—now no more, but then most fashionably placed in the West End.

That tenement had a certain quiet distinction; there was no sign upon its face that he made for any of the Royal Family—merely his own German name of Gessler Brothers: and in the window a few pairs of boots. I remember that it always troubled me to account for those unvarying boots in the window, for he made only what was ordered, reaching nothing down, and it seemed so inconceivable that what he made could ever have failed to fit. Had he bought them to put there? That, too, seemed inconceivable. He would never have tolerated in his house leather on which he had not worked himself. Besides, they were too beautiful—the pair of pumps, so inexpressibly slim, the patent leathers with cloth tops, making water come into one's mouth, the tall brown riding boots with marvellous sooty glow, as if, though new, they had been worn a hundred years. Those pairs could only have been made by one who saw before him the Soul of Boot—so truly were they prototypes incarnating the very spirit of all foot-gear. These thoughts, of course, came to me later, though even when I was promoted to him, at the age of perhaps fourteen, some inkling haunted me of the dignity of himself

* From "The Inn of Tranquillity," by John Galsworthy. Copyright, 1912, by Charles Scribner's Sons.

and brother. For to make boots—such boots as he made —seemed to me then, and still seems to me, mysterious and wonderful.

I remember well my shy remark, one day, while stretching out to him my youthful foot:

" Isn't it awfully hard to do, Mr. Gessler? "

And his answer, given with a sudden smile from out of the sardonic redness of his beard: " Id is an Ardt! "

Himself, he was a little as if made from leather, with his yellow crinkly face, and crinkly reddish hair and beard, and neat folds slanting down his cheeks to the corners of his mouth, and his guttural and one-toned voice; for leather is a sardonic substance, and stiff and slow of purpose. And that was the character of his face, save that his eyes, which were gray-blue, had in them the simple gravity of one secretly possessed by the Ideal. His elder brother was so very like him—though watery, paler in every way, with a great industry—that sometimes in early days I was not quite sure of him until the interview was over. Then I knew that it was he, if the words, " I will ask my brudder," had not been spoken; and that, if they had, it was his elder brother.

When one grew old and wild and ran up bills, one somehow never ran them up with Gessler Brothers. It would not have seemed becoming to go in there and stretch out one's foot to that blue iron-spectacled glance, owing him for more than—say—two pairs, just the comfortable reassurance that one was still his client.

For it was not possible to go to him very often—his boots lasted terribly, having something beyond the temporary—some, as it were, essence of boot stitched into them.

One went in, not as into most shops, in the mood of: " Please serve me, and let me go! " but restfully, as one enters a church; and, sitting on the single wooden chair, waited—for there was never anybody there. Soon, over the top edge of that sort of well—rather dark, and smelling soothingly of leather—which formed the shop, there would be seen his face, or that of his elder brother, peering down. A guttural sound, and the tip-tap of bast slippers beating the narrow wooden stairs, and he would stand before one without coat, a little bent, in leather apron, with sleeves turned back, blinking—as if awakened from some dream of boots, or like an owl surprised in daylight and annoyed at this interruption.

And I would say: "How do you do, Mr. Gessler? Could you make me a pair of Russia leather boots?"

Without a word he would leave me, retiring whence he came, or into the other portion of the shop, and I would continue to rest in the wooden chair, inhaling the incense of his trade. Soon he would come back, holding in his thin, veined hand a piece of gold-brown leather. With eyes fixed on it, he would remark: "What a beautiful biece!" When I, too, had admired it, he would speak again. "When do you wand dem?" And I would answer: "Oh! As soon as you conveniently can." And he would say: "To-morrow fordnighd?" Or if he were his elder brother: "I will ask my brudder!"

Then I would murmur: "Thank you! Good-morning, Mr. Gessler." "Goot-morning!" he would reply, still looking at the leather in his hand. And as I moved to the door, I would hear the tip-tap of his bast slippers restoring him, up the stairs, to his dream of boots. But if it were some new kind of foot-gear that he had not yet made me, then indeed he would observe ceremony—divesting me of my boot and holding it long in his hand, looking at it with eyes at once critical and loving, as if recalling the glow with which he had created it, and rebuking the way in which one had disorganized this masterpiece. Then, placing my foot on a piece of paper, he would two or three times tickle the outer edges with a pencil and pass his nervous fingers over my toes, feeling himself into the heart of my requirements.

I cannot forget that day on which I had occasion to say to him: "Mr. Gessler, that last pair of town walking-boots creaked, you know."

He looked at me for a time without replying, as if expecting me to withdraw or qualify the statement, then said:

"Id shouldn'd 'ave greaked."

"It did, I'm afraid."

"You goddem wed before dey found demselves?"

"I don't think so."

At that he lowered his eyes, as if hunting for memory of those boots, and I felt sorry I had mentioned this grave thing.

"Zend dem back!" he said; "I will look at dem."

A feeling of compassion for my creaking boots surged up in me, so well could I imagine the sorrowful long curiosity of regard which he would bend on them.

"Zome boods," he said slowly, "are bad from birdt. If I can do noding wid dem, I dake dem off your bill."

Once (once only) I went absent-mindedly into his shop in a pair of boots bought in an emergency at some large firm's. He took my order without showing me any leather, and I could feel his eyes penetrating the inferior integument of my foot. At last he said:

"Dose are nod my boods."

The tone was not one of anger, nor of sorrow, not even of contempt, but there was in it something quiet that froze the blood. He put his hand down and pressed a finger on the place where the left boot, endeavoring to be fashionable, was not quite comfortable.

"Id 'urds you dere," he said. "Dose big virms 'ave

no self-respect. Drash!'' And then, as if something had given way within him, he spoke long and bitterly. It was the only time I ever heard him discuss the conditions and hardships of his trade.

'' Dey get id all,'' he said, '' dey get id by adverdisement, nod by work. Dey dake it away from us, who lofe our boods. Id gomes to this—bresently I haf no work. Every year id gets less—you will see.'' And looking at his lined face I saw things I had never noticed before, bitter things and bitter struggle—and what a lot of gray hairs there seemed suddenly in his red beard!

As best I could, I explained the circumstances of the purchase of those ill-omened boots. But his face and voice made so deep impression that during the next few minutes I ordered many pairs. Nemesis fell! They lasted more terribly than ever. And I was not able conscientiously to go to him for nearly two years.

When at last I went I was surprised to find that outside one of the two little windows of his shop another name was painted, also that of a bootmaker—making, of course, for the Royal Family. The old familiar boots, no longer in dignified isolation, were huddled in the single window. Inside, the now contracted well of the one little shop was more scented and darker than ever. And it was longer than usual, too, before a face peered down, and the tip-tap of the bast slippers began. At last he stood before me, and, gazing through those rusty iron spectacles, said:

'' Mr. ——, isn'd it?''

'' Ah! Mr. Gessler,'' I stammered, '' but your boots are really *too* good, you know! See, these are quite decent still!'' And I stretched out to him my foot. He looked at it.

'' Yes,'' he said, '' beople do nod wand good boods, id seems.''

To get away from his reproachful eyes and voice I hastily remarked: "What have you done to your shop?"

He answered quietly: "Id was too exbensif. Do you wand some boods?"

I ordered three pairs, though I had only wanted two, and quickly left. I had, I do not know quite what feeling of being part, in his mind, of a conspiracy against him; or not perhaps so much against him as against his idea of boot. One does not, I suppose, care to feel like that; for it was again many months before my next visit to his shop, paid, I remember, with the feeling: "Oh! well, I can't leave the old boy—so here goes! Perhaps it'll be his elder brother!"

For his elder brother, I knew, had not character enough to reproach me, even dumbly.

And, to my relief, in the shop there did appear to be his elder brother, handling a piece of leather.

"Well, Mr. Gessler," I said, "how are you?"

He came close, and peered at me.

"I am breddy well," he said slowly; "but my elder brudder is dead."

And I saw that it was indeed himself—but how aged and wan! And never before had I heard him mention his brother. Much shocked, I murmured: "Oh! I am sorry!"

"Yes," he answered, "he was a good man, he made a good bood; but he is dead." And he touched the top of his head, where the hair had suddenly gone as thin as it had been on that of his poor brother, to indicate, I suppose, the cause of death. "He could nod ged over losing de oder shop. Do you wand any boods?" And he held up the leather in his hand: "Id's a beaudiful biece."

I ordered several pairs. It was very long before they

came—but they were better than ever. One simply could not wear them out. And soon after that I went abroad.

It was over a year before I was again in London. And the first shop I went to was my old friend's. I had left a man of sixty, I came back to one of seventy-five, pinched and worn and tremulous, who genuinely, this time, did not at first know me.

" Oh! Mr. Gessler," I said, sick at heart; " how splendid your boots are! See, I've been wearing this pair nearly all the time I've been abroad; and they're not half worn out, are they? "

He looked long at my boots—a pair of Russia leather, and his face seemed to regain steadiness. Putting his hand on my instep, he said:

" Do dey vid you here? I 'ad drouble wid dat bair, I remember."

I assured him that they had fitted beautifully.

" Do you wand any boods? " he said. " I can make dem quickly; id is a slack dime."

I answered: " Please, please! I want boots all round —every kind! "

" I will make a vresh model. Your food must be bigger." And with utter slowness, he traced round my foot, and felt my toes, only once looking up to say:

" Did I dell you my brudder was dead? "

To watch him was painful, so feeble had he grown; I was glad to get away.

I had given those boots up, when one evening they came. Opening the parcel, I set the four pairs out in a row. Then one by one I tried them on. There was no doubt about it. In shape and fit, in finish and quality of leather, they were the best he had ever made me. And in the mouth of one of the town walking-boots I found his bill. The amount was the same as usual, but it gave me quite a shock. He had never before sent it in till quarter day. I flew down-stairs, and wrote a check, and posted it at once with my own hand.

A week later, passing the little street, I thought I would go in and tell him how splendidly the new boots fitted. But when I came to where his shop had been, his name was gone. Still there, in the window, were the slim pumps, the patent leathers with cloth tops, the sooty riding boots.

I went in, very much disturbed. In the two little shops—again made into one—was a young man with an English face.

" Mr. Gessler in? " I said.

He gave me a strange, ingratiating look.

" No, sir," he said, " no. But we can attend to anything with pleasure. We've taken the shop over. You've seen our name, no doubt, next door. We make for some very good people."

" Yes, yes," I said; " but Mr. Gessler? "

" Oh! " he answered; " dead."

" Dead! But I only received these boots from him last Wednesday week."

" Ah! " he said; " a shockin' go. Poor old man starved 'imself."

" Good God! "

" Slow starvation, the doctor called it! You see he went to work in such a way! Would keep the shop on; wouldn't have a soul touch his boots except himself. When he got an order, it took him such a time. People won't wait. He lost everybody. And there he'd sit, goin' on and on—I will say that for him—not a man in London made a better boot! But look at the competition! He never advertised! Would 'ave the best leather, too, and do it all 'imself. Well, there it is. What could you expect with his ideas? "

" But starvation——! "

" That may be a bit flowery, as the sayin' is—but I know myself he was sittin' over his boots day and night, to the very last. You see I used to watch him. Never gave 'imself time to eat; never had a penny in the house. All went in rent and leather. How he lived so long I don't know. He regular let his fire go out. He was a character. But he made good boots."

" Yes," I said, " he made good boots."

And I turned and went out quickly, for I did not want that youth to know that I could hardly see.

THE TRIUMPH OF NIGHT

BY

EDITH WHARTON

This is a mystery plot in which the supernatural furnishes the interest. In dealing with the supernatural Mrs. Wharton does not allow it to become horrible or grotesque. She secures plausibility by having for its leading characters practical business men—not a woman, hysterical or otherwise, really appears—and by placing them in a perfectly conventional setting. The apparition is not accompanied by blood stains, shroud, or uncanny noises. Sometimes the writer of the supernatural feels that he must explain his mystery by material agencies. The effect is to disappoint the reader who has yielded himself to the conditions imposed by the author, and is willing, for the time at least, to believe in ghosts. Mrs. Wharton makes no such mistake. She does not spoil the effect by commonplace explanation.

In characterization Mrs. Wharton reveals the power not only to analyze subtly temperaments and motives, but also to describe vividly with a few words. This phrasal power is illustrated when she says of Faxon that he "had a healthy face, but dying hands," and of Lavington that "his pinched smile was screwed to his blank face like a gas-light to a white-washed wall."

THE TRIUMPH OF NIGHT *

I

It was clear that the sleigh from Weymore had not
come; and the shivering young traveller from Boston,
who had so confidently counted on jumping into it when
he left the train at Northridge Junction, found himself
standing alone on the open platform, exposed to the full
assault of night-fall and winter.

The blast that swept him came off New Hampshire
snow-fields and ice-hung forests. It seemed to have
traversed interminable leagues of frozen silence, filling
them with the same cold roar and sharpening its edge
against the same bitter black-and-white landscape.
Dark, searching, and sword-like, it alternately muffled
and harried its victim, like a bull-fighter now whirling
his cloak and now planting his darts. This analogy
brought home to the young man the fact that he himself had no cloak, and that the overcoat in which he
had faced the relatively temperate airs of Boston seemed
no thicker than a sheet of paper on the bleak heights
of Northridge. George Faxon said to himself that the
place was uncommonly well-named. It clung to an exposed ledge over the valley from which the train had
lifted him, and the wind combed it with teeth of steel
that he seemed actually to hear scraping against the
wooden sides of the station. Other building there was
none: the village lay far down the road, and thither—
since the Weymore sleigh had not come—Faxon saw

* From *Scribner's Magazine*, August, 1914.

himself under the immediate necessity of plodding through several feet of snow.

He understood well enough what had happened at Weymore: his hostess had forgotten that he was coming. Young as Faxon was, this sad lucidity of soul had been acquired as the result of long experience, and he knew that the visitors who can least afford to hire a carriage are almost always those whom their hosts forget to send for. Yet to say Mrs. Culme had forgotten him was perhaps too crude a way of putting it. Similar incidents led him to think that she had probably told her maid to tell the butler to telephone the coachman to tell one of the grooms (if no one else needed him) to drive over to Northridge to fetch the new secretary; but on a night like this what groom who respected his rights would fail to forget the order?

Faxon's obvious course was to struggle through the drifts to the village, and there rout out a sleigh to convey him to Weymore; but what if, on his arrival at Mrs. Culme's, no one remembered to ask him what this devotion to duty had cost? That, again, was one of the contingencies he had expensively learned to look out for, and the perspicacity so acquired told him it would be cheaper to spend the night at the Northridge inn, and advise Mrs. Culme of his presence there by telephone. He had reached this decision, and was about to entrust his luggage to a vague man with a lantern who seemed to have some loose connection with the railway company, when his hopes were raised by the sound of sleighbells.

Two vehicles were just dashing up to the station, and from the foremost there sprang a young man swathed in furs.

'' Weymore?— No, these are not the Weymore sleighs.''

The voice was that of the youth who had jumped to the platform—a voice so agreeable that, in spite of the words, it fell reassuringly on Faxon's ears. At the same moment the wandering station-lantern, casting a transient light on the speaker, showed his features to be in the pleasantest harmony with his voice. He was very fair and very young—hardly in the twenties, Faxon thought—but his face, though full of a morning freshness, was a trifle too thin and fine-drawn, as though a vivid spirit contended in him with a strain of physical weakness. Faxon was perhaps the quicker to notice such delicacies of balance because his own temperament hung on lightly vibrating nerves, which yet, as he believed, would never quite swing him beyond the arc of a normal sensibility.

" You expected a sleigh from Weymore? " the youth continued, standing beside Faxon like a slender column of fur.

Mrs. Culme's secretary explained his difficulty, and the new-comer brushed it aside with a contemptuous " Oh, *Mrs. Culme!* " that carried both speakers a long way toward reciprocal understanding.

" But then you must be——" The youth broke off with a smile of interrogation.

" The new secretary? Yes. But apparently there are no notes to be answered this evening." Faxon's laugh deepened the sense of solidarity which had so promptly established itself between the two.

The new-comer laughed also. " Mrs. Culme," he explained, " was lunching at my uncle's to-day, and she said you were due this evening. But seven hours is a long time for Mrs. Culme to remember anything."

" Well," said Faxon philosophically, " I suppose that's one of the reasons why she needs a secretary. And I've always the inn at Northridge," he concluded.

The youth laughed again. He was at the age when predicaments are food for gaiety.

" Oh, but you haven't, though! It burned down last week."

" The deuce it did! " said Faxon; but the humor of the situation struck him also before its inconvenience. His life, for years past, had been mainly a succession of resigned adaptations, and he had learned, before dealing practically with his embarrassments, to extract from most of them a small tribute of amusement.

" Oh, well, there's sure to be somebody in the place who can put me up."

" No one *you* could put up with. Besides, Northridge is three miles off, and our place—in the opposite direction—is a little nearer." Through the darkness, Faxon saw his friend sketch a gesture of self-introduction. " My name's Frank Rainer, and I'm staying with my uncle at Overdale. I've driven over to meet two friends of his, who are due in a few minutes from New York. If you don't mind waiting till they arrive I'm sure Overdale can do you better than Northridge. We're only down from town for a few days, but the house is always ready for a lot of people."

" But your uncle——? " Faxon could only object, with the odd sense, through his embarrassment, that it would be magically dispelled by his invisible friend's next words.

" Oh, my uncle—you'll see! I answer for *him!* I dare say you've heard of him—John Lavington? "

John Lavington! There was a certain irony in asking if one had heard of John Lavington! Even from a post of observation as obscure as that of Mrs. Culme's secretary, the rumor of John Lavington's money, of his pictures, his politics, his charities and his hospitality, was as difficult to escape as the roar of a cataract in a

mountain solitude. It might almost have been said that
the one place in which one would not have expected
to come upon him was in just such a solitude as now
surrounded the speakers—at least in this deepest hour
of its desertedness. But it was just like Lavington's
brilliant ubiquity to put one in the wrong even there.

" Oh, yes, I've heard of your uncle."

" Then you *will* come, won't you? We've only five
minutes to wait," young Rainer urged, in the tone that
dispels scruples by ignoring them; and Faxon found
himself accepting the invitation as simply as it was offered.

A delay in the arrival of the New York train lengthened their five minutes to fifteen; and as they paced
the icy platform Faxon began to see why it had seemed
the most natural thing in the world to accede to his
new acquaintance's suggestion. It was because Frank
Rainer was one of the privileged beings who simplify
human intercourse by the atmosphere of confidence and
good humor they diffuse. He produced this effect,
Faxon noted, by the exercise of no gift save his youth,
of no art save his sincerity; but these qualities were
revealed in a smile of such appealing sweetness that
Faxon felt, as never before, what Nature can achieve
when she deigns to match the face with the mind.

He learned that the young man was the ward, and
only nephew, of John Lavington, with whom he had
made his home since the death of his mother, the great
man's sister. Mr. Lavington, Rainer said, had been " a
regular brick " to him—" But then he is to every one,
you know "—and the young fellow's situation seemed
in fact to be perfectly in keeping with his person. Apparently the only shade that had ever rested on him
was cast by the physical weakness which Faxon had
already detected. Young Rainer had been threatened

with a disease of the lungs which, according to the highest authorities, made banishment to Arizona or New Mexico inevitable. "But luckily my uncle didn't pack me off, as most people would have done, without getting another opinion. Whose? Oh, an awfully clever chap, a young doctor with a lot of new ideas, who simply laughed at my being sent away, and said I'd do perfectly well in New York if I didn't dine out too much, and if I dashed off occasionally to Northridge for a little fresh air. So it's really my uncle's doing that I'm not in exile—and I feel no end better since the new chap told me I needn't bother." Young Rainer went on to confess that he was extremely fond of dining out, dancing, and other urban distractions; and Faxon, listening to him, concluded that the physician who had refused to cut him off altogether from these pleasures was probably a better psychologist than his seniors.

"All the same you ought to be careful, you know." The sense of elder-brotherly concern that forced the words from Faxon made him, as he spoke, slip his arm impulsively through Frank Rainer's.

The latter met the movement with a responsive pressure. "Oh, I *am:* awfully, awfully. And then my uncle has such an eye on me!"

"But if your uncle has such an eye on you, what does he say to your swallowing knives out here in this Siberian wild?"

Rainer raised his fur collar with a careless gesture. "It's not that that does it—the cold's good for me."

"And it's not the dinners and dances? What is it, then?" Faxon good-humoredly insisted; to which his companion answered with a laugh: "Well, my uncle says it's being bored; and I rather think he's right!"

His laugh ended in a spasm of coughing and a struggle for breath that made Faxon, still holding his arm, guide him hastily into the shelter of the fireless waiting-room.

Young Rainer had dropped down on the bench against the wall and pulled off one of his fur gloves to grope for a handkerchief. He tossed aside his cap and drew the handkerchief across his forehead, which was intensely white, and beaded with moisture, though his face retained a healthy glow. But Faxon's gaze remained fastened to the hand he had uncovered: it was so long, so colorless, so wasted, so much older than the brow he passed it over.

"It's queer—a healthy face but dying hands," the secretary mused; he somehow wished young Rainer had kept on his glove.

The whistle of the express drew the young men to their feet, and the next moment two heavily-furred gentlemen had descended to the platform and were breasting the rigor of the night. Frank Rainer introduced them as Mr. Grisben and Mr. Balch, and Faxon, while their luggage was being lifted into the second sleigh, discerned them, by the roving lantern-gleam, to be an elderly gray-headed pair, apparently of the average prosperous business cut.

They saluted their host's nephew with friendly familiarity, and Mr. Grisben, who seemed the spokesman of the two, ended his greeting with a genial—"and many many more of them, dear boy!" which suggested to Faxon that their arrival coincided with an anniversary. But he could not press the inquiry, for the seat allotted him was at the coachman's side, while Frank Rainer joined his uncle's guests inside the sleigh.

A swift flight (behind such horses as one could be sure of John Lavington's having) brought them to tall gate-posts, an illuminated lodge, and an avenue on which the snow had been levelled to the smoothness of marble. At the end of the avenue the long house loomed through trees, its principal bulk dark but one wing sending out a ray of welcome; and the next moment Faxon was receiving a violent impression of warmth and light, of hot-house plants, hurrying servants, a vast spectacular oak hall like a stage-setting, and, in its unreal middle distance, a small concise figure, correctly dressed, conventionally featured, and utterly unlike his rather florid conception of the great John Lavington.

The shock of the contrast remained with him through his hurried dressing in the large impersonally luxurious bedroom to which he had been shown. "I don't see where he comes in," was the only way he could put it, so difficult was it to fit the exuberance of Lavington's public personality into his host's contracted frame and manner. Mr. Lavington, to whom Faxon's case had been rapidly explained by young Rainer, had welcomed him with a sort of dry and stilted cordiality that exactly matched his narrow face, his stiff hand, the whiff of scent on his evening handkerchief. "Make yourself at home—at home!" he had repeated, in a tone that suggested, on his own part, a complete inability to perform the feat he urged on his visitor. "Any friend of Frank's . . . delighted . . . make yourself thoroughly at home!"

II

In spite of the balmy temperature and complicated conveniences of Faxon's bedroom, the injunction was not easy to obey. It was wonderful luck to have found a night's shelter under the opulent roof of Overdale, and he tasted the physical satisfaction to the full. But the place, for all its ingenuities of comfort, was oddly cold and unwelcoming. He couldn't have said why, and could only suppose that Mr. Lavington's intense personality—intensely negative, but intense all the same—must, in some occult way, have penetrated every corner of his dwelling. Perhaps, though, it was merely that Faxon himself was tired and hungry, more deeply chilled than he had known till he came in from the cold, and unutterably sick of all strange houses, and of the prospect of perpetually treading other people's stairs.

"I hope you're not famished?" Rainer's slim figure was in the doorway. "My uncle has a little business to attend to with Mr. Grisben, and we don't dine for half an hour. Shall I fetch you, or can you find your way down? Come straight to the dining-room—the second door on the left of the long gallery."

He disappeared, leaving a ray of warmth behind him, and Faxon, relieved, lit a cigarette and sat down by the fire.

Looking about with less haste, he was struck by a detail that had escaped him. The room was full of flowers—a mere "bachelor's room," in the wing of a house opened only for a few days, in the dead middle of a New Hampshire winter! Flowers were everywhere, not in senseless profusion, but placed with the same conscious art he had remarked in the grouping of the blossoming shrubs that filled the hall. A vase of arums stood on the writing-table, a cluster of strange-hued carnations on the stand at his elbow, and from wide bowls of glass and porcelain clumps of freesia-bulbs diffused their melting fragrance. The fact implied acres of glass—but that was the least interesting part of it. The flowers themselves, their quality, selection and arrangement, attested on some one's part—and on whose but John Lavington's?—a solicitous and sensitive passion for that particular embodiment of beauty. Well, it simply made the man, as he had appeared to Faxon, all the harder to understand!

The half-hour elapsed, and Faxon, rejoicing at the near prospect of food, set out to make his way to the dining-room. He had not noticed the direction he had followed in going to his room, and was puzzled, when he left it, to find that two staircases, of apparently equal importance, invited him. He chose the one to his right, and reached, at its foot, a long gallery such as Rainer had described. The gallery was empty, the doors down its length were closed; but Rainer had said: " The second to the left," and Faxon, after pausing for some chance enlightenment which did not come, laid his hand on the second knob to the left.

The room he entered was square, with dusky picture-hung walls. In its centre, about a table lit by veiled lamps, he fancied Mr. Lavington and his guests to be already seated at dinner; then he perceived that the table was covered not with viands but with papers, and that he had blundered into what seemed to be his host's study. As he paused in the irresolution of embarrassment Frank Rainer looked up.

" Oh, here's Mr. Faxon. Why not ask him——? "

Mr. Lavington, from the end of the table, reflected his nephew's smile in a glance of impartial benevolence.

" Certainly. Come in, Mr. Faxon. If you won't think it a liberty—— "

Mr. Grisben, who sat opposite his host, turned his solid head toward the door. " Of course Mr. Faxon's an American citizen? "

Frank Rainer laughed. " That all right! . . . Oh, no, not one of your pin-pointed pens, Uncle Jack! Haven't you got a quill somewhere? "

Mr. Balch, who spoke slowly and as if reluctantly, in a muffled voice of which there seemed to be very little left,

raised his hand to say: "One moment: you acknowledge this to be——?"

"My last will and testament?" Rainer's laugh
redoubled. "Well, I won't answer for the 'last.' It's
the first one, anyway."

"It's a mere formula," Mr. Balch explained.

"Well, here goes." Rainer dipped his quill in the
inkstand his uncle had pushed in his direction, and
dashed a gallant signature across the document.

Faxon, understanding what was expected of him, and
conjecturing that the young man was signing his will
on the attainment of his majority, had placed himself
behind Mr. Grisben, and stood awaiting his turn to affix
his name to the instrument. Rainer, having signed, was
about to push the paper across the table to Mr. Balch;
but the latter, again raising his hand, said in his sad
imprisoned voice: "The seal——?"

"Oh, does there have to be a seal?"

Faxon, looking over Mr. Grisben at John Lavington,
saw a faint frown between his impassive eyes. "Really,
Frank!" He seemed, Faxon thought, slightly irritated
by his nephew's frivolity.

"Who's got a seal?" Frank Rainer continued, glancing about the table. "There doesn't seem to be one
here."

Mr. Grisben interposed. "A wafer will do. Lavington, you have a wafer?"

Mr. Lavington had recovered his serenity. "There
must be some in one of the drawers. But I'm ashamed
to say I don't know where my secretary keeps these
things. He ought, of course, to have seen to it that a
wafer was sent with the document."

"Oh, hang it——" Frank Rainer pushed the paper
aside: "It's the hand of God—and I'm hungry as a
wolf. Let's dine first, Uncle Jack."

" I think I've a seal upstairs," said Faxon suddenly.

Mr. Lavington sent him a barely perceptible smile.
" So sorry to give you the trouble——"

" Oh, I say, don't send him after it now. Let's wait till after dinner! "

Mr. Lavington continued to smile on his guest, and the latter, as if under the faint coercion of the smile, turned from the room and ran upstairs. Having taken the seal from his writing-case he came down again, and once more opened the door of the study. No one was speaking when he entered—they were evidently awaiting his return with the mute impatience of hunger, and he put the seal in Rainer's reach, and stood watching while Mr. Grisben struck a match and held it to one of the candles flanking the inkstand. As the wax descended on the paper Faxon remarked again the singular emaciation, the premature physical weariness, of the hand that held it: he wondered if Mr. Lavington had ever noticed his nephew's hand, and if it were not poignantly visible to him now.

With this thought in his mind, Faxon raised his eyes to look at Mr. Lavington. The great man's gaze rested on Frank Rainer with an expression of untroubled benevolence; and at the same instant Faxon's attention was attracted by the presence in the room of another person, who must have joined the group while he was upstairs searching for the seal. The new-comer was a man of about Mr. Lavington's age and figure, who stood directly behind his chair, and who, at the moment when Faxon first saw him, was gazing at young Rainer with an equal intensity of attention. The likeness between the two men—perhaps increased by the fact that the hooded lamps on the table left the figure behind the chair in shadow—struck Faxon the more because of

the strange contrast in their expression. John Lavington, during his nephew's blundering attempt to drop
the wax and apply the seal, continued to fasten on him
a look of half-amused affection; while the man behind
the chair, so oddly reduplicating the lines of his features
and figure, turned on the boy a face of pale hostility.

The impression was so startling Faxon forgot what
was going on about him. He was just dimly aware of
young Rainer's exclaiming: "Your turn, Mr. Grisben!" of Mr. Grisben's ceremoniously protesting:
"No—no; Mr. Faxon first," and of the pen's being
thereupon transferred to his own hand. He received it
with a deadly sense of being unable to move, or even to
understand what was expected of him, till he became
conscious of Mr. Grisben's paternally pointing out the
precise spot on which he was to leave his autograph.
The effort to fix his attention and steady his hand pro-
longed the process of signing, and when he stood up—a
strange weight of fatigue on all his limbs—the figure
behind Mr. Lavington's chair was gone.

Faxon felt an immediate sense of relief. It was puzzling that the man's exit should have been so rapid
and noiseless, but the door behind Mr. Lavington was
screened by a tapestry hanging, and Faxon concluded
that the unknown looker-on had merely had to raise it
to pass out. At any rate, he was gone, and with his
withdrawal the strange weight was lifted. Young Rainer
was lighting a cigarette, Mr. Balch meticulously inscrib-
ing his name at the foot of the document, Mr. Lavington
—his eyes no longer on his nephew—examining a
strange white-winged orchid in the vase at his elbow.
Everything suddenly seemed to have grown natural and
simple again, and Faxon found himself responding with
a smile to the affable gesture with which his host declared: " And now, Mr. Faxon, we'll dine."

III

" I wonder how I blundered into the wrong room just now; I thought you told me to take the second door to the left," Faxon said to Frank Rainer as they followed the older men down the gallery.

" So I did; but I probably forgot to tell you which staircase to take. Coming from your bedroom, I ought to have said the fourth door to the right. It's a puzzling house, because my uncle keeps adding to it from year to year. He built this room last summer for his modern pictures."

Young Rainer, pausing to open another door, touched an electric button which sent a circle of light about the walls of a long room hung with canvases of the French impressionist school.

Faxon advanced, attracted by a shimmering Monet, but Rainer laid a hand on his arm.

" He bought that last week for a thundering price. But come along—I'll show you all this after dinner. Or *he* will rather—he loves it."

" Does he really love things? "

Rainer stared, clearly perplexed at the question. " Rather! Flowers and pictures especially! Haven't you noticed the flowers? I suppose you think his manner's cold; it seems so at first; but he's really awfully keen about things."

Faxon looked quickly at the speaker. " Has your uncle a brother? "

" Brother? No—never had. He and my mother were the only ones."

" Or any relation who—who looks like him? Who might be mistaken for him? "

" Not that I ever heard of. Does he remind you of some one? "

" Yes."

" That's queer. We'll ask him if he's got a double. Come on! "

But another picture had arrested Faxon, and some minutes elapsed before he and his young host reached the dining-room. It was a large room, with the same conventionally handsome furniture and delicately grouped flowers; and Faxon's first glance showed him that only three men were seated about the dining-table. The man who had stood behind Mr. Lavington's chair was not present, and no seat awaited him.

When the young men entered, Mr. Grisben was speaking, and his host, who faced the door, sat looking down at his untouched soup-plate and turning the spoon about in his small dry hand.

" It's pretty late to call them rumors—they were devilish close to facts when we left town this morning," Mr. Grisben was saying, with an unexpected incisiveness of tone.

Mr. Lavington laid down his spoon and smiled interrogatively. " Oh, facts—what *are* facts? Just the way a thing happens to look at a given minute."

" You haven't heard anything from town? " Mr. Grisben persisted.

" Not a syllable. So you see . . . Balch, a little more of that *petite marmite*. Mr. Faxon . . . between Frank and Mr. Grisben, please."

The dinner progressed through a series of complicated courses, ceremoniously dispensed by a stout butler attended by three tall footmen, and it was evident that Mr. Lavington took a somewhat puerile satisfaction in the pageant. That, Faxon reflected, was probably the joint in his armor—that and the flowers. He had changed the subject—not abruptly but firmly—when the young men entered, but Faxon perceived that it still

possessed the thoughts of the two elderly visitors, and
Mr. Balch presently observed, in a voice that seemed to
come from the last survivor down a mine-shaft: "If
it *does* come, it will be the biggest crash since '93."

Mr. Lavington looked bored but polite. "Wall Street
can stand crashes better than it could then. It's got a
robuster constitution."

"Yes; but——"

"Speaking of constitutions," Mr. Grisben intervened:
"Frank, are you taking care of yourself?"

A flush rose to young Rainer's cheeks.

"Why, of course! Isn't that what I'm here for?"

"You're here about three days in the month, aren't
you? And the rest of the time it's crowded restaurants
and hot ballrooms in town. I thought you were to be
shipped off to New Mexico?"

"Oh, I've got a new man who says that's rot."

"Well, you don't look as if your new man were right,"
said Mr. Grisben bluntly.

Faxon saw the lad's color fade, and the rings of
shadow deepen under his gay eyes. At the same moment
his uncle turned to him with a renewed intensity of
attention. There was such solicitude in Mr. Lavington's
gaze that it seemed almost to fling a tangible shield between his nephew and Mr. Grisben's tactless scrutiny.

"We think Frank's a good deal better," he began;
"this new doctor——"

The butler, coming up, bent discreetly to whisper a
word in his ear, and the communication caused a sudden change in Mr. Lavington's expression. His face
was naturally so colorless that it seemed not so much
to pale as to fade, to dwindle and recede into something blurred and blotted-out. He half rose, sat down
again and sent a rigid smile about the table.

"Will you excuse me? The telephone. Peters, go

on with the dinner.'' With small precise steps he walked
out of the door which one of the footmen had hastened
to throw open.

A momentary silence fell on the group; then Mr.
Grisben once more addressed himself to Rainer. '' You
ought to have gone, my boy; you ought to have gone.''

The anxious look returned to the youth's eyes. '' My
uncle doesn't think so, really.''

'' You're not a baby, to be always governed on your
uncle's opinion. You came of age to-day, didn't you?
Your uncle spoils you . . . that's what's the matter. . . .''

The thrust evidently went home, for Rainer laughed
and looked down with a slight accession of color.

'' But the doctor——''

'' Use your common sense, Frank! You had to try
twenty doctors to find one to tell you what you wanted
to be told.''

A look of apprehension overshadowed Rainer's
gaiety. '' Oh, come—I say! . . . What would *you*
do? '' he stammered.

'' Pack up and jump on the first train.'' Mr. Grisben
leaned forward and laid a firm hand on the young man's
arm. '' Look here: my nephew Jim Grisben is out
there ranching on a big scale. He'll take you in and be
glad to have you. You say your new doctor thinks it
won't do you any good; but he doesn't pretend to say
it will do you harm, does he? Well, then—give it a trial.
It'll take you out of hot theatres and night restaurants,
anyhow. . . . And all the rest of it. . . . Eh,
Balch? ''

'' Go! '' said Mr. Balch hollowly. '' Go *at once*,'' he
added, as if a closer look at the youth's face had impressed on him the need of backing up his friend.

Young Rainer had turned ashy-pale. He tried to

stiffen his mouth into a smile. " Do I look as bad as all that ? "

Mr. Grisben was helping himself to terrapin. " You look like the day after an earthquake," he said concisely.

The terrapin had encircled the table, and been deliberately enjoyed by Mr. Lavington's three visitors (Rainer, Faxon noticed, left his plate untouched) before the door was thrown open to re-admit their host.

Mr. Lavington advanced with an air of recovered composure. He seated himself, picked up his napkin, and consulted the gold-monogrammed menu. " No, don't bring back the filet. . . . Some terrapin; yes. . . ." He looked affably about the table. " Sorry to have deserted you, but the storm has played the deuce with the wires, and I had to wait a long time before I could get a good connection. It must be blowing up for a blizzard."

" Uncle Jack," young Rainer broke out, " Mr. Grisben's been lecturing me."

Mr. Lavington was helping himself to terrapin. " Ah —what about ? "

" He thinks I ought to have given New Mexico a show."

" I want him to go straight out to my nephew at Santa Paz and stay there till his next birthday." Mr. Lavington signed to the butler to hand the terrapin to Mr. Grisben, who, as he took a second helping, addressed himself again to Rainer. " Jim's in New York now, and going back the day after to-morrow in Olyphant's private car. I'll ask Olyphant to squeeze you in if you'll go. And when you've been out there a week or two, in the saddle all day and sleeping nine hours a night, I suspect you won't think much of the doctor who prescribed New York."

Faxon spoke up, he knew not why. " I was out there once: it's a splendid life. I saw a fellow—oh, a really *bad* case—who'd been simply made over by it."

" It *does* sound jolly," Rainer laughed, a sudden eagerness of anticipation in his tone.

His uncle looked at him gently. " Perhaps Grisben's right. It's an opportunity——"

Faxon looked up with a start: the figure dimly perceived in the study was now more visibly and tangibly planted behind Mr. Lavington's chair.

" That's right, Frank: you see your uncle approves. And the trip out there with Olyphant isn't a thing to be missed. So drop a few dozen dinners and be at the Grand Central the day after to-morrow at five."

Mr. Grisben's pleasant gray eye sought corroboration of his host, and Faxon, in a cold anguish of suspense, continued to watch him as he turned his glance on Mr. Lavington. One could not look at Lavington without seeing the presence at his back, and it was clear that, the next minute, some change in Mr. Grisben's expression must give his watcher a clue.

But Mr. Grisben's expression did not change: the gaze he fixed on his host remained unperturbed, and the clue he gave was the startling one of not seeming to see the other figure.

Faxon's first impulse was to look away, to look anywhere else, to resort again to the champagne glass the watchful butler had already brimmed; but some fatal attraction, at war in him with an overwhelming physical resistance, held his eyes upon the spot they feared.

The figure was still standing, more distinctly, and therefore more resemblingly, at Mr. Lavington's back; and while the latter continued to gaze affectionately at his nephew, his counterpart, as before, fixed young Rainer with eyes of deadly menace.

Faxon, with what felt like an actual wrench of the muscles, dragged his own eyes from the sight to scan the other countenances about the table; but not one revealed the least consciousness of what he saw, and a sense of mortal isolation sank upon him.

" It's worth considering, certainly——" he heard Mr. Lavington continue; and as Rainer's face lit up, the face behind his uncle's chair seemed to gather into its look all the fierce weariness of old unsatisfied hates. That was the thing that, as the minutes labored by, Faxon was becoming most conscious of. The watcher behind the chair was no longer merely malevolent: he had grown suddenly, unutterably tired. His hatred seemed to well up out of the very depths of balked effort and thwarted hopes, and the fact made him more pitiable, and yet more dire.

Faxon's look reverted to Mr. Lavington, as if to surprise in him a corresponding change. At first none was visible: his pinched smile was screwed to his blank face like a gas-light to a white-washed wall. Then the fixity of the smile became ominous: Faxon saw that its wearer was afraid to let it go. It was evident that Mr. Lavington was unutterably tired too, and the discovery sent a colder current through Faxon's veins. Looking down at his untouched plate, he caught the soliciting twinkle of the champagne glass; but the sight of the wine turned him sick.

" Well, we'll go into the details presently," he heard Mr. Lavington say, still on the question of his nephew's future. " Let's have a cigar first. No—not here, Peters." He turned his smile on Faxon. " When we've had coffee I want to show you my pictures."

" Oh, by the way, Uncle Jack—Mr. Faxon wants to know if you've got a double? "

" A double? " Mr. Lavington, still smiling, continued

to address himself to his guest. "Not that I know of.
Have you seen one, Mr. Faxon?"

Faxon thought: "My God, if I look up now they'll
both be looking at me!" To avoid raising his eyes he
made as though to lift the glass to his lips; but his hand
sank inert, and he looked up. Mr. Lavington's glance
was politely bent on him, but with a loosening of the
strain about his heart he saw that the figure behind
the chair still kept its gaze on Rainer.

"Do you think you've seen my double, Mr. Faxon?"

Would the other face turn if he said yes? Faxon
felt a dryness in his throat. "No," he answered.

"Ah? It's possible I've a dozen. I believe I'm
extremely usual-looking," Mr. Lavington went on
conversationally; and still the other face watched
Rainer.

"It was . . . a mistake . . . a confusion of memory . . ." Faxon heard himself stammer. Mr. Lavington pushed back his chair, and as he did so Mr. Grisben
suddenly leaned forward.

"Lavington! What have we been thinking of? We
haven't drunk Frank's health!"

Mr. Lavington reseated himself. "My dear boy! . . .
Peters, another bottle. . . ." He turned to his nephew.
"After such a sin of omission I don't presume to
propose the toast myself . . . but Frank knows. . . .
Go ahead, Grisben!"

The boy shone on his uncle. "No, no, Uncle Jack!
Mr. Grisben won't mind. Nobody but *you*—to-day!"

The butler was replenishing the glasses. He filled
Mr. Lavington's last, and Mr. Lavington put out his
small hand to raise it. . . . As he did so, Faxon looked
away.

"Well, then—All the good I've wished you in all the
past years. . . . I put it into the prayer that the com-

ing ones may be healthy and happy and many . . . and *many,* dear boy! ' '

Faxon saw the hands about him reach out for their glasses. Automatically, he made the same gesture. His eyes were still on the table, and he repeated to himself with a trembling vehemence: '' I won't look up! I won't. . . . I won't. . . .''

His fingers clasped the stem of the glass, and raised it to the level of his lips. He saw the other hands making the same motion. He heard Mr. Grisben's genial '' Hear! Hear! '' and Mr. Balch's hollow echo. He said to himself, as the rim of the glass touched his lips: '' I won't look up! I swear I won't!——'' and he looked.

The glass was so full that it required an extraordinary effort to hold it there, brimming and suspended, during the awful interval before he could trust his hand to lower it again, untouched, to the table. It was this merciful preoccupation which saved him, kept him from crying out, from losing his hold, from slipping down into the bottomless blackness that gaped for him. As long as the problem of the glass engaged him he felt able to keep his seat, manage his muscles, fit unnoticeably into the group; but as the glass touched the table his last link with safety snapped. He stood up and dashed out of the room.

IV

In the gallery, the instinct of self-preservation helped him to turn back and sign to young Rainer not to follow. He stammered out something about a touch of dizziness, and joining them presently; and the boy waved an unsuspecting hand and drew back.

At the foot of the stairs Faxon ran against a servant.

"I should like to telephone to Weymore," he said with dry lips.

"Sorry, sir; wires all down. We've been trying the last hour to get New York again for Mr. Lavington."

Faxon shot on to his room, burst into it, and bolted the door. The mild lamplight lay on furniture, flowers, books, in the ashes a log still glimmered. He dropped down on the sofa and hid his face. The room was utterly silent, the whole house was still: nothing about him gave a hint of what was going on, darkly and dumbly, in the horrible room he had flown from, and with the covering of his eyes oblivion and reassurance seemed to fall on him. But they fell for a moment only; then his lids opened again to the monstrous vision. There it was, stamped on his pupils, a part of him forever, an indelible horror burnt into his body and brain. But why into his—just his? Why had he alone been chosen to see what he had seen? What business was it of *his*, in God's name? Any one of the others, thus enlightened, might have exposed the horror and defeated it; but *he*, the one weaponless and defenceless spectator, the one whom none of the others would believe or understand if he attempted to reveal what he knew—*he* alone had been singled out as the victim of this atrocious initiation!

Suddenly he sat up, listening: he had heard a step on the stairs. Some one, no doubt, was coming to see how he was—to urge him, if he felt better, to go down and join the smokers. Cautiously he opened his door; yes, it was young Rainer's step. Faxon looked down the passage, remembered the other stairway, and darted to it. All he wanted was to get out of the house. Not another instant would he breathe its abominable air! What business was it of *his*, in God's name?

He reached the opposite end of the lower gallery, and

beyond it saw the hall by which he had entered. It was empty, and on a long table he recognized his coat and cap among the furs of the other travellers. He got into his coat, unbolted the door, and plunged into the purifying night.

The darkness was deep, and the cold so intense that for an instant it stopped his breathing. Then he perceived that only a thin snow was falling, and resolutely set his face for flight. The trees along the avenue dimly marked his way as he hastened with long strides over the beaten snow. Gradually, while he walked, the tumult in his brain subsided. The impulse to fly still drove him forward, but he began to feel that he was flying from a terror of his own creating, and that the most urgent reason for escape was the need of hiding his state, of shunning other eyes' scrutiny till he should regain his balance.

He had spent the long hours in the train in fruitless broodings on a discouraging situation, and he remembered how his bitterness had turned to exasperation when he found that the Weymore sleigh was not awaiting him. It was absurd, of course; but, though he had joked with Rainer over Mrs. Culme's forgetfulness, to confess it had cost a pang. That was what his rootless life had brought him to: for lack of a personal stake in things his sensibility was at the mercy of such trivial accidents. . . . Yes; that, and the cold and fatigue, the absence of hope and the haunting sense of starved aptitudes, all these had brought him to the perilous verge over which, once or twice before, his terrified brain had hung.

Why else, in the name of any imaginable logic, human or devilish, should he, a stranger, be singled out for this experience? What could it mean to him, how was

he related to it, what bearing had it on his case? . . .
Unless, indeed, it was just because he was a stranger—
a stranger everywhere—because he had no personal life,
no warm strong screen of private egotisms to shield
him from exposure, that he had developed this abnormal
sensitiveness to the vicissitudes of others. The thought
pulled him up with a shudder. No! Such a fate was
too abominable; all that was strong and sound in him
rejected it. A thousand times better regard himself
as ill, disorganized, deluded, than as the predestined
victim of such warnings!

He reached the gates and paused before the darkened lodge. The wind had risen and was sweeping the
snow into his face in lacerating streamers. The cold had
him in its grasp again, and he stood uncertain. Should
he put his sanity to the test and go back? He turned
and looked down the dark drive to the house. A single
ray shone through the trees, evoking a picture of the
lights, the flowers, the faces grouped about that fatal
room. He turned and plunged out into the road.

He remembered that, about a mile from Overdale,
the coachman had pointed out the road to Northridge;
and he began to walk in that direction. Once in the
road, he had the gale in his face, and the wet snow on
his moustache and eye-lashes instantly hardened to
metal. The same metal seemed to be driving a million
blades into his throat and lungs, but he pushed on,
desperately determined, the vision of the warm room
pursuing him.

The snow in the road was deep and uneven. He
stumbled across ruts and sank into drifts, and the wind
rose before him like a granite cliff. Now and then he
stopped, gasping, as if an invisible hand had tightened
an iron band about his body; then he started again,
stiffening himself against the stealthy penetration of the

cold. The snow continued to descend out of a pall of inscrutable darkness, and once or twice he paused, fearing he had missed the road to Northridge; but, seeing no sign of a turn, he ploughed on doggedly.

At last, feeling sure that he had walked for more than a mile, he halted and looked back. The act of turning brought immediate relief, first because it put his back to the wind, and then because, far down the road, it showed him the advancing gleam of a lantern. A sleigh was coming—a sleigh that might perhaps give him a lift to the village! Fortified by the hope, he began to walk back toward the light. It seemed to come forward very slowly, with unaccountable zigzags and waverings; and even when he was within a few yards of it he could catch no sound of sleigh-bells. Then the light paused and became stationary by the roadside, as though carried by a pedestrian who had stopped, exhausted by the cold. The thought made Faxon hasten on, and a moment later he was stooping over a motionless figure huddled against the snow-bank. The lantern had dropped from its bearer's hand, and Faxon, fearfully raising it, threw its light into the face of Frank Rainer.

" Rainer! What on earth are you doing here? "

The boy smiled back through his pallor. " What are *you*, I'd like to know? " he retorted; and, scrambling to his feet with a clutch on Faxon's arm, he added gaily: " Well, I've run you down, anyhow! "

Faxon stood confounded, his heart sinking. The lad's face was gray.

" What madness——" he began.

" Yes, it *is*. What on earth did you do it for? "

" I? Do what? . . . Why, I . . . I was just taking a walk. . . . I often walk at night. . . . "

Frank Rainer burst into a laugh. " On such nights?
Then you hadn't bolted? "

" Bolted? "

" Because I'd done something to offend you? My
uncle thought you had."

Faxon grasped his arm. " Did your uncle send you
after me? "

" Well, he gave me an awful rowing for not going
up to your room with you when you said you were ill.
And when we found you'd gone we were frightened—
and he was awfully upset—so I said I'd catch you. . . .
You're *not* ill, are you? "

" Ill? No. Never better." Faxon picked up the
lantern. " Come; let's go back. It was awfully hot in
that dining-room," he added.

" Yes; I hoped it was only that."

They trudged on in silence for a few minutes; then
Faxon questioned: " You're not too done up? "

" Oh, no. It's a lot easier with the wind behind us."

" All right. Don't talk any more."

They pushed ahead, walking, in spite of the light
that guided them, more slowly than Faxon had walked
alone into the gale. The fact of his companion's stumbling against a drift gave him a pretext for saying:
" Take hold of my arm," and Rainer, obeying, gasped
out: " I'm blown! "

" So am I. Who wouldn't be? "

" What a dance you led me! If it hadn't been for
one of the servants' happening to see you——"

" Yes: all right. And now, won't you kindly shut
up? "

Rainer laughed and hung on him. " Oh, the cold
doesn't hurt me. . . ."

For the first few minutes after Rainer had over-
taken him, anxiety for the lad had been Faxon's only

thought. But as each laboring step carried them nearer to the spot he had been fleeing, the reasons for his flight grew more ominous and more insistent. No, he was not ill; he was not distraught and deluded—he was the instrument singled out to warn and save; and here he was, irresistibly driven, dragging the victim back to his doom!

The intensity of the conviction had almost checked his steps. But what could he do or say? At all costs he must get Rainer out of the cold, into the house and into his bed. After that he would act.

The snow-fall was thickening, and as they reached a stretch of the road between open fields the wind took them at an angle, lashing their faces with barbed thongs. Rainer stopped to take breath, and Faxon felt the heavier pressure of his arm.

" When we get to the lodge, can't we telephone to the stable for a sleigh? "

" If they're not all asleep at the lodge."

" Oh, I'll manage. Don't talk! " Faxon ordered; and they plodded on. . . .

At length the lantern ray showed ruts that curved away from the road under tree-darkness.

Faxon's spirits rose. " There's the gate! We'll be there in five minutes."

As he spoke he caught, above the boundary hedge, the gleam of a light at the farther end of the dark avenue. It was the same light that had shone on the scene of which every detail was burnt into his brain; and he felt again its overpowering reality. No—he couldn't let the boy go back!

They were at the lodge at last, and Faxon was hammering on the door. He said to himself: " I'll get him inside first, and make them give him a hot drink. Then I'll see—I'll find an argument. . . ."

There was no answer to his knocking, and after an interval Rainer said: "Look here—we'd better go on."

"No!"

"I can, perfectly——"

"You sha'n't go to the house, I say!" Faxon furiously redoubled his blows, and at length steps sounded on the stairs. Rainer was leaning against the lintel, and as the door opened the light from the hall flashed on his pale face and fixed eyes. Faxon caught him by the arm and drew him in.

"It *was* cold out there," he sighed; and then, abruptly, as if invisible shears at a single stroke had cut every muscle in his body, he swerved, drooped on Faxon's arm, and seemed to sink into nothing at his feet.

The lodge-keeper and Faxon bent over him, and somehow, between them, lifted him into the kitchen and laid him on a sofa by the stove.

The lodge-keeper, stammering: "I'll ring up the house," dashed out of the room. But Faxon heard the words without heeding them: omens mattered nothing now, beside this woe fulfilled. He knelt down to undo the fur collar about Rainer's throat, and as he did so he felt a warm moisture on his hands. He held them up, and they were red. . . .

V

The palms threaded their endless line along the yellow river. The little steamer lay at the wharf, and George Faxon, sitting in the veranda of the wooden hotel, idly watched the coolies carrying the freight across the gang-plank.

He had been looking at such scenes for two months. Nearly five had elapsed since he had descended from the train at Northridge and strained his eyes for the sleigh that was to take him to Weymore: Weymore, which he was never to behold! . . . Part of the interval—the first part—was still a great gray blur. Even now he could not be quite sure how he had got back to Boston, reached the house of a cousin, and been thence transferred to a quiet room looking out on snow under bare trees. He looked out a long time at the same scene, and finally one day a man he had known at Harvard came to see him and invited him to go out on a business trip to the Malay Peninsula.

" You've had a bad shake-up, and it'll do you no end of good to get away from things."

When the doctor came the next day it turned out that he knew of the plan and approved it. " You ought to be quiet for a year. Just loaf and look at the landscape," he advised.

Faxon felt the first faint stirrings of curiosity.

" What's been the matter with me, anyhow? "

" Well, over-work, I suppose. You must have been bottling up for a bad breakdown before you started for New Hampshire last December. And the shock of that poor boy's death did the rest."

Ah, yes—Rainer had died. He remembered. . . .

He started for the East, and gradually, by imperceptible degrees, life crept back into his weary bones and leaden brain. His friend was very considerate and forbearing, and they travelled slowly and talked little. At first Faxon had felt a great shrinking from whatever touched on familiar things. He seldom looked at a newspaper, he never opened a letter without a moment's contraction of the heart. It was not that he had any special cause for apprehension, but merely that a great trail of darkness lay on everything. He had looked too deep down into the abyss. . . . But little by little health and energy returned to him, and with them the common promptings of curiosity. He was beginning to wonder how the world was going, and when, presently, the hotel-keeper told him there were no letters for him in the steamer's mail-bag, he felt a distinct sense of disappointment. His friend had gone into the jungle on a long excursion, and he was lonely, unoccupied, and wholesomely bored. He got up and strolled into the stuffy reading-room.

There he found a game of dominoes, a mutilated picture-puzzle, some copies of *Zion's Herald,* and a pile of New York and London newspapers.

He began to glance through the papers, and was disappointed to find that they were less recent than he had hoped. Evidently the last numbers had been carried off by luckier travellers. He continued to turn them over, picking out the American ones first. These, as it happened, were the oldest: they dated back to December and January. To Faxon, however, they had all the flavor of novelty, since they covered the precise period during which he had virtually ceased to exist. It had never before occurred to him to wonder what had happened in the world during that interval of obliteration; but now he felt a sudden desire to know.

To prolong the pleasure, he began by sorting the papers chronologically, and as he found and spread out the earliest number, the date at the top of the page entered into his consciousness like a key slipping into a lock. It was the seventeenth of December: the date of the day after his arrival at Northridge. He glanced at the first page and read in blazing characters: " Reported Failure of Opal Cement Company. Lavington's Name Involved. Gigantic Exposure of Corruption Shakes Wall Street to Its Foundations."

He read on, and when he had finished the first paper

he turned to the next. There was a gap of three days, but the Opal Cement "Investigation" still held the centre of the stage. From its complex revelations of greed and ruin his eye wandered to the death notices, and he read: "Rainer. Suddenly, at Northridge, New Hampshire, Francis John, only son of the late. . . ."

His eyes clouded, and he dropped the newspaper and sat for a long time with his face in his hands. When he looked up again he noticed that his gesture had pushed the other papers from the table and scattered them on the floor at his feet. The uppermost lay spread out before him, and heavily his eyes began their search again. "John Lavington comes forward with plan for reconstructing Company. Offers to put in ten millions of his own—The proposal under consideration by the District Attorney."

Ten millions . . . ten millions of his own. But if John Lavington was ruined? . . . Faxon stood up with a cry. That was it, then—that was what the warning meant! And if he had not fled from it, dashed wildly away from it into the night, he might have broken the spell of iniquity, the powers of darkness might not have prevailed! He caught up the pile of newspapers and began to glance through each in turn for the head-line: "Wills Admitted to Probate." In the last of all he found the paragraph he sought, and it stared up at him as if with Rainer's dying eyes.

That—*that* was what he had done! The powers of pity had singled him out to warn and save, and he had closed his ears to their call, had washed his hands of it, and fled. Washed his hands of it! That was the word. It caught him back to the dreadful moment in the lodge when, raising himself up from Rainer's side, he had looked at his hands and seen that they were red. . . .

A MESSENGER

BY

MARY RAYMOND SHIPMAN ANDREWS

The Berserker of the North, because he believed in the directing power of the gods, knew no fear. Death or life—it was meted out by a destiny that could not err. In song and story he has been one of the most attractive figures of the past; far more attractive in his savage virtues than the more sensuous heroes of Greece and Rome. In this story he lives again in the American boy who has his ancestor's inexplicable uplift of spirit in the presence of danger and his implicit faith in " the God of battles and the beauty of holiness." The ideal of Miles Morgan is such a man as Chinese Gordon, who, not only in youth but all through life, had eyes for " the vision splendid."

The ethical value of " A Messenger " may be summed up in the words of the General: " There is nothing in Americanism to prevent either inspiration or heroism."

A MESSENGER *

How oft do they their silver bowers leave,
To come to succour us that succour want!
How oft do they with golden pineons cleave
The flitting skyes, like flying Pursuivant,
Against fowle feendes to ayd us militant!
They for us fight, they watch and dewly ward,
And their bright Squadrons round about us plant;
And all for love, and nothing for reward.
O! Why should heavenly God to men have such regard?
—Spenser's "Faerie Queene."

That the other world of our hope rests on no distant, shining star, but lies about us as an atmosphere, unseen yet near, is the belief of many. The veil of material life shades earthly eyes, they say, from the glories in which we ever are. But sometimes when the veil wears thin in mortal stress, or is caught away by a rushing, mighty wind of inspiration, the trembling human soul, so bared, so purified, may look down unimagined heavenly vistas, and messengers may steal across the shifting boundary, breathing hope and the air of a brighter world. And of him who speaks his vision, men say "He is mad," or "He has dreamed."

The group of officers in the tent was silent for a long half minute after Colonel Wilson's voice had stopped. Then the General spoke.

"There is but one thing to do," he said. "We must get word to Captain Thornton at once."

* From "The Militants," by Mary R. S. Andrews. Copyright, 1907, by Charles Scribner's Sons.

The Colonel thought deeply a moment, and glanced at the orderly outside the tent. " Flannigan! " The man, wheeling swiftly, saluted. " Present my compliments to Lieutenant Morgan and say that I should like to see him here at once," and the soldier went off, with the quick military precision in which there is no haste and no delay.

" You have some fine, powerful young officers, Colonel," said the General casually. " I suppose we shall see in Lieutenant Morgan one of the best. It will take strength and brains both, perhaps, for this message."

A shadow of a smile touched the Colonel's lips. " I think I have chosen a capable man, General," was all he said.

Against the doorway of the tent the breeze blew the flap lazily back and forth. A light rain fell with muffled gentle insistence on the canvas over their heads, and out through the opening the landscape was blurred —the wide stretch of monotonous, billowy prairie, the sluggish, shining river, bending in the distance about the base of Black Wind Mountain—Black Wind Mountain, whose high top lifted, though it was almost June, a white point of snow above dark pine ridges of the hills below. The five officers talked a little as they waited, but spasmodically, absent-mindedly. A shadow blocked the light of the entrance, and in the doorway stood a young man, undersized, slight, blond. He looked inquiringly at the Colonel.

" You sent for me, sir? " and the General and his aide, and the grizzled old Captain, and the big, fresh-faced young one, all watched him.

In direct, quiet words—words whose bareness made them dramatic for the weight of possibility they carried—the Colonel explained. Black Wolf and his band were out on the war-path. A soldier coming in wounded, escaped from the massacre of the post at Devil's Hoof Gap, had reported it. With the large command known to be here camped on Sweetstream Fork, they would not come this way; they would swerve up the Gunpowder River twenty miles away, destroying the settlement and Little Fort Slade, and would sweep on, probably for a general massacre, up the Great Horn as far as Fort Doncaster. He himself, with the regiment, would try to save Fort Slade, but in the meantime Captain Thornton's troop, coming to join him, ignorant that Black Wolf had taken the war-path, would be directly in their track. Some one must be sent to warn them, and of course the fewer the quicker. Lieutenant Morgan would take a sergeant, the Colonel ordered quietly, and start at once.

In the misty light inside the tent, the young officer looked hardly more than seventeen years old as he stood listening. His small figure was light, fragile; his hair was blond to an extreme, a thick thatch of pale gold; and there was about him, among these tanned, stalwart men in uniform, a presence, an effect of something unusual, a simplicity out of place yet harmonious, which might have come with a little child into a scene like this. His large blue eyes were fixed on the Colonel as he talked, and in them was just such a look of innocent, pleased wonder, as might be in a child's eyes, who had been told to leave studying and go pick violets. But as the Colonel ended he spoke, and the few words he said, the few questions he asked, were full of poise, of crisp directness. As the General volunteered a word or two, he turned to him and answered with a very charming deference, a respect that was yet full of gracious ease, the unconscious air of a man to whom generals are first as men, and then as generals. The slight figure in its dark uniform was already beyond the tent doorway when the Colonel spoke again, with a shade of hesitation in his manner.

"Mr. Morgan!" and the young officer turned quickly. "I think it may be right to warn you that there is likely to be more than usual danger in your ride."

"Yes, sir." The fresh, young voice had a note of inquiry.

"You will—you will"—what was it the Colonel wanted to say? He finished abruptly. "Choose the man carefully who goes with you."

"Thank you, Colonel," Morgan responded heartily, but with a hint of bewilderment. "I shall take Sergeant O'Hara," and he was gone.

There was a touch of color in the Colonel's face, and he sighed as if glad to have it over. The General watched him, and slowly, after a pause, he demanded:

"May I ask, Colonel, why you chose that blond baby to send on a mission of uncommon danger and importance?"

The Colonel answered quietly: "There were several reasons, General—good ones. The blond baby"—that ghost of a smile touched the Colonel's lips again—"the blond baby has some remarkable qualities. He never loses his head; he has uncommon invention and facility of getting out of bad holes; he rides light and so can make a horse last longer than most, and"—the Colonel considered a moment—"I may say he has no fear of death. Even among my officers he is known for the quality of his courage. There is one more reason: he is the most popular man I have, both with officers and men; if anything happened to Morgan the whole command would race into hell after the devils that did it before they would miss their revenge."

The General reflected, pulling at his moustache. "It seems a bit like taking advantage of his popularity," he said.

"It is," the Colonel threw back quickly. "It's just that. But that's what one must do—a commanding officer—isn't it so, General? In this war music we play on human instruments, and if a big chord comes out stronger for the silence of a note, the note must be silenced—that's all. It's cruel, but it's fighting; it's the game."

The General, as if impressed with the tense words, did not respond, and the other officers stared at the Colonel's face, as carved, as stern as if done in marble—a face from which the warm, strong heart seldom shone, held back always by the stronger will.

The big, fresh-colored young Captain broke the silence. "Has the General ever heard of the trick Morgan played on Sun Boy, sir?" he asked.

"Tell the General, Captain Booth," the Colonel said briefly, and the Captain turned toward the higher officer.

"It was apropos of what the Colonel said of his inventive faculties, General," he began. "A year ago the youngster with a squad of ten men walked into Sun Boy's camp of seventy-five warriors. Morgan had made quite a pet of a young Sioux, who was our prisoner for five months, and the boy had taught him a lot of the language, and assured him that he would have the friendship of the band in return for his kindness to Blue Arrow—that was the chap's name. So he thought he was safe; but it turned out that Blue Arrow's father, a chief, had got into a row with Sun Boy, and the latter would not think of ratifying the boy's promise. So there was Morgan with his dozen men, in a nasty enough fix. He knew plenty of Indian talk to understand that they were discussing what they would do with him, and it wasn't pleasant.

" All of a sudden he had an inspiration. He tells the story himself, sir, and I assure you he'd make you laugh—Morgan is a wonderful mimic. Well, he remembered suddenly, as I said, that he was a mighty good ventriloquist, and he saw his chance. He gave a great jump like a startled fawn, and threw up his arms and stared like one demented into the tree over their heads. There was a mangy-looking crow sitting up there on a branch, and Morgan pointed at him as if at something marvellous, supernatural, and all those fool Indians stopped pow-wowing and stared up after him, as curious as monkeys. Then to all appearances, the crow began to talk. Morgan said they must have thought that spirits didn't speak very choice Sioux, but he did his best. The bird cawed out:

" ' Oh, Sun Boy, great chief, beware what you do! '

" And then the real bird flapped its wings and Morgan thought it was going to fly, and he was lost. But it settled back again on the branch, and Morgan proceeded to caw on:

" ' Hurt not the white man, or the curses of the gods will come upon Sun Boy and his people.'

" And he proceeded to give a list of what would happen if the Indians touched a hair of their heads. By this time the red devils were all down on their stomachs, moaning softly whenever Morgan stopped cawing. He said he quite got into the spirit of it, and would have liked to go on some time, but he was beginning to get hoarse, and besides he was in deadly terror for fear the crow would fly before he got to the point. So he had the spirit order them to give the white men their horses and turn them loose instanter; and just as he got all through, off went the thing with a big flap and a parting caw on its own account. I wish I could tell it as Morgan does—you'd think he was a bird and an Indian rolled together. He's a great actor spoiled, that lad.''

'' You leave out a fine point, to my mind, Captain Booth,'' the Colonel said quickly. '' About his going back.''

'' Oh! certainly that ought to be told,'' said the Captain, and the General's eyes turned to him again. '' Morgan forgot to see young Blue Arrow, his friend, before he got away, and nothing would do but that he should go back and speak to him. He said the boy would be disappointed. The men were visibly uneasy at his going, but that didn't affect him. He ordered them to wait, and back he went, pell-mell, all alone into that horde of fiends. They hadn't got over their funk, luckily, and he saw Blue Arrow and made his party call and got out again all right. He didn't tell that himself, but Sergeant O'Hara made the camp ring with it. He adores Morgan, and claims that he doesn't know what fear is. I believe it's about so. I've seen him in a fight three times now. His cap always goes off—he loses a cap every blessed scrimmage—and with that yellow mop of hair, and a sort of rapt expression he gets, he looks like a child saying its prayers all the time he is slashing and shooting like a berserker.'' Captain Booth faced abruptly toward the Colonel. '' I beg your pardon for talking so long, sir,'' he said. '' You know we're all rather keen about little Miles Morgan.''

The General lifted his head suddenly. '' Miles Morgan? '' he demanded. '' Is his name Miles Morgan? ''

The Colonel nodded. '' Yes. The grandson of the old Bishop—named for him.''

'' Lord! '' ejaculated the General. '' Miles Morgan was my earliest friend, my friend until he died! This must be Jim's son—Miles's only child. And Jim is dead these ten years," he went on rapidly. " I've lost track of him since the Bishop died, but I knew Jim left children. Why, he married "—he searched rapidly in his memory—" he married a daughter of General Fitzbrian's. This boy's got the church and the army both in him. I knew his mother," he went on, talking to the Colonel, garrulous with interest. " Irish and fascinating she was—believed in fairies and ghosts and all that, as her father did before her. A clever woman, but with the superstitious, wild Irish blood strong in her. Good Lord! I wish I'd known that was Miles Morgan's grandson."

The Colonel's voice sounded quiet and rather cold after the General's impulsive enthusiasm. " You have summed him up by his antecedents, General," he said. " The church and the army—both strains are strong. He is deeply religious."

The General looked thoughtful. " Religious, eh? And popular? They don't always go together."

Captain Booth spoke quickly. " It's not that kind, General," he said. " There's no cant in the boy. He's more popular for it—that's often so with the genuine thing, isn't it? I sometimes think "—the young Captain hesitated and smiled a trifle deprecatingly—" that Morgan is much of the same stuff as Gordon—Chinese Gordon; the martyr stuff, you know. But it seems a bit rash to compare an every-day American youngster to an inspired hero."

" There's nothing in Americanism to prevent either inspiration or heroism that I know of," the General affirmed stoutly, his fine old head up, his eyes gleaming with pride of his profession.

Out through the open doorway, beyond the slapping tent-flap, the keen, gray eyes of the Colonel were fixed musingly on two black points which crawled along the edge of the dulled silver of the distant river—Miles Morgan and Sergeant O'Hara had started.

"Sergeant!" They were eight miles out now, and the camp had disappeared behind the elbow of Black Wind Mountain. "There's something wrong with your horse. Listen! He's not loping evenly." The soft cadence of eight hoofs on earth had somewhere a lighter and then a heavier note; the ear of a good horseman tells in a minute, as a musician's ear at a false note, when an animal saves one foot ever so slightly, to come down harder on another.

"Yessirr. The Lieutenant'll remimber 'tis the horrse that had a bit of a spavin. Sure I thot 'twas cured, and 'tis the kindest baste in the rigiment f'r a pleasure ride, sorr—that willin' 'tis. So I tuk it. I think 'tis only the stiffness at furrst aff. 'Twill wurruk aff later. Plaze God, I'll wallop him." And the Sergeant walloped with a will.

But the kindest beast in the regiment failed to respond except with a plunge and increased lameness. Soon there was no more question of his incapacity.

Lieutenant Morgan halted his mount, and, looking at the woe-begone O'Hara, laughed. "A nice trick this is, Sergeant," he said, "to start out on a trip to dodge Indians with a spavined horse. Why didn't you get a broomstick? Now go back to camp as fast as you can go; and that horse ought to be blistered when you get there. See if you can't really cure him. He's too good to be shot." He patted the gray's nervous head, and the beast rubbed it gently against his sleeve, quiet under his hand.

"Yessirr. The Lieutenant'll ride slow, sorr, f'r me to catch up on ye, sorr?"

Miles Morgan smiled and shook his head. " Sorry, Sergeant, but there'll be no slow riding in this. I'll have to press right on without you; I must be at Massacre Mountain to-night to catch Captain Thornton to-morrow."

Sergeant O'Hara's chin dropped. " Sure the Lieutenant'll niver be thinkin' to g'wan alone—widout *me?* " and with all the Sergeant's respect for his superiors, it took the Lieutenant ten valuable minutes to get the man started back, shaking his head and muttering forebodings, to the camp.

It was quiet riding on alone. There were a few miles to go before there was any chance of Indians, and no particular lookout to be kept, so he put the horse ahead rapidly while he might, and suddenly he found himself singing softly as he galloped. How the words had come to him he did not know, for no conscious train of thought had brought them; but they surely fitted to the situation, and a pleasant sense of companionship, of safety, warmed him as the swing of an old hymn carried his voice along with it.

> " God shall charge His angel legions
> Watch and ward o'er thee to keep;
> Though thou walk through hostile regions,
> Though in desert wilds thou sleep."

Surely a man riding toward—perhaps through— skulking Indian hordes, as he must, could have no better message reach him than that. The bent of his mind was toward mysticism, and while he did not think the train of reasoning out, could not have said that he believed it so, yet the familiar lines flashing suddenly, clearly, on the curtain of his mind, seemed to him, very simply, to be sent from a larger thought than his own. As a child might take a strong hand held out as it walked over rough country, so he accepted this quite readily and happily, as from that Power who was never far from him, and in whose service, beyond most people, he lived and moved. Low but clear and deep his voice went on, following one stanza with its mate:

> " Since with pure and firm affection
> Thou on God hast set thy love,
> With the wings of His protection
> He will shield thee from above."

The simplicity of his being sheltered itself in the broad promise of the words.

Light-heartedly he rode on and on, though now more carefully; lying flat and peering over the crests of hills a long time before he crossed their tops; going miles perhaps through ravines; taking advantage of every bit of cover where a man and a horse might be hidden; travelling as he had learned to travel in three years of experience in this dangerous Indian country, where a shrub taken for granted might mean a warrior, and that warrior a hundred others within signal. It was his plan to ride until about twelve—to reach Massacre Mountain, and there rest his horse and himself till gray daylight. There was grass there and a spring—two good and innocent things that had been the cause of the bad, dark thing which had given the place its name. A troop under Captain James camping at this point, because of the water and grass, had been surprised and wiped out by five hundred Indian braves of the wicked and famous Red Crow. There were ghastly signs about the place yet; Morgan had seen them, but soldiers may not have nerves, and it was good camping ground.

On through the valleys and half-way up the slopes, which rolled here far away into a still wilder world, the young man rode. Behind the distant hills in the east a glow like fire flushed the horizon. A rim of pale gold lifted sharply over the ridge; a huge round ball of light pushed faster, higher, and lay, a bright world on the edge of the world, great against the sky—the moon had risen. The twilight trembled as the yellow rays struck into its depths, and deepened, dying into purple shadows. Across the plain zigzagged the pools of a level stream, as if a giant had spilled handfuls of quicksilver here and there.

Miles Morgan, riding, drank in all the mysterious, wild beauty, as a man at ease; as open to each fair impression as if he were not riding each moment into deeper danger, as if his every sense were not on guard. On through the shining moonlight and in the shadow of the hills he rode, and, where he might, through the trees, and stopped to listen often, to stare at the hilltops, to question a heap of stones or a bush.

At last, when his leg-weary horse was beginning to stumble a bit, he saw, as he came around a turn, Massacre Mountain's dark head rising in front of him, only half a mile away. The spring trickled its low song, as musical, as limpidly pure as if it had never run scarlet. The picketed horse fell to browsing and Miles sighed restfully as he laid his head on his saddle and fell instantly to sleep with the light of the moon on his damp, fair hair. But he did not sleep long. Suddenly with a start he awoke, and sat up sharply, and listened. He heard the horse still munching grass near him, and made out the shadow of its bulk against the sky; he heard the stream, softly falling and calling to the waters where it was going. That was all. Strain his hearing as he might he could hear nothing else in the still night. Yet there was something. It might not be sound or sight, but there was a presence, a something—he could not explain. He was alert in every nerve. Suddenly

the words of the hymn he had been singing in the afternoon flashed again into his mind, and, with his cocked
revolver in his hand, alone, on guard, in the midnight
of the savage wilderness, the words came that were not
even a whisper:

> "God shall charge His angel legions
> Watch and ward o'er thee to keep;
> Though thou walk through hostile regions,
> Though in desert wilds thou sleep."

He gave a contented sigh and lay down. What was
there to worry about? It was just his case for which
the hymn was written. "Desert wilds"—that surely
meant Massacre Mountain, and why should he not sleep
here quietly, and let the angels keep their watch and
ward? He closed his eyes with a smile. But sleep
did not come, and soon his eyes were open again, staring into blackness, thinking, thinking.

It was Sunday when he started out on this mission,
and he fell to remembering the Sunday nights at home—
long, long ago they seemed now. The family sang hymns
after supper always; his mother played, and the children stood around her—five of them, Miles and his
brothers and sisters. There was a little sister with
brown hair about her shoulders, who always stood by
Miles, leaned against him, held his hand, looked up at
him with adoring eyes—he could see those uplifted
eyes now, shining through the darkness of this lonely
place. He remembered the big, home-like room; the
crackling fire; the peaceful atmosphere of books and
pictures; the dumb things about its walls that were yet
eloquent to him of home and family; the sword that his
great-grandfather had worn under Washington; the old
ivories that another great-grandfather, the Admiral, had
brought from China; the portraits of Morgans of half a

dozen generations which hung there; the magazine table, the books and books and books. A pang of desperate homesickness suddenly shook him. He wanted them—his own. Why should he, their best-beloved, throw away his life—a life filled to the brim with hope and energy and high ideals—on this futile quest? He knew quite as well as the General or the Colonel that his ride was but a forlorn hope. As he lay there, longing so, in the dangerous dark, he went about the library at home in his thought and placed each familiar belonging where he had known it all his life. And as he finished, his mother's head shone darkly golden by the piano; her fingers swept over the keys; he heard all their voices, the dear never-forgotten voices. Hark! They were singing his hymn—little Alice's reedy note lifted above the others—" God shall charge His angel legions——"

Now! He was on his feet with a spring, and his revolver pointed steadily. This time there was no mistaking—something had rustled in the bushes. There was but one thing for it to be—Indians. Without realizing what he did, he spoke sharply.

" Who goes there? " he demanded, and out of the darkness a voice answered quietly:

" A friend."

" A friend? " With a shock of relief the pistol dropped by his side, and he stood tense, waiting. How might a friend be here, at midnight in this desert? As the thought framed itself swiftly the leaves parted, and his straining eyes saw the figure of a young man standing before him.

" How came you here? " demanded Miles sternly. " Who are you? "

Even in the dimness he could see the radiant smile that answered him. The calm voice spoke again: " You will understand that later. I am here to help you."

As if a door had suddenly opened into that lighted room of which he dreamed, Miles felt a sense of tranquillity, of happiness stirring through him. Never in his life had he known such a sudden utter confidence in any one, such a glow of eager friendliness as this half-seen, mysterious stranger inspired. " It is because I was lonelier than I knew," he said mentally. " It is because human companionship gives courage to the most self-reliant of us; " and somewhere in the words he was aware of a false note, but he did not stop to place it.

The low, even voice of the stranger spoke again. " There are Indians on your trail," he said. " A small band of Black Wolf's scouts. But don't be troubled. They will not hurt you."

" You escaped from them? " demanded Miles eagerly, and again the light of a swift smile shone into the night. " You came to save me—how was it? Tell me, so that we can plan. It is very dark yet, but hadn't we better ride? Where is your horse? "

He threw the earnest questions rapidly across the black night, and the unhurried voice answered him. " No," it said, and the verdict was not to be disputed. " You must stay here."

Who this man might be or how he came Miles could not tell, but this much he knew, without reason for knowing it; it was some one stronger than he, in whom he could trust. As the new-comer had said, it would be time enough later to understand the rest. Wondering a little at his own swift acceptance of an unknown authority, wondering more at the peace which wrapped him as an atmosphere at the sound of the stranger's voice, Miles made a place for him by his side, and the two talked softly to the plashing undertone of the stream.

Easily, naturally, Miles found himself telling how he had been homesick, longing for his people. He told him of the big familiar room, and of the old things that were in it, that he loved; of his mother; of little Alice, and her baby adoration for the big brother; of how they had always sung hymns together Sunday night; he never for a moment doubted the stranger's interest and sympathy—he knew that he cared to hear.

"There is a hymn," Miles said, "that we used to sing a lot—it was my favorite; 'Miles's hymn,' the family called it. Before you came to-night, while I lay there getting lonelier every minute, I almost thought I heard them singing it. You may not have heard it, but it has a grand swing. I always think"—he hesitated—"it always seems to me as if the God of battles and the beauty of holiness must both have filled the man's mind who wrote it." He stopped, surprised at his own lack of reserve, at the freedom with which, to this friend of an hour, he spoke his inmost heart.

"I know," the stranger said gently. There was silence for a moment, and then the wonderful low tones, beautiful, clear, beyond any voice Miles had ever heard, began again, and it was as if the great sweet notes of an organ whispered the words:

"God shall charge His angel legions
    Watch and ward o'er thee to keep;
Though thou walk through hostile regions,
    Though in desert wilds thou sleep."

"Great Heavens!" gasped Miles. "How could you know I meant that? Why, this is marvellous—why, this"—he stared, speechless, at the dim outlines of the face which he had never seen before to-night, but which seemed to him already familiar and dear beyond all reason. As he gazed the tall figure rose, lightly towering above him. " Look! " he said, and Miles was on his feet. In the east, beyond the long sweep of the prairie, was a faint blush against the blackness; already threads of broken light, of pale darkness, stirred through the pall of the air; the dawn was at hand.

" We must saddle," Miles said, " and be off. Where is your horse picketed? " he demanded again.

But the strange young man stood still; and now his arm was stretched pointing. " Look," he said again, and Miles followed the direction with his eyes.

From the way he had come, in that fast-growing glow at the edge of the sky, sharp against the mist of the little river, crept slowly half a dozen pin points, and Miles, watching their tiny movement, knew that they were ponies bearing Indian braves. He turned hotly to his companion.

" It's your fault," he said. " If I'd had my way we'd have ridden from here an hour ago. Now here we are caught like rats in a trap; and who's to do my work and save Thornton's troop—who's to save them— God! " The name was a prayer, not an oath.

" Yes," said the quiet voice at his side, " God,"— and for a second there was a silence that was like an Amen.

Quickly, without a word, Miles turned and began to saddle. Then suddenly, as he pulled at the girth, he stopped. " It's no use," he said. " We can't get away except over the rise, and they'll see us there; " he nodded at the hill which rose beyond the camping ground three hundred yards away, and stretched in a long, level sweep into other hills and the west. " Our chance is that they're not on my trail after all—it's quite possible." There was a tranquil unconcern about

the figure near him; his own bright courage caught the
meaning of its relaxed lines with a bound of pleasure.
" As you say, it's best to stay here," he said, and as if
thinking aloud—" I believe you must always be right."
Then he added, as if his very soul would speak itself
to this wonderful new friend: " We can't be killed,
unless the Lord wills it, and if he does it's right. Death
is only the step into life; I suppose when we know that
life, we will wonder how we could have cared for this
one."

Through the gray light the stranger turned his face
swiftly, bent toward Miles, and smiled once again, and
the boy thought suddenly of the martyrdom of St. Ste-
phen, and how those who were looking " saw his face
as it had been the face of an angel."

Across the plain, out of the mist-wreaths, came rushing, scurrying, the handful of Indian braves. Pale light
streamed now from the east, filtering over a hushed
world. Miles faced across the plain, stood close to the
tall stranger whose shape, as the dawn touched it, seemed
to rise beyond the boy's slight figure wonderfully large
and high. There was a sense of unending power, of
alertness, of great, easy movement about him; one might
have looked at him, and looking away again, have said
that wings were folded about him. But Miles did not
see him. His eyes were on the fast-nearing, galloping
ponies, each with its load of filthy, cruel savagery. This
was his death coming; there was disgust, but not dread
in the thought for the boy. In a few minutes he should
be fighting hopelessly, fiercely against this froth of a
lower world; in a few minutes after that he should be
lying here still—for he meant to be killed; he had that
planned. They should not take him—a wave of sick repulsion at that thought shook him. Nearer, nearer, right
on his track came the riders pell-mell. He could hear

their weird, horrible cries; now he could see gleaming through the dimness the huge head-dress of the foremost, the white coronet of feathers, almost the stripes of paint on the fierce face.

Suddenly a feeling that he knew well caught him, and he laughed. It was the possession that had held in him in every action which he had so far been in. It lifted his high-strung spirit into an atmosphere where there was no dread and no disgust, only a keen rapture in throwing every atom of soul and body into physical intensity; it was as if he himself were a bright blade, dashing, cutting, killing, a living sword rejoicing to destroy. With the coolness that may go with such a frenzy he felt that his pistols were loose; saw with satisfaction that he and his new ally were placed on the slope to the best advantage, then turned swiftly, eager now for the fight to come, toward the Indian band. As he looked, suddenly in mid-career, pulling in their plunging ponies with a jerk that threw them, snorting, on their haunches, the warriors halted. Miles watched in amazement. The bunch of Indians, not more than a hundred yards away, were staring, arrested, startled, back of him to his right, where the lower ridge of Massacre Mountain stretched far and level over the valley that wound westward beneath it on the road to Fort Rain-and-Thunder. As he gazed, the ponies had swept about and were galloping back as they had come, across the plain.

Before he knew if it might be true, if he were not dreaming this curious thing, the clear voice of his companion spoke in one word again, like the single note of a deep bell. "Look!" he said, and Miles swung about toward the ridge behind, following the pointing finger.

In the gray dawn the hill-top was clad with the still strength of an army. Regiment after regiment, silent, motionless, it stretched back into silver mist, and the mist rolled beyond, above, about it; and through it he saw, as through rifts in broken gauze, lines interminable of soldiers, glitter of steel. Miles, looking, knew.

He never remembered how long he stood gazing, earth and time and self forgotten, at a sight not meant for mortal eyes; but suddenly, with a stab it came to him, that if the hosts of heaven fought his battle it was that he might do his duty, might save Captain Thornton and his men; he turned to speak to the young man who had been with him. There was no one there. Over the bushes the mountain breeze blew damp and cold; they rustled softly under its touch; his horse stared at him mildly; away off at the foot-hills he could see the diminishing dots of the fleeing Indian ponies; as he wheeled again and looked, the hills that had been covered with the glory of heavenly armies, lay hushed and empty. And his friend was gone.

Clatter of steel, jingle of harness, an order ringing out far but clear—Miles threw up his head sharply and listened. In a second he was pulling at his horse's girth, slipping the bit swiftly into its mouth—in a moment more he was off and away to meet them, as a body of cavalry swung out of the valley where the ridge had hidden them.

" Captain Thornton's troop? " the officer repeated carelessly. " Why, yes; they are here with us. We picked them up yesterday, headed straight for Black Wolf's war-path. Mighty lucky we found them. How about you—seen any Indians, have you? "

Miles answered slowly: " A party of eight were on my trail; they were riding for Massacre Mountain, where I camped, about an hour—about half an hour—awhile ago." He spoke vaguely, rather oddly, the officer thought. " Something—stopped them about a hundred yards from the mountain. They turned, and rode away.''

'' Ah,'' said the officer. '' They saw us down the valley.''

'' I couldn't see you,'' said Miles.

The officer smiled. '' You're not an Indian, Lieutenant. Besides, they were out on the plain and had a farther view behind the ridge.'' And Miles answered not a word.

General Miles Morgan, full of years and of honors, has never but twice told the story of that night of forty years ago. But he believes that when his time comes, and he goes to join the majority, he will know again the presence which guarded him through the blackness of it, and among the angel legions he looks to find an angel, a messenger, who was his friend.

MARKHEIM

BY

ROBERT LOUIS STEVENSON

In one of the old Greek tragedies, after the actors on the stage have played their parts and the chorus in the orchestra below has hinted mysteriously of crime and retribution, the doors of the palace in the background suddenly fly apart. There stands the criminal queen. She confesses her crime and explains the reason for it. So sometimes a story opens the doors of a character's heart and mind, and invites us to look within. Such a story is called psychological. Sometimes there is action, not for action's sake, but for its revelation of character. Sometimes nothing happens. "This," says Bliss Perry, "may be precisely what most interests us, because we are made to understand what it is that inhibits action." In the story of this type we see the moods of the character; we watch motives appear, encounter other motives, and retreat or advance. In short, we are allowed to observe the man's mental processes until we understand him.

The emotional value of this story may be stated in the words of C. T. Winchester:

"We may lay it down as a rule that those emotions which are intimately related to the conduct of life are of higher rank than those which are not; and that, consequently, the emotions highest of all are those related to the deciding forces of life, the affections, and the conscience."

MARKHEIM *

" Yes," said the dealer, " our windfalls are of various kinds. Some customers are ignorant, and then I touch a dividend on my superior knowledge. Some are dishonest," and here he held up the candle, so that the light fell strongly on his visitor, " and in that case," he continued, " I profit by my virtue."

Markheim had but just entered from the daylight streets, and his eyes had not yet grown familiar with the mingled shine and darkness in the shop. At these pointed words, and before the near presence of the flame, he blinked painfully and looked aside.

The dealer chuckled. " You come to me on Christmas Day," he resumed, " when you know that I am alone in my house, put up my shutters, and make a point of refusing business. Well, you will have to pay for that; you will have to pay for my loss of time, when I should be balancing my books; you will have to pay, besides, for a kind of manner that I remark in you to-day very strongly. I am the essence of discretion, and ask no awkward questions; but when a customer cannot look me in the eye, he has to pay for it." The dealer once more chuckled; and then, changing to his usual business voice, though still with a note of irony, " You can give, as usual, a clear account of how you came into the possession of the object? " he continued. " Still your uncle's cabinet? A remarkable collector, sir! "

From "The Merry Men and Other Tales and Fables," by Robert Louis Stevenson, published by Charles Scribner's Sons.

And the little pale, round-shouldered dealer stood almost on tip-toe, looking over the top of his gold spectacles, and nodding his head with every mark of disbelief. Markheim returned his gaze with one of infinite pity, and a touch of horror.

" This time," said he, " you are in error. I have not come to sell, but to buy. I have no curios to dispose of; my uncle's cabinet is bare to the wainscot; even were it still intact, I have done well on the Stock Exchange, and should more likely add to it than otherwise, and my errand to-day is simplicity itself. I seek a Christmas present for a lady," he continued, waxing more fluent as he struck into the speech he had prepared; " and certainly I owe you every excuse for thus disturbing you upon so small a matter. But the thing was neglected yesterday; I must produce my little compliment at dinner; and, as you very well know, a rich marriage is not a thing to be neglected."

There followed a pause, during which the dealer seemed to weigh this statement incredulously. The ticking of many clocks among the curious lumber of the shop, and the faint rushing of the cabs in a near thoroughfare, filled up the interval of silence.

" Well, sir," said the dealer, " be it so. You are an old customer after all; and if, as you say, you have the chance of a good marriage, far be it from me to be an obstacle. Here is a nice thing for a lady now," he went on, " this hand glass—fifteenth century, warranted; comes from a good collection, too; but I reserve the name, in the interests of my customer, who was just like yourself, my dear sir, the nephew and sole heir of a remarkable collector."

The dealer, while he thus ran on in his dry and biting voice, had stooped to take the object from its place; and, as he had done so, a shock had passed through

Markheim, a start both of hand and foot, a sudden leap of many tumultuous passions to the face. It passed as swiftly as it came, and left no trace beyond a certain trembling of the hand that now received the glass.

"A glass," he said hoarsely, and then paused, and repeated it more clearly. "A glass? For Christmas? Surely not?"

"And why not?" cried the dealer. "Why not a glass?"

Markheim was looking upon him with an indefinable expression. "You ask me why not?" he said. "Why, look here—look in it—look at yourself! Do you like to see it? No! nor I—nor any man."

The little man had jumped back when Markheim had so suddenly confronted him with the mirror; but now, perceiving there was nothing worse on hand, he chuckled. "Your future lady, sir, must be pretty hard favored," said he.

"I ask you," said Markheim, "for a Christmas present, and you give me this—this damned reminder of years, and sins, and follies—this hand-conscience! Did you mean it? Had you a thought in your mind? Tell me. It will be better for you if you do. Come, tell me about yourself. I hazard a guess now, that you are in secret a very charitable man?"

The dealer looked closely at his companion. It was very odd, Markheim did not appear to be laughing; there was something in his face like an eager sparkle of hope, but nothing of mirth.

"What are you driving at?" the dealer asked.

"Not charitable?" returned the other, gloomily. "Not charitable; not pious; not scrupulous; unloving, unbeloved; a hand to get money, a safe to keep it. Is that all? Dear God, man, is that all?"

"I will tell you what it is," began the dealer, with

some sharpness, and then broke off again into a chuckle.
"But I see this is a love match of yours, and you have
been drinking the lady's health."

"Ah!" cried Markheim, with a strange curiosity.
"Ah, have you been in love? Tell me about that."

"I," cried the dealer. "I in love! I never had the
time, nor have I the time to-day for all this nonsense.
Will you take the glass?"

"Where is the hurry?" returned Markheim. "It
is very pleasant to stand here talking; and life is so
short and insecure that I would not hurry away from
any pleasure—no, not even from so mild a one as this.
We should rather cling, cling to what little we can get,
like a man at a cliff's edge. Every second is a cliff, if
you think upon it—a cliff a mile high—high enough,
if we fall, to dash us out of every feature of humanity.
Hence it is best to talk pleasantly. Let us talk of each
other; why should we wear this mask? Let us be con-
fidential. Who knows, we might become friends?"

"I have just one word to say to you," said the
dealer. "Either make your purchase, or walk out of
my shop."

"True, true," said Markheim. "Enough fooling.
To business. Show me something else."

The dealer stooped once more, this time to replace
the glass upon the shelf, his thin blond hair falling over
his eyes as he did so. Markheim moved a little nearer,
with one hand in the pocket of his greatcoat; he drew
himself up and filled his lungs; at the same time many
different emotions were depicted together on his face—
terror, horror, and resolve, fascination and a physical
repulsion; and through a haggard lift of his upper lip,
his teeth looked out.

"This, perhaps, may suit," observed the dealer; and
then, as he began to re-arise, Markheim bounded from

behind upon his victim. The long, skewerlike dagger flashed and fell. The dealer struggled like a hen, striking his temple on the shelf, and then tumbled on the floor in a heap.

Time had some score of small voices in that shop, some stately and slow as was becoming to their great age; others garrulous and hurried. All these told out the seconds in an intricate chorus of tickings. Then the passage of a lad's feet, heavily running on the pavement, broke in upon these smaller voices and startled Markheim into the consciousness of his surroundings. He looked about him awfully. The candle stood on the counter, its flame solemnly wagging in a draught; and by that inconsiderable movement, the whole room was filled with noiseless bustle and kept heaving like a sea: the tall shadows nodding, the gross blots of darkness swelling and dwindling as with respiration, the faces of the portraits and the china gods changing and wavering like images in water. The inner door stood ajar, and peered into that leaguer of shadows with a long slit of daylight like a pointing finger.

From these fear-stricken rovings, Markheim's eyes returned to the body of his victim, where it lay both humped and sprawling, incredibly small and strangely meaner than in life. In these poor, miserly clothes, in that ungainly attitude, the dealer lay like so much sawdust. Markheim had feared to see it, and, lo! it was nothing. And yet, as he gazed, this bundle of old clothes and pool of blood began to find eloquent voices. There it must lie; there was none to work the cunning hinges or direct the miracle of locomotion—there it must lie till it was found. Found! ay, and then? Then would this dead flesh lift up a cry that would ring over England, and fill the world with the echoes of pursuit. Ay, dead or not, this was still the enemy. "Time was that when the brains were out,'' he thought; and the first word struck into his mind. Time, now that the deed was accomplished—time, which had closed for the victim, had become instant and momentous for the slayer.

The thought was yet in his mind, when, first one and then another, with every variety of pace and voice— one deep as the bell from a cathedral turret, another ringing on its treble notes the prelude of a waltz—the clocks began to strike the hour of three in the afternoon.

The sudden outbreak of so many tongues in that dumb chamber staggered him. He began to bestir himself, going to and fro with the candle, beleaguered by moving shadows, and startled to the soul by chance reflections. In many rich mirrors, some of home designs, some from Venice or Amsterdam, he saw his face repeated and repeated, as it were an army of spies; his own eyes met and detected him; and the sound of his own steps, lightly as they fell, vexed the surrounding quiet. And still as he continued to fill his pockets, his mind accused him, with a sickening iteration, of the thousand faults of his design. He should have chosen a more quiet hour; he should have prepared an alibi; he should not have used a knife; he should have been more cautious, and only bound and gagged the dealer, and not killed him; he should have been more bold, and killed the servant also; he should have done all things otherwise; poignant regrets, weary, incessant toiling of the mind to change what was unchangeable, to plan what was now useless, to be the architect of the irrevocable past. Meanwhile, and behind all this activity, brute terrors, like the scurrying of rats in a deserted attic, filled the more remote chambers of his brain with riot; the hand of the constable would fall heavy on his shoulder, and his nerves would jerk like a hooked fish;

or he beheld, in galloping defile, the dock, the prison, the gallows, and the black coffin.

Terror of the people in the street sat down before his mind like a besieging army. It was impossible, he thought, but that some rumor of the struggle must have reached their ears and set on edge their curiosity; and now, in all the neighboring houses, he divined them sitting motionless and with uplifted ear—solitary people, condemned to spend Christmas dwelling alone on memories of the past, and now startlingly recalled from that tender exercise; happy family parties, struck into silence round the table, the mother still with raised finger: every degree and age and humor, but all, by their own hearts, prying and hearkening and weaving the rope that was to hang him. Sometimes it seemed to him he could not move too softly; the clink of the tall Bohemian goblets rang out loudly like a bell; and alarmed by the bigness of the ticking, he was tempted to stop the clocks. And then, again, with a swift transition of his terrors, the very silence of the place appeared a source of peril, and a thing to strike and freeze the passer-by; and he would step more boldly, and bustle aloud among the contents of the shop, and imitate, with elaborate bravado, the movements of a busy man at ease in his own house.

But he was now so pulled about by different alarms that, while one portion of his mind was still alert and cunning, another trembled on the brink of lunacy. One hallucination in particular took a strong hold on his credulity. The neighbor hearkening with white face beside his window, the passer-by arrested by a horrible surmise on the pavement—these could at worst suspect, they could not know; through the brick walls and shuttered windows only sounds could penetrate. But here, within the house, was he alone? He knew he was; he had watched the servant set forth sweethearting, in her poor best, " out for the day " written in every ribbon and smile. Yes, he was alone, of course; and yet, in the bulk of empty house above him, he could surely hear a stir of delicate footing—he was surely conscious, inexplicably conscious of some presence. Ay, surely; to every room and corner of the house his imagination followed it; and now it was a faceless thing, and yet had eyes to see with; and again it was a shadow of himself; and yet again behold the image of the dead dealer, reinspired with cunning and hatred.

At times, with a strong effort, he would glance at the open door which still seemed to repel his eyes. The house was tall, the skylight small and dirty, the day blind with fog; and the light that filtered down to the ground story was exceedingly faint, and showed dimly on the threshold of the shop. And yet, in that strip of doubtful brightness, did there not hang wavering a shadow?

Suddenly, from the street outside, a very jovial gentleman began to beat with a staff on the shop-door, accompanying his blows with shouts and railleries in which the dealer was continually called upon by name. Markheim, smitten into ice, glanced at the dead man. But no! he lay quite still; he was fled away far beyond earshot of these blows and shoutings; he was sunk beneath seas of silence; and his name, which would once have caught his notice above the howling of a storm, had become an empty sound. And presently the jovial gentleman desisted from his knocking and departed.

Here was a broad hint to hurry what remained to be done, to get forth from this accusing neighborhood, to plunge into a bath of London multitudes, and to reach, on the other side of day, that haven of safety and apparent innocence—his bed. One visitor had come:

at any moment another might follow and be more obstinate. To have done the deed, and yet not to reap the profit, would be too abhorrent a failure. The money, that was now Markheim's concern; and as a means to that, the keys.

He glanced over his shoulder at the open door, where the shadow was still lingering and shivering; and with no conscious repugnance of the mind, yet with a tremor of the belly, he drew near the body of his victim. The human character had quite departed. Like a suit half-stuffed with bran, the limbs lay scattered, the trunk doubled, on the floor; and yet the thing repelled him. Although so dingy and inconsiderable to the eye, he feared it might have more significance to the touch. He took the body by the shoulders, and turned it on its back. It was strangely light and supple, and the limbs, as if they had been broken, fell into the oddest postures. The face was robbed of all expression; but it was as pale as wax, and shockingly smeared with blood about one temple. That was, for Markheim, the one displeasing circumstance. It carried him back, upon the instant, to a certain day in a fishers' village: a gray day, a piping wind, a crowd upon the street, the blare of brasses, the booming of drums, the nasal voice of a ballad singer; and a boy going to and fro, buried over head in the crowd and divided between interest and fear, until, coming out upon the chief place of concourse, he beheld a booth and a great screen with pictures, dismally designed, garishly colored: Brownrigg with her apprentice; the Mannings with their murdered guest; Weare in the death-grip of Thurtell; and a score besides of famous crimes. The thing was as clear as an illusion; he was once again that little boy; he was looking once again, and with the same sense of physical revolt, at these vile pictures; he was still stunned by the thumping of the drums. A bar of that day's music returned upon his memory; and at that, for the first time, a qualm came over him, a breath of nausea, a sudden weakness of the joints, which he must instantly resist and conquer.

He judged it more prudent to confront than to flee from these considerations; looking the more hardily in the dead face, bending his mind to realize the nature and greatness of his crime. So little a while ago that face had moved with every change of sentiment, that pale mouth had spoken, that body had been all on fire with governable energies; and now, and by his act, that piece of life had been arrested, as the horologist, with interjected finger, arrests the beating of the clock. So he reasoned in vain; he could rise to no more remorseful consciousness; the same heart which had shuddered before the painted effigies of crime, looked on its reality unmoved. At best, he felt a gleam of pity for one who had been endowed in vain with all those faculties that can make the world a garden of enchantment, one who had never lived and who was now dead. But of penitence, no, not a tremor.

With that, shaking himself clear of these considerations, he found the keys and advanced towards the open door of the shop. Outside, it had begun to rain smartly; and the sound of the shower upon the roof had banished silence. Like some dripping cavern, the chambers of the house were haunted by an incessant echoing, which filled the ear and mingled with the ticking of the clocks. And, as Markheim approached the door, he seemed to hear, in answer to his own cautious tread, the steps of another foot withdrawing up the stair. The shadow still palpitated loosely on the threshold. He threw a ton's weight of resolve upon his muscles, and drew back the door.

The faint, foggy daylight glimmered dimly on the bare floor and stairs; on the bright suit of armor posted, halbert in hand, upon the landing; and on the dark wood-carvings, and framed pictures that hung against the yellow panels of the wainscot. So loud was the beating of the rain through all the house that, in Markheim's ears, it began to be distinguished into many different sounds. Footsteps and sighs, the tread of regiments marching in the distance, the chink of money in the counting, and the creaking of doors held stealthily ajar, appeared to mingle with the patter of the drops upon the cupola and the gushing of the water in the pipes. The sense that he was not alone grew upon him to the verge of madness. On every side he was haunted and begirt by presences. He heard them moving in the upper chambers; from the shop, he heard the dead man getting to his legs; and as he began with a great effort to mount the stairs, feet fled quietly before him and followed stealthily behind. If he were but deaf, he thought, how tranquilly he would possess his soul! And then again, and hearkening with ever fresh attention, he blessed himself for that unresting sense which held the outposts and stood a trusty sentinel upon his life. His head turned continually on his neck; his eyes, which seemed starting from their orbits, scouted on every side, and on every side were half-rewarded as with the tail of something nameless vanishing. The four-and-twenty steps to the first floor were four-and-twenty agonies.

On that first story, the doors stood ajar, three of them like three ambushes, shaking his nerves like the throats of cannon. He could never again, he felt, be sufficiently immured and fortified from men's observing eyes; he longed to be home, girt in by walls, buried among bedclothes, and invisible to all but God. And at that thought he wondered a little, recollecting tales of other murderers and the fear they were said to entertain of heavenly avengers. It was not so, at least, with him. He feared the laws of nature, lest, in their callous and immutable procedure, they should preserve some damning evidence of his crime. He feared tenfold more, with a slavish, superstitious terror, some scission in the continuity of man's experience, some wilful illegality of nature. He played a game of skill, depending on the rules, calculating consequence from cause; and what if nature, as the defeated tyrant overthrew the chess-board, should break the mould of their succession? The like had befallen Napoleon (so writers said) when the winter changed the time of its appearance. The like might befall Markheim: the solid walls might become transparent and reveal his doings like those of bees in a glass hive; the stout planks might yield under his foot like quicksands and detain him in their clutch; ay, and there were soberer accidents that might destroy him: if, for instance, the house should fall and imprison him beside the body of his victim; or the house next door should fly on fire, and the firemen invade him from all sides. These things he feared; and, in a sense, these things might be called the hands of God reached forth against sin. But about God himself he was at ease; his act was doubtless exceptional, but so were his excuses, which God knew; it was there, and not among men, that he felt sure of justice.

When he had got safe into the drawing-room, and shut the door behind him, he was aware of a respite from alarms. The room was quite dismantled, uncarpeted besides, and strewn with packing-cases and incongruous furniture; several great pier-glasses, in which he beheld himself at various angles, like an actor on a stage; many pictures, framed and unframed, standing, with

their faces to the wall; a fine Sheraton sideboard, a
cabinet of <u>marquetry</u>, and a great old bed, with tapestry hangings. The windows opened to the floor; but
by great good fortune the lower part of the shutters had
been closed, and this concealed him from the neighbors. Here, then, Markheim drew in a packing-case
before the cabinet, and began to search among the keys.
It was a long business, for there were many; and it was
irksome, besides; for, after all, there might be nothing
in the cabinet, and time was on the wing. But the
closeness of the occupation sobered him. With the tail
of his eye he saw the door—even glanced at it from
time to time directly, like a besieged commander pleased
to verify the good estate of his defences. But in truth
he was at peace. The rain falling in the street sounded
natural and pleasant. Presently, on the other side, the
notes of a piano were wakened to the music of a hymn,
and the voices of many children took up the air and
words. How stately, how comfortable was the melody!
How fresh the youthful voices! Markheim gave ear
to it smilingly, as he sorted out the keys; and his mind
was thronged with answerable ideas and images;
church-going children and the pealing of the high organ;
children afield, bathers by the brookside, ramblers
on the brambly common, kite-fliers in the windy and
cloud-navigated sky; and then, at another cadence of
the hymn, back again to church, and the somno-
lence of summer Sundays, and the high genteel voice
of the parson (which he smiled a little to recall)
and the painted Jacobean tombs, and the dim letter-
ing of the Ten Commandments in the chancel.

And as he sat thus, at once busy and absent, he was
startled to his feet. A flash of ice, a flash of fire, a
bursting gush of blood, went over him, and then he
stood transfixed and thrilling. A step mounted the

stair slowly and steadily, and presently a hand was laid upon the knob, and the lock clicked, and the door opened.

Fear held Markheim in a vice. What to expect he knew not, whether the dead man walking, or the official ministers of human justice, or some chance witness blindly stumbling in to consign him to the gallows. But when a face was thrust into the aperture, glanced round the room, looked at him, nodded and smiled as if in friendly recognition, and then withdrew again, and the door closed behind it, his fear broke loose from his control in a hoarse cry. At the sound of this the visitant returned.

" Did you call me? " he asked, pleasantly, and with that he entered the room and closed the door behind him.

Markheim stood and gazed at him with all his eyes. Perhaps there was a film upon his sight, but the outlines of the new-comer seemed to change and waver like those of the idols in the wavering candle-light of the shop; and at times he thought he knew him; and at times he thought he bore a likeness to himself; and always, like a lump of living terror, there lay in his bosom the conviction that this thing was not of the earth and not of God.

And yet the creature had a strange air of the commonplace, as he stood looking on Markheim with a smile; and when he added: " You are looking for the money, I believe? " it was in the tones of every-day politeness.

Markheim made no answer.

" I should warn you," resumed the other, " that the maid has left her sweetheart earlier than usual and will soon be here. If Mr. Markheim be found in this house, I need not describe to him the consequences."

" You know me?" cried the murderer.

The visitor smiled. " You have long been a favorite of mine," he said; " and I have long observed and often sought to help you."

" What are you?" cried Markheim: " the devil?"

" What I may be," returned the other, " cannot affect the service I propose to render you."

" It can," cried Markheim; " it does! Be helped by you? No, never; not by you! You do not know me yet; thank God, you do not know me!"

" I know you," replied the visitant, with a sort of kind severity or rather firmness. " I know you to the soul."

" Know me!" cried Markheim. " Who can do so? My life is but a travesty and slander on myself. I have lived to belie my nature. All men do; all men are better than this disguise that grows about and stifles them. You see each dragged away by life, like one whom bravos have seized and muffled in a cloak. If they had their own control—if you could see their faces, they would be altogether different, they would shine out for heroes and saints! I am worse than most; my self is more overlaid; my excuse is known to me and God. But, had I the time, I could disclose myself."

" To me?" inquired the visitant.

" To you before all," returned the murderer. " I supposed you were intelligent. I thought—since you exist—you would prove a reader of the heart. And yet you would propose to judge me by my acts! Think of it; my acts! I was born and I have lived in a land of giants; giants have dragged me by the wrists since I was born out of my mother—the giants of circumstance. And you would judge me by my acts! But can you not look within? Can you not understand that evil is hateful to me? Can you not see within me the clear writing of conscience, never blurred by any wilful sophistry, although too often disregarded? Can you not read me for a thing that surely must be common as humanity—the unwilling sinner?"

"All this is very feelingly expressed," was the reply, "but it regards me not. These points of consistency are beyond my province, and I care not in the least by what compulsion you may have been dragged away, so as you are but carried in the right direction. But time flies; the servant delays, looking in the faces of the crowd and at the pictures on the hoardings, but still she keeps moving nearer; and remember, it is as if the gallows itself was striding towards you through the Christmas streets! Shall I help you; I, who know all? Shall I tell you where to find the money?"

"For what price?" asked Markheim.

"I offer you the service for a Christmas gift," returned the other.

Markheim could not refrain from smiling with a kind of bitter triumph. "No," said he, "I will take nothing at your hands; if I were dying of thirst, and it was your hand that put the pitcher to my lips, I should find the courage to refuse. It may be credulous, but I will do nothing to commit myself to evil."

"I have no objection to a death-bed repentance," observed the visitant.

"Because you disbelieve their efficacy!" Markheim cried.

"I do not say so," returned the other; "but I look on these things from a different side, and when the life is done my interest falls. The man has lived to serve me, to spread black looks under color of religion, or to sow tares in the wheat-field, as you do, in a course of weak compliance with desire. Now that he draws so near to his deliverance, he can add but one act of service

—to repent, to die smiling, and thus to build up in confidence and hope the more timorous of my surviving followers. I am not so hard a master. Try me. Accept my help. Please yourself in life as you have done hitherto; please yourself more amply, spread your elbows at the board; and when the night begins to fall and the curtains to be drawn, I tell you, for your greater comfort, that you will find it even easy to compound your quarrel with your conscience, and to make a truckling peace with God. I came but now from such a death-bed, and the room was full of sincere mourners, listening to the man's last words: and when I looked into that face, which had been set as a flint against mercy, I found it smiling with hope."

"And do you, then, suppose me such a creature?" asked Markheim. "Do you think I have no more generous aspirations than to sin, and sin, and sin, and, at last, sneak into heaven? My heart rises at the thought. Is this, then, your experience of mankind? or is it because you find me with red hands that you presume such baseness? and is this crime of murder indeed so impious as to dry up the very springs of good?"

"Murder is to me no special category," replied the other. "All sins are murder, even as all life is war. I behold your race, like starving mariners on a raft, plucking crusts out of the hands of famine and feeding on each other's lives. I follow sins beyond the moment of their acting; I find in all that the last consequence is death; and to my eyes, the pretty maid who thwarts her mother with such taking graces on a question of a ball, drips no less visibly with human gore than such a murderer as yourself. Do I say that I follow sins? I follow virtues also; they differ not by the thickness of a nail, they are both scythes for the reaping angel of Death. Evil, for which I live, consists not in action but in character. The bad man is dear to me; not the bad act, whose fruits, if we could follow them far enough down the hurtling cataract of the ages, might yet be found more blessed than those of the rarest virtues. And it is not because you have killed a dealer, but because you are Markheim, that I offered to forward your escape.''

'' I will lay my heart open to you,'' answered Markheim. '' This crime on which you find me is my last. On my way to it I have learned many lessons; itself is a lesson, a momentous lesson. Hitherto I have been driven with revolt to what I would not; I was a bond-slave to poverty, driven and scourged. There are robust virtues that can stand in these temptations; mine was not so: I had a thirst of pleasure. But to-day, and out of this deed, I pluck both warning and riches—both the power and a fresh resolve to be myself. I become in all things a free actor in the world; I begin to see myself all changed, these hands the agents of good, this heart at peace. Something comes over me out of the past; something of what I have dreamed on Sabbath evenings to the sound of the church organ, of what I forecast when I shed tears over noble books, or talked, an innocent child, with my mother. There lies my life; I have wandered a few years, but now I see once more my city of destination.''

'' You are to use this money on the Stock Exchange, I think? '' remarked the visitor; '' and there, if I mistake not, you have already lost some thousands? ''

'' Ah,'' said Markheim, '' but this time I have a sure thing.''

'' This time, again, you will lose,'' replied the visitor quietly.

'' Ah, but I keep back the half! '' cried Markheim.

"That also you will lose," said the other.

The sweat started upon Markheim's brow. "Well, then, what matter?" he exclaimed. "Say it be lost, say I am plunged again in poverty, shall one part of me, and that the worst, continue until the end to override the better? Evil and good run strong in me, haling me both ways. I do not love the one thing, I love all. I can conceive great deeds, renunciations, martyrdoms; and though I be fallen to such a crime as murder, pity is no stranger to my thoughts. I pity the poor; who knows their trials better than myself? I pity and help them; I prize love, I love honest laughter; there is no good thing nor true thing on earth but I love it from my heart. And are my vices only to direct my life, and my virtues to lie without effect, like some passive lumber of the mind? Not so; good, also, is a spring of acts."

But the visitant raised his finger. "For six-and-thirty years that you have been in this world," said he, "through many changes of fortune and varieties of humor, I have watched you steadily fall. Fifteen years ago you would have started at a theft. Three years back you would have blenched at the name of murder. Is there any crime, is there any cruelty or meanness, from which you still recoil?—five years from now I shall detect you in the fact! Downward, downward, lies your way; nor can anything but death avail to stop you."

"It is true," Markheim said huskily, "I have in some degree complied with evil. But it is so with all: the very saints, in the mere exercise of living, grow less dainty, and take on the tone of their surroundings."

"I will propound to you one simple question," said the other; "and as you answer, I shall read to you your moral horoscope. You have grown in many things more lax; possibly you do right to be so; and at any account, it is the same with all men. But granting that, are you in any one particular, however trifling, more difficult to please with your own conduct, or do you go in all things with a looser rein?"

"In any one?" repeated Markheim, with an anguish of consideration. "No," he added, with despair, "in none! I have gone down in all."

"Then," said the visitor, "content yourself with what you are, for you will never change; and the words of your part on this stage are irrevocably written down."

Markheim stood for a long while silent, and indeed it was the visitor who first broke the silence. "That being so," he said, "shall I show you the money?"

"And grace?" cried Markheim.

"Have you not tried it?" returned the other. "Two or three years ago, did I not see you on the platform of revival meetings, and was not your voice the loudest in the hymn?"

"It is true," said Markheim; "and I see clearly what remains for me by way of duty. I thank you for these lessons from my soul; my eyes are opened, and I behold myself at last for what I am."

At this moment, the sharp note of the door-bell rang through the house; and the visitant, as though this were some concerted signal for which he had been waiting, changed at once in his demeanor.

"The maid!" he cried. "She has returned, as I forewarned you, and there is now before you one more difficult passage. Her master, you must say, is ill; you must let her in, with an assured but rather serious countenance—no smiles, no overacting, and I promise you success! Once the girl within, and the door closed, the same dexterity that has already rid you of the dealer will relieve you of this last danger in your path. Thenceforward you have the whole evening—the whole night, if needful—to ransack the treasures of the house and to make good your safety. This is help that comes to you with the mask of danger. Up!" he cried: "up, friend; your life hangs trembling in the scales: up, and act!"

Markheim steadily regarded his counsellor. "If I be condemned to evil acts," he said, "there is still one door of freedom open—I can cease from action. If my life be an ill thing, I can lay it down. Though I be, as you say truly, at the beck of every small temptation, I can yet, by one decisive gesture, place myself beyond the reach of all. My love of good is damned to barrenness; it may, and let it be! But I have still my hatred of evil; and from that, to your galling disappointment, you shall see that I can draw both energy and courage."

The features of the visitor began to undergo a wonderful and lovely change: they brightened and softened with a tender triumph; and, even as they brightened, faded and dislimned. But Markheim did not pause to watch or understand the transformation. He opened the door and went downstairs very slowly, thinking to himself. His past went soberly before him; he beheld it as it was, ugly and strenuous like a dream, random as chance-medley—a scene of defeat. Life, as he thus reviewed it, tempted him no longer; but on the further side he perceived a quiet haven for his bark. He paused in the passage, and looked into the shop, where the candle still burned by the dead body. It was strangely silent. Thoughts of the dealer swarmed into his mind, as he stood gazing. And then the bell once more broke out into impatient clamor.

He confronted the maid upon the threshold with something like a smile.

"You had better go for the police," said he: "I have killed your master."